DYNAMICS IN CIVIL ENGINEERING

ANALYSIS AND DESIGN

VOLUME I

FUNDAMENTALS IN VIBRATION THEORY AND PRACTICE INCLUDING MACHINE FOUNDATIONS. SOIL DYNAMICS. INSTRUMENTATION. VIBRATION TOLERANCES

ALEXANDER MAJOR

Dr. Tech. Sc., Dr. Eng.

Professor of Civil Engineering

AKADÉMIAI KIADÓ · BUDAPEST 1980

Revised and enlarged edition of

VIBRATION ANALYSIS AND DESIGN OF FOUNDATIONS FOR MACHINES AND TURBINES

published jointly
by
Akadémiai Kiadó, Budapest
and
Collet's Holdings Limited, London

ISBN 963 05 2206 3 (Vols. I–IV)
ISBN 963 05 2219 5 Vol. I

Printed in Hungary

CONTENTS*

PART ONE

THEORY AND PRACTICE OF MACHINE FOUNDATION

CHAPTER I

CHAPTER II

  * The preface, the list of symbols, the abbreviations, and the conversion factors are given in this volume; the bibliography and the index are incorporated in the fourth volume. Detailed contents are given in each volume. For orientation, brief contents of subsequent volumes are also given.

CHAPTER III

CLASSIFICATION OF MACHINE FOUNDATIONS AND MACHINES 130

CHAPTER IV

FUNDAMENTAL PRINCIPLES FOR THE DESIGN OF MACHINE FOUNDATIONS . 133

CHAPTER V

BUILDING MATERIALS FOR MACHINE FOUNDATIONS 137

CHAPTER VI

PRINCIPLES OF COMPUTATION FOR MACHINE FOUNDATIONS 154

CHAPTER VII

INSTRUMENTATION AND EQUIPMENT FOR GENERATING DYNAMIC FORCES FOR VIBRATION MEASUREMENTS 177

PART TWO

INTERACTION BETWEEN SOIL AND FOUNDATION

CHAPTER VIII

DYNAMIC EFFECTS ON THE SOIL AND THEIR EXAMINATION 205

CHAPTER IX

THE ELASTIC PROPERTIES OF THE SOIL 226

CHAPTER X

THE BEHAVIOUR OF SOILS UNDER DYNAMIC LOADS 241

CHAPTER XI

DYNAMIC SOIL PROPERTIES FOR DESIGN PURPOSES 254

BRIEF CONTENTS OF SUBSEQUENT VOLUMES

PREFACE

Since the author's last English publication on machine and turbine foundations, industrial development together with the concomitant important problems in dynamics have increased greatly over the whole field of civil engineering.

The original edition of this work and its translations into various languages have been out of print for some years and it was therefore felt that a most useful purpose would be served by publishing a new treatise to include the widespread problems of dynamics in civil engineering. Consequently, the title and the layout of the book are different from the original.

In connection with the design of diesel-electric power plants in Egypt the author had to face complicated problems, owing to very unfavourable subsoil conditions, usually necessitating pile foundations. He also took part in the designing of the high-capacity Bánhida power station in Hungary where he was able to use the experience gained in connection with the unfavourable settlements observed during the construction of the Klingenberg power station in Berlin. Engaged further in the analysis and design of a number of power stations and industrial plants both in Hungary and abroad the author has had ample opportunity for studying the foundations of generators, reciprocating engines, machines having impact loads and various other machines, and thus could follow in practice the development of this branch of science over a considerable period of time. The experience gained induced him to write his original book covering mainly the vibration analysis and design of foundations for machines and turbines. Lectures delivered at the Technical University of Budapest, at the Institute for Postgraduate Education and at the Hungarian Academy of Sciences—which lectures also included prestressing and prefabrications—are now incorporated.

Information concerning soil properties, the physical treatment of soils, and advances in the research into reliable computation methods by the use of computer programming together with other appropriate methods such as the finite element method have all resulted in significant progress being made regarding problems in dynamics in civil engineering. In machine foundations the trend has led towards slender low-tuned structures preferably utilizing—also at high output units—spring mounted foundations. In addition to the fact that machines have increased greatly in size as well as in efficiency, up-to-date building materials and constructions together with lightweight prefabricated structures are more sensitive to machine-induced or other types of vibrations. In recent years, therefore, substantial efforts have been made to deal with dynamical problems in civil engineering from a more theoretical point of view—with due regard to safety and economy. Much of this effort has been carried out through experimentation using modern instruments. New problems have arisen in connection with vibrations in tall buildings, in industrial structures including those of nuclear plants and in connection with problems of wind loading, blasting and in those resulting from earthquakes. These problems in particular made it necessary to take into account the use of high-speed high-capacity electronic computers—these having paved the way to more correct research and economization in the dynamics of civil engineering.

The first Hungarian edition of this book used in various departments of the Technical University, at the Scientific Institute for Building Research, in the Design Office for Civil Engineering, in the Office for Bridge Design and in the Design Office for Industrial Plants was sold out within a relatively short time. As a consequence of the practical applicability of the book, a number of foreign editions were published. The expanded and revised German edition was adopted as the basis for the first English version (this was also translated into Chinese) which endeavoured to make allowances for a large number of particular practices and included the then latest achievements. To this, the following should be added thereby briefly emphasizing the general activities in the field. The first international symposium on machine foundations (which also dealt with other dynamical problems in civil engineering), was organized in Budapest by the author within the framework of RILEM. In addition, many other congresses and symposia have been organized on the topic but mainly on problems other than machine foundations. Tall buildings were dealt with in Lehigh, USA, in Warsaw and in Bratislava; conferences on earthquake problems have been held all over the world; machine foundations (among other topics), were treated at a symposium organized by the British National Section of the International Association for Earthquake Engineering in London, and at the Soil Dynamics Specialty Conference held in Mexico. Machine foundations have also been dealt with at meetings held in the USA and in the USSR, and at a joint meeting of the Institution of Civil Engineers and the Institution of Mechanical Engineers organized by the Steam Plant Group about turbo-machinery in London. Within the framework of the Royal Society (U. K.) at the 44th Euromech Symposium held in Bucharest the special theme of machine foundations was once more treated as the main topic. The same theme was touched on at the FIP Congress in New York and at the ACI Fall Convention in Houston, Texas, USA. In addition to his lectures given at the Technical University of Budapest, several lectures and lecture series have been given by the author over the last decade as visiting professor at 45 institutions—including 25 universities, research institutes and engineering companies in the United States—and in a large number of institutions in Europe, Africa and Asia. This background, together with his cooperation within the framework of RILEM, has enabled the author to gain a great deal of experience putting him in the advantageous position of being able to appreciate the demands from many points of view.

As expressed in the previous book, it is only during the last few decades that really detailed theoretical and experimental scientific research has been carried out on problems connected with the foundation of machines giving rise to dynamic effects. The development and practical application of the comparatively new branch of science, industrial seismology, as well as many scientific achievements in the field of soil mechanics during the last decades, have contributed greatly to this progress.

Problems other than those of machine foundations were treated briefly in the previous editions but since then not only have important developments taken place but quite new areas have been opened up. This enlarged edition covers a wider area in the main branches of the dynamics in civil engineering containing those new problems which have emerged since the previous editions, thus presenting a quite new concept in its new form. This has meant omitting a number of parts to ensure sufficient room for the new problems. The early stages and types of development are also partially given in this book not only to demonstrate the history and the development in the field, but also to avoid suppositions or investigations which have been overtaken by new research results. The importance of such material should also be emphasized from the viewpoints of the readers of the developing countries, where the local conditions do not always ensure the most up-to-date solutions. Informative ways are presented here in which it is possible to arrive step by step at better solutions. Critical viewpoints are given in the light of recent investigations and by this procedure the state-of-the-art and the outlines for future developments are laid down in the book in order to ensure as complete a survey of the complex theme as is possible.

The contents are arranged in a sequence that introduces the reader to the theory of vibrations and vibration measurements before dealing with the methods of analysis. The purpose of this is to enable him to appreciate the practical significance of frequency and amplitude prior to enlarging on the detailed analysis of various machine foundations. These details are accompanied by the operating principles of the machines themselves to acquaint the civil engineer with the machine to be accomodated. Endeavours have been made to include the methods of calculation published so far. When discussing the various types of machines, the description of the theory of computation is followed by a comparison of different methods. The prime aim has been to present the principles on which good practice is based and this is illustrated by a great many examples given in the different chapters of the book.

Because of the increased material, because of practical considerations, and in order to ensure easy handling of the book, the new edition is divided into four volumes. Since the four volumes are to be handled as a whole, the Preface, the Contents, the Symbols and the Conversion Factors are incorporated in the first volume; the fourth volume contains the Bibliography and the Index.

Volume One, Part One contains the basic problems of vibration analysis and the general principles of the theory and practice of machine foundations which are in fact valuable for most problems arising in civil engineering. In addition, soil dynamics, including interaction between the soil and its foundation, are comprehensively treated. Design methods for dynamically loaded foundations regarding the subgrade coefficients and worked out and revised in the USSR are given here as well as a detailed treatment of problems relating to the supposition of an elastic half space which led, suggested by prominent authors in the USA, to the development of the widely used lumped parameter system. Instrumentation and vibration tolerances are also treated here. Volume Two contains a review of the machine types and a detailed treatment of the structural analysis and design of the various types of foundations for hammers, reciprocating engines and the problems of vibration isolation and damping. Furthermore, foundations for various other machines and those such as are directly set on the workshop floor are handled. The multifarious possibilities for close cooperation between civil and mechanical engineers are also treated here by considering the mechanical methods of vibration elimination, useful also for high-speed machinery. Volume Three is concerned with the operating principles of the machinery and the details of the foundations of the high-speed types, especially of turbogenerators. These machines have been developed in the course of industrial development in units of increasing dimensions both for steam and nuclear facilities and the structural design of the plants and their foundations have introduced ideas which affect theoretical investigations in a decisive manner. Structural details are also treated here. Volume Four concerns itself with the vibrations in buildings and industrial structures due to dynamic loads. Dynamic problems in hydraulic structures and those of bridges are also considered. Any concept, wherever encountered in this book, uses the same symbol: this principle has been strictly adhered to except where agreement with the literature was inevitably required. The more important denotations are given in the list of symbols. In the previous English edition all dimensions were given in the metric system, with the foot-pound system being given in brackets. As the metric system is now fully accepted in the U. K. and the acceptance of it is also under way in the USA, the present work uses conventional metric units, foot-pound units being presented only in cases where the research results are still given in this system. Conversion factors, as has already been mentioned, are given separately in the first volume.

In keeping with the purpose of this book, all problems related to machine foundations and other questions of vibrations in civil engineering have been considered from a general point of view and every effort has been made to give proper credit to the latest possible theoretical and practical results. Reference to a multitude of sources is the natural consequence of this. The sources listed in the Bibliography also include works suitable for advanced studies in the corresponding branches of science. Some sources are mentioned in the text, others in the footnotes. Names of the authors and their activities are to some extent given where the different themes are developed. The writer is indebted to all authors whose works were used for reference purposes or who are mentioned in the book—as for instance to those listed on pp. 35–6 of Volume One where the development regarding machine foundations and the connected branches such as soil dynamics, etc. are treated—

and wishes to express his appreciation to firms, factories, manufacturers and engineering companies, whose products or activities are mentioned. The names of a number of firms are listed in the Abbreviations in Volume One and are also mentioned in the Index at the end of Volume Four. Where references are given, these are in square brackets—either in the text or in the captions or in both. Where it was considered necessary, such as where works are mentioned in the description of the developments, often only the year of publication is given. As a result of the rapid development of this field, the number of references is large. Due to the lack of space, it was sometimes only possible to refer to certain investigations by outlining the researches with their results or giving just the title in order to facilitate further studies.

Sincere acknowledgements are expressed to all colleagues for the part they have played in personal discussions at consultations, seminars or round table conferences at the different universities, scientific and research institutions, and at engineering and construction companies. The author feels obliged to admit that in view of the amount of material contained in the book, which in keeping with its character extends to various branches of science, it may well be that credit to some authors, editors, firms and factories may, in spite the extreme care with which the sources have been compiled, have escaped attention; it is more likely that this is the case if the relevant details are quoted second-hand. Any remarks concerning the origin of such material will be gratefully acknowledged and the necessary corrections made in subsequent editions.

In order to acknowledge some individuals who were of help in previous editions, a part of the Preface of the first English edition is given. The reader of the first Hungarian edition was Mr. M. Cséry, Eng.; Mr. W. Hermann, Dr. Eng., of the German version. The English translation was the work of Mr. A. Frankovszky, Mr. J. Tóth and Mr. Z. Szilvássy, Eng. who also revised the text linguistically. In checking the numerical examples valuable aid was given by Mr. S. Szücs, Eng. The entire text was revised by the author.

With regard to the present work the author acknowledges the assistance on certain examples of Prof. M. Harasta, Cand. Sc. Techn., Technical University of Budapest. The useful help of F. Hunyadi, Dr. Techn., of the Institute for Geodesie and Geotechniques, Budapest, whose critical reading while the work was in the manuscript stage, is gratefully acknowledged. Concerning some examples regarding turbogenerator foundations, the useful cooperation of his former student P. Shrinivasulu, Dr. Techn., now active at the Structural Engineering Research Centre, Madras, India, should be mentioned. Zoltan S. Szabo, B. Sc., registered civil engineer, is thanked for his help in obtaining some data from the United States literature; the latter is also thanked for his help in compiling the section on computer applications. The text for the present edition was revised and edited by Mr. Harvey Shenker of Akadémiai Kiadó, the Publishing House of the Hungarian Academy of Sciences. The author wishes to acknowledge his debt to the staff of Akadémiai Kiadó for their painstaking work relating to all aspects of publication.

Special thanks are due to my wife, the most inspiring companion.

This book is intended primarily for civil engineers, but is nevertheless of help to mechanical engineers; at the same time it serves the needs of students and researchers at universities and scientific institutes.

Author's address: *A. MAJOR*
1068 Budapest,
Gorkij fasor 40,
Hungary

LIST OF SYMBOLS

Within the individual letter-groups the more important symbols are given here in the order of their appearance in the text. Certain symbols, not listed below, are defined in the text

a_i distance of the weights G_i from the vertical through the centre of gravity
a_d amplitude of the forced vibrations of the vibration damper
a_k amplitude of the forced vibrations of the construction
a velocity of propagation of pressure waves in an elastic medium
a_1 lever arm ratio (factor)
A amplitude in general
A_d vibration amplitude with damping
A_z vertical amplitude
A_x horizontal amplitude of the translational vibrations
A_ϕ amplitude of the rotational vibrations
A_ψ amplitude of torsional vibrations
A_1 vibration amplitude of the foundation
A_2 amplitude of vibration of the anvil
A_3 vibrational amplitude of the foundation under the springs
A_2^* maximum amplitude of the vibrations at the centre of the frame-beam
A_1 amplitude of vibration of the frame-beam
A_2 amplitude of vibration of the frame-column
A_t area of steel in tension
A_x amplitude of the translational vibrations of the foundation
A_ϕ amplitude of the rotational vibrations of the foundation
α reduction factor in the case of soil stresses
α_1 coefficient depending on the characteristics of the hammer
α increment of the free surface at the rubber springs
α degree of instantaneousness
b thickness of the pad
b_i distance of the forces H_i from their resultant, which passes through the centre of elasticity
β_i crank displacement of the corresponding cylinder
β angle of the cone
c spring-constant
c_1 coefficient of stiffness of the bedding
c_2 coefficient of stiffness of the pad under the anvil
c_3 coefficient of stiffness of the bedding
c_{1sp} stiffness of a single spring
c_2 factor of rigidity of the beam
c_1 factor of rigidity of the columns
c_i factor of rigidity of the individual frames
c_a stiffness factor of the absorber
c_k stiffness factor of the construction
c_d stiffness factor of the vibration damper
c_z vertical stiffness factor
c_x horizontal stiffness factor
c_ϕ stiffness factor for rotation in the vertical plane

c_ψ	stiffness factor torsion in the horizontal plane
c	propagation velocity
C	centrifugal force
C_b	cube strength of the concrete
C_z	coefficient of uniform compression of the soil
C_x	coefficient of uniform displacement of the soil
C_ϕ	coefficient of non-uniform compression of the soil
C_ψ	coefficient of non-uniform displacement of the soil
C_{st}	spring constant in the static state
C_d	spring constant in the dynamic state
γ_x, γ_y	ratio of the moments of mass inertia
γ	factor which is proportional to λ at the method of successive approximation
γ_s	specific weight of the soil
γ_v	volume weight of the soil
d	diameter of the spring steel
D	damping ratio
D	relative density
D	diameter of the spring coil
D	diameter of the pipe
δ_c	elastic shortening of the pile
δ_l	settlement of the pile regarded as a rigid body
δ_1	deflection due to bending
δ_2	deflection due to shear
δ_3	compression of the columns
δ_s	displacement of the soil
δ_h	displacement of the upper slab
δ_H	horizontal displacement of the frame due to unit force
δ_c	deflection of the foundation element in the examined horizontal or vertical direction due to the static effect of the generating force
Δ	logarithmic decrement
e	distance between the centre of inertia and the centre of elasticity
e_1	eccentricity of the rotating mass
e_2	eccentricity of the blow
e_c	eccentricity of the resultant of the centrifugal forces related to the centre of elasticity
e	wall thickness of the pipe
E	Young's modulus
E_2	modulus of elasticity of the pad
E_0	energy of impact of the hammer
E_c	modulus of elasticity of the cork
ε	void ratio
ε	strain of rubber
ε	modulus of elasticity of the water
f	surface area of the piston
f_a	base area related to the unit weight of the hammer head
f_2	static settlement due to the weight of the foundation and to the anvil for hammer foundations
f_0	natural frequency (cps) (in Chapter V of Vol. II)
F_2	base area of the pad
F_1	base area of the foundation
F_b	cross-sectional area of the frame beam
F_c	cross-sectional area of the column
$F_l\, F_f$	loaded and free surfaces, respectively of the rubber block
Φ	ratio of the amplitudes of the building and the soil
ζ	vertical distance of the mass forces from the centre of rotation

ζ ratio of the natural frequency to the rpm

g gravitational acceleration

G_h weight of the upper scale in the computations of the horizontal natural frequency

G^* shear modulus

G_a weight of the foundation

G_m weight of the machine

G_0 weight of the hammer head

G_2 weight of the anvil

G_1 weight of the stand and that of the backfill above the foundation

G_s weight of the stand

G_3 weight of the foundation below the spring

G_r weight of the rotor if the foundation and anvil form a rigid body

G weight of the foundation by stiffened connection between foundation and anvil

G time constant of the conduct valve

η correction factor in the equation for velocity of the hammer head

h_0 drop height

h height of the spring compressed by the loading P

h_0 height of the frame-column

H' horizontal mass force

H_n horizontal stiffness of the frame

H_d horizontal dynamic force

$\Theta_x, \Theta_y, \Theta_z$ moment of mass inertia related to the axes x, y and z passing through the common centroid of machine and foundation

Θ_{sx}, Θ_{sy} moment of mass inertia related to the axes passing through the centre of gravity of the base surface

Θ mass moment of inertia of the equivalent masses about the centre of inertia

i number of cylinders

i number of turns

i_1 radius of inertia at the hammer foundations

I moment of inertia of flat foundations

I'_x, I'_y moment of inertia of flat foundations

I_z polar moment of inertia of flat foundations

I_b moment of inertia of the beam

I_c moment of inertia of the column

k coefficient of correction in the calculation for hammer foundations of the factor of uniform compression C_z

k constant of the linear damping force

k_z, k_x, k_ϕ ratios for C_z, C_x, and C_ϕ

k_c coefficient of impact

k frame constant

K_z vertical component of the generating force in direction z

K_x horizontal component of the generating force in direction x

K_y horizontal component of the generating force in direction y

κ dynamic factor value for impulsive load

l^* critical length of piles

l length of piles

l_0 length of the frame-girder

L_1 distance between the centre of gravity of the connecting rod and big end

L length of connecting rod

λ circular frequency of the natural frequency

λ_z circular frequency of the vertical natural frequency

λ_z vertical natural frequency at the hammer foundations

λ_b vertical limit frequency of the anvil

λ_ϕ limit frequency of the rotational natural vibrations of the foundation

λ_x limit frequency of the natural translational vibrations of the foundation

λ_1, λ_2 principal frequencies

λ_ψ torsional angular frequency

λ_b limit frequency of the transverse beam with absolutely rigid columns

λ_c limit frequency of the column with absolutely rigid beam

m mass in general

m_0 mass of the hammer head

m_1 mass of the hammer foundation with stand

m_2 mass of the anvil

m_a mass of the moving parts of the drive mechanism acting on the crankshaft

m_b mass of the moving parts of the crankshaft acting on the cross-head

m_2 equivalent weight assumed to be concentrated at the centre of the transverse beam

m_0 concentrated mass of the load due to mechanical equipment carried by the girder via the bearing

m_0 mass of the falling load

m_b mass of the beam

m_1 equivalent weight acting at the end of the columns

m_a mass of the longitudinal beams and the mechanical equipment carried by them

m_c mass of the columns

m_b mass of the moving crushing plate

m_c mass of the arm

m_0 mass of the eccentric

m_d mass of the counterweights

m_I mass of the main shaft and the crushing cone coupled to it

m_{II} mass of the crankshaft, the gear and the counterweights, etc. attached to it

m' mass reduced to O

m', m'' masses of the counterweights

m_d mass of the vibration damper

m_k reduced mass of the construction and the machine

m_M mass of the machine

$M (\sin \omega t)$ periodical generating moment

M_x, M_y, M_z components of the generating moment to the axis x, y and z

M'_x, M'_y, M'_z mass moments

M_{xd}, M_{yd}, M_{zd} dynamic effects of the moments

M_s moment of the frictional forces

M_{sp} moment on the spring force

M_v deviation moment

μ fatigue factor

μ mass per unit length

μ_t ratio of the masses of foundation and hammer head

μ_m ratio of the masses of anvil and hammer head

μ_1 ratio of the masses of anvil and foundation

μ_3 ratio of the masses of the hammer foundation above the spring support and the base slab under the spring support

μ ratio of the masses at the computation of the vertical natural frequency of the turbine upper slab

n number of revolutions per second

$2n$ constant of the linear damping force

n_a weight of foundation related to the unit weight of the hammer head

n_m machine weight related to the unit weight of the hammer head

N_1 number of springs casing

n_2 number of springs

N number of revolutions per minute

N_m speed of the machine (rpm)

N_0	operating speed of the machine (rpm)
N_z	vertical natural frequency (cpm)
N_e	natural frequency (cpm)
N_ψ	natural frequency (cpm) for torsion in the horizontal plane
N_h, N_{eh1}, N_{eh2}	horizontal natural frequencies of the upper slab (cpm)
N_y	natural frequency in turbine foundations corrected by a factor $(1 \pm a_e)$
N_k	critical frequency of the beam
v	dynamic factor in general
v_z	dynamic factor for vertical vibrations
v_r	dynamic factor in the case of resonance
v_d	dynamic factor in the case of damping
O'	momentary position of the bearing
p_1, p_2	centres of rotation from the centroid
p	mean pressure on the piston
p	stress in the case of a rubber block
P_d	vertical dynamic force
P_t	generating force
P_{1sp}	permissible load on a single spring
P_z	vertical mass force in the case of crushers
P_x	horizontal mass force in the case of crushers
$P(t)$	impulsive load
$p(x)$	probability density
ξ	horizontal distance of the mass forces from the centre of rotation
q	relative moisture content
q_1	weight of crank
q_2	weight of the reciprocating part of piston, piston rod and cross-head
q_3	weight of the connecting rod
Q	load of the foundation
Q	force of inertia produced by the vibration damper
Q	discharge through the pipe in time t
r_I	distance between the shaft of the crusher and the centre of gravity of the main shaft
r_{II}	distance between the shaft of the crusher and the centre of gravity of the camshaft
R	radius of the crank
R	generating force in the case of crushers
R_1	distance between the centre of gravity of the rotational axis and of the crankshaft.
Re	Reynold's number
ρ	deflection of the shaft
ρ	density of soil
ρ	gate ratio
s	distance of the combined centroid of machine and foundation from the elastic bedding supporting the foundation
s	circumference of a single pile
s	momentary position of the centre of gravity of the rotating part
s	Strouhal number
s	impulse force
s_2	displacement of the frame beam due to unit load
σ	stress in general
σ_p	permissible soil stress
σ_{perm}	permissible stress
σ_{st}	static stress
σ_d	dynamic stress
t	permissible tensile stress in reinforcement
τ	time for the free effect
T	time interval of one period

T_1, T_2	cable forces of hoisting towers
T	time of closure of the conduit valve
φ	phase angle
φ	initial angular velocity of rotation at hammer foundations
φ_0	an auxiliary value introduced in the calculation of the horizontal natural frequency of turbine foundations
v	velocity in general
v	velocity of the mass of the foundation if anvil and foundation are connected stiffly
v_M	velocity of the hammer head
v_2	velocity of the anvil
v	spouting velocity at the downstream end of the pipe
v_1	issuing velocity
V	vertical mass force
V_d	vertical dynamic force
ψ	rotational angle of the foundation
ψ	specific internal resistance of the elastic connection of the vibration damper
$\psi(\tau)$	autocorrelation function
$w(f)$	spectral density
W_1	output of the asynchronous motor
W_2	demand of the rolling mill motor
W	point of intersection of the momentary axis of rotation with the rotating part
x	horizontal displacement
x_s	coordinate of the centre of rotation
y_0	horizontal distance from the centroid
z	vertical displacement
z_1	vertical displacement of the hammer foundations
z_2	vertical displacement of the anvil
z	raising of the bearing
z	height of W above O
z_s	coordinate of the centre of rotation
ω	angular velocity of circular motion
ω	circular frequency of the generating force
ω_0	circular frequency of the natural vibration
ω_a	natural frequency of the absorbers
ω_k	natural frequency of the construction
ω_d	natural frequency of the vibration damper
ω_k	natural frequency of the machine generating vibrations
$\omega_{1,2}$	common natural frequency of the construction and the vibration damper

ABBREVIATIONS

Selected, mostly repeatedly occurring, abbreviations are listed below

AASHO	American Associations of State Highway Officials
ACI	American Concrete Institute
AEC	Atomic Energy Commission
AEG	Allgemeine Elektrizitätsgesellschaft
Ann. I. T. B. T. P.	*Annales de l'Institute Technique du Bâtiment et des Travaux Publics*
ANS	American National Standard
ASCE	American Society of Civil Engineers
ASME	American Society of Mechanical Engineers
ASTM	American Society of Testing and Materials
B. & K.	Brüel and Kjaer, Copenhagen
Bauing.	*Der Bauingenieur*
Bautechn.	*Die Bautechnik*
Baupl.–Bautechn.	*Bauplanung–Bautechnik*
BBC	Brown Boveri Company, Switzerland
BECHTEL	Bechtel Corporation, Engineers and Builders for Industry, San Francisco
Beton u. Stahlb.	*Beton und Stahlbetonbau*
BLUM	J. A. Blum and Associates, Engineers, San Francisco
BORSIG	Borsig AG. Berlin–Tegel
BR	British Railways
BRAUN	C. F. Braun Corporation, Los Angeles
BRS	Building Research Station, U. K.
BS	British Standards Institution
BSC	British Standard Code
BST	Brown Boveri–Sulzer Turbomachinery Ltd., Switzerland
BWR	Boiling Water Reactor
CALTECH	California Institute of Technology
CDF	Cumulative Distribution Function
CEGB	Central Electricity Generating Board, UK
CFF	Chemin de Fer Fédéral de la Suisse
CIB	Conseil International du Bâtiment pour la Recherche, l'Étude et la Documentation

CO	Construction Division of the ASCE
CPC	Cahier des Prescriptions Communes, France
CSEPEL	Csepel Machine Works for Unit Production, Hungary
DB	Deutsche Bundesbahn
DEGEBO	Deutsche Gesellschaft für Bodenforschung
DIN	FRG Norm
Disc.	Discussion
EFAS	Eigenform Methode plus Antwort-Spektrum Methode
EM	Mechanics Division of the ASCE
EMPA	Federal Laboratories for Testing Materials and Research
ENERGO-MACHEXPORT	Society for the Export of Machinery, USSR
ER	Energy Ratio
ERŐTERV	Erőmű- és HálózattervezőVállalat (Office for Power Station and Network Design), Hungary
ESL	Engineering Societies Library
ESSO	Research Laboratories of the Standard Oil Co., USA
EUMUCO	Aktiengesellschaft für Maschinenbau, Leverkusen, FRG
FHWA	Federal Highway Administration, USA
FIP	Fédération International de la Précontrainte
GANZ–MÁVAG	GANZ–MÁVAG Machine Factory, Budapest
GEC	General Electric Company
GT	Geotechnical Engineering Division of the ASCE
HY	Hydraulics Division of the ASCE
IABS	International Association for Bridge and Structural Engineering
IAEE	International Association of Earthquake Engineering
IBM	International Business Machines
ICE	Institution of Civil Engineers, U.K.
ICSMFE	International Conference on Soil Mechanics and Foundation Engineering
IME	Institution of Mechanical Engineers, U.K.
IPARTERV	Ipari és Mezőgazdasági Tervező Vállalat (Design Bureau for Industrial and Agricultural Building) Hungary
IRC	Indian Road Congress
ISI	Indian Standards Institution
ISO	International Organization for Standardization
IUTAM	International Union of Theoretical and Applied Mechanics

J.	*Journal*
J. ACI	*Journal of the American Concrete Institute*
J. Appl. Mech.	*Journal of Applied Mechanics*
KRUPP	Krupp Works, Bochum, FRG
KWU	Kraftwerk Union Aktiengesellschaft, Erlangen, FRG
KTC	The Kobe, Commerce, Industry and Trade Center, Japan
LÁNG	Láng Machine Factory, Budapest
Ljungström	Ljungström Works for Steam Turbines, Sweden
MAN	Maschinenfabrik Augsburg Nürnberg, FRG
MÉLYÉPTERV	Mélyépítési Tervező Vállalat (Design Office for Civil Engineering) Hungary
MIT	Massachusetts Institute of Technology
MSC	Mercantil-Sieberg-Cancani Scale
NSSS	Nuclear Steam Power Supply System
NS	Nederlandsche Spoorwegen
OBE	Operating Basis Earthquake
ODRA	Polish Computer Type
ORE	Office for Research and Experiment
PAFEC	Program for Automatic Finite Element Calculations
PARSONS	C. A. Parsons and Co. Ltd., U. K.
PCA	Portland Cement Association
PCCV	Prestressed Concrete Containment Vessel
PWR	Pressurized Water Reactor
Proc.	*Proceedings*
PO	Power Division of the ASCE
RMS	Root Mean Square
RCCV	Reinforced Concrete Containment Vessel
RILEM	Réunion International des Laboratoires d'Éssais et de Recherches sur les Matériaux et les Constructions
ROSS	R. G. Ross and Son Ltd. Eglington Engine Works, U. K.
SCHLOEMANN	Schloemann Aktiengesellschaft, Düsseldorf
SDDA	Seismic Design Decision Analysis
SI	Système International d'Unités
SIEMENS	Siemens Aktiengesellschaft, Elektrische Maschinen für Wasserkraftwerke, West Berlin
SM	Soil Mechanics and Foundation Division of the ASCE

SNCB   Société National de Chemin de Fer Belges
SNCF   Société National des Chemin de Fer Français
SOM   Skidmore, Owings and Merrill, USA
SPL   Sound Pressure Level
SSE   Safe Shutdown Earthquake
SSI   Soil Structure Interaction
ST   Structural Division of the ASCE
SULZER   Sulzer Brothers Ltd., Winterthur, Switzerland
SYMP   Symposium

TELEDYNE   Company for Instrumentation, Garland, Texas
  GEOTECH
TGL   GDR Norm
Trans.   Transactions

UBC   Uniform Building Code
UIC   Union Internationales des Chemins der Fer
USAEC   United States Atomic Energy Commission
USBR   United States Bureau of Reclamation

VDI   Verein Deutscher Ingenieure
VÍZITERV   Vízépítési Tervező Vállalat (Design Office for Hydraulical
              Structures), Hungary

WES   US Army Engineers Waterways Experimental Station

WCEE   World Conference on Earthquake Engineering

Z. d. VDI   *Zeitschrift des Vereines Deutscher Ingenieure*

CONVERSION FACTORS

As the Metric System is already generally used in the United Kingdom and the introduction of this system is also advanced in the United States, conventional metric units are given in this book in place of the units of the foot–pound system; units of this latter system are only presented where research results are still given in this form.

The SI (Système International d'Unités: International System of Units) recommendations are not yet generally adopted in practice, especially not in the European countries where the use of the metric system can still be foreseen for several years. In some countries the term *pond* (kilopond) was adopted.

The term *newton*, although it has been coordinated with the unit of force *pond*, cannot be visualized in engineering practice as easily as the *kilogram* (kg).

The unit of mass "m" is the same in the SI system as that of force in the conventional metric system, viz. the "kg"; the unit of force, depending upon Newton's second law, is equal to $g \cdot m$, where "g" is the acceleration due to gravity of mass "m". Acceleration due to gravity amounts to about 9.81 m s^{-2} on the surface of the earth. It is emphasized that the unit of force is marked in the conventional metric system by "kg" although this unit is sometimes termed "kgf", or in the pond system "kp".

The corresponding force term in the SI system in newtons is $N = 1 \text{ kg/s}^2 \cdot 9.81$. The conversion factor is thus a round value of 10.

As the value 9.81 is negligibly less than the round value of 10, no practical difficulties will arise by using the conventional system of units because in engineering practice such small deviations can in most cases be ignored.

Since, as has been mentioned above, metrification is now being used in the UK, and in the FRG (see Funk, [343a]), and introduction is under way in the USA (see Hopkins [470a], Leffel [673a], and Milton [833a]), it seems advisable to include here a conversion table with appropriate conversion factors. This table is from an ASCE publication and is based on the ASTM guide (ASTM E-380).

To convert	To	Multiply by
inches (in.)	millimetres (mm)	25.40
inches (in.)	centimetres (cm)	2.540
inches (in.)	metres (m)	0.0254
feet(ft)	metres (m)	0.305
miles (miles)	kilometres (km)	1.61
yards (yd)	metres (m)	0.91
square inches (sq in.)	square centimetres (cm^2)	6.45
square feet (sq ft)	square metres (m^2)	0.093
square yards (sq yd)	square metres (m^2)	0.836
acres (acre)	square metres (m^2)	4047
square miles (sq miles)	square kilometres (km^2)	2.59
cubic inches (cu in.)	cubic centimetres (cm^3)	16.4
cubic feet (cu ft)	cubic metres (m^3)	0.028
cubic yards (cu yd)	cubic metres (m^3)	0.765
pounds (lb)	kilograms (kg)	0.453
tons (ton)	kilograms (kg)	907.2
one pound force (lbf)	newtons (N)	4.45
one kilogram force (kgf)	newtons (N)	9.81
pounds per square foot (psf)	newtons per square metre (N/m^2)	47.9
pounds per square inch (psi)	kilonewtons per square metre (kN/m^2)	6.9
gallons (gal)	cubic metres (m^3)	0.0038
acre-feet (acre-ft)	cubic metres (m^3)	1233
gallons per minute (gal/min)	cubic metres per minute (m^3/min)	0.0038
newtons per square metre (N/m^2)	pascals (Pa)	1.00

PART ONE

THEORY AND PRACTICE OF MACHINE FOUNDATION

CHAPTER I

MACHINE FOUNDATIONS IN GENERAL

Before dealing with machine foundations in detail, let us examine their importance in both civil and mechanical engineering design.

1. The importance of machine foundations

All machine foundations, except very small ones, should be regarded as serious engineering problems. The larger ones give rise to dynamic loads, causing vibrations which the designer must take into account if he is to choose a solution which is both technically sound and economical. For foundations with static loads it is enough to know the loads and the results of mechanical tests of the subsoil. But machine foundations with dynamic loads confront the designer with a much more complex problem. When constructing the foundations, the effects of static and dynamic loads must be considered if objectionable unequal settlement and harmful cracking are to be avoided. Care must further be taken to ensure the smooth running of the machine by avoiding harmful vibration in the base or in the subsoil or, if the foundation does not rest on the ground, in the floor which supports it and which may transmit vibrations to its surroundings.

Machine bases generally carry heavy loads requiring broad or deep foundations. Works below ground-water level are often necessary, for which pile driving or open caissons should be envisaged. In some cases densification of the soil or stabilization, e.g. sand soils with chemicals, could be adopted. In many instances care must be taken to guard against the effects of heat or chemical action, and harmful vibration. The requirements of machine foundations must be considered as early as when the ground plan of the building is designed. The foundations necessary for the machines to be housed determine the layout of the buildings and govern the choice between single, or multi-storey buildings. To ensure a technically correct and economical solution, close cooperation between mechanical and civil engineers is required.

The importance of machine foundation design was not recognized in the past. Simple methods of calculation were used most often involving the multiplication of the static loads by an estimated "dynamic factor", the result being treated as an increased static load without any knowledge of the actual safety factor. Because of this uncertainty the value of the adopted "dynamic factor" was usually too high, although practice showed that harmful deformations resulted during operation even when these excessive factors were used. This made a deeper scientific investigation of dynamic loading necessary. A more detailed study became urgent also because of the great development of machine technique. Machines several times more powerful than the old ones give rise to considerable stresses thereby posing problems which are partly in the field of vibration techniques and partly in that of soil mechanics. It is not sufficient for machine manufacturers to give brief instructions on their drawings, such as "the machine must rest on suitable load-bearing subsoil", with, at the most, approximate values for the various forces of inertia. Recently, new theoretical procedures have been developed for calculating the dynamic responses of foundations.

Most civil engineers responsible for the foundation of similar machines were formerly familiar only with the conventional computation methods based, as mentioned before, on the principles of statics. During investigations into the dynamic loads of machine foundations a certain time was necessary before the design methods derived on the basis of various theoretical considerations could be verified by a satisfactory number of experiments. The first phase in the development of design methods for machine foundations may be regarded as the one in which the estimation of the dynamic forces relied upon practical experience only. Later it was thought, erroneously of course, that all problems could be solved theoretically and a great number of factors had to be assumed in an arbitrary manner. This approach could not be justified without corroboration by adequate experimental evidence. Laboratory and field measurements have been introduced to determine carefully the effect of the subsoil, the interaction of soil and vibrating foundation. Sometimes isolation design of the machine is necessary because of ground motion excited by, say, another foundation.

Foundation vibration and its results, viz. differential settlement of the foundation, deformations and cracks, may greatly disturb the operation of the machine. Potential uneven wear may result in hot running or even in shaft failure—with the consequent standstill of the machine and perhaps the shutdown of the works thereby involving serious loss in production.

The virtually complete elimination (for all practical purposes) of vibrations is especially important where pipelines are connected to the foundations because vibration may impair the tightness of the pipe joints, with the consequent possibility of gas leakage and explosion, leading to the further possibility of considerable damage.

Workers' health, too, requires the avoidance of vibration as it may have a harmful effect on them. Care must be taken that laboratories using precision instruments are sited sufficiently far away to avoid soil vibration which might be detrimental.

Particularly dangerous oscillations may arise if tower-like industrial structures such as silos and chimney stacks are subject to periodic forces. Since machine loads cannot be changed, and it is not usually possible to change the speed of the machine to produce a different frequency, prior attention must be given to the elimination of harmful oscillations.

One way to avoid vibration is to establish an inner balance in the machine. This can be done, for example by the use of revolving masses of equal size, acting in opposite directions. However, a similar balancing of masses is seldom practical except in instances where special foundations would result in very high cost, or where the foundation work would be very difficult. Spring foundations designed on the basis of vibration technique are in most cases suitable for the absorption of vibrations, to largely eliminate the harmful effects of the moving loads.

The cost of machine foundations is but a small fraction of that of the engineering equipment, and inadequately constructed foundations may result in failures and shutdowns exceeding many times the cost of the capital investment required for properly designed and built foundations. It is clear, therefore, that the proper design of machine foundations is of the greatest importance for the entire structure.

2. The development of methods used for machine foundation design

Scientific investigations of machine foundations have been carried out only in the last few decades. Sad experiences have established the fact that it is not enough to base the design on vertical loads only, multiplied by a dynamic factor, even if this factor introduces a "dynamic" load many times greater than the original one. It should be remembered that the operation of the machines generates not only vertical forces, acting upwards and downwards, but also forces acting perpendicular to the axis; it is thus not enough simply to take into account the vertical load and to multiply it by a selected dynamic factor.

It has also been found that the suitability of machine foundations depends not only on the forces to which they will be subjected but also on their behaviour when exposed to dynamic loads. This latter depends on the relation between the speed of the machine concerned and the natural frequency of the foundation. This makes vibration analysis necessary.

It should be realized finally that the elastic properties of the soil exercise considerable influence on the design of the foundation. Hence careful dynamical investigations into the dynamics of the soil are essential.

It was as early as in 1922–23 that Geiger carried out investigations to determine the natural frequencies of foundations. Later, in 1925, Ehlers and in 1927–30 Prager, studied the theory of vibrations and its practical applications. The development of the calculation of natural frequencies by exact theoretical, as well as by empirical methods, will be treated later in detail (cf. Chapter II, Section 7, pp. 79 ff).

Rausch dealt with machine and turbine foundations in 1924 and contributed greatly to the practical and theoretical development of the science. His basic work on machine foundations was published first in the period 1936–42. A new edition came out in 1959 and a further supplement in 1968. Questions relating to machine foundations have also been dealt with by Schleicher, Schönburg, Spilker, Steinbach, Kayser, Troche, Fratschner, Guéraud, Zeller, Hartz, Haller, Klein, Koch, Hüffmann, Müller, Henselein, Scheiter and by Irish and Walker and many others. In addition, the latest book of Buzdugan and of Lipinski, both published in 1972 and a handbook of Srinivasulu and Vaidyanathan published in 1976 should be mentioned.

Particular vibration problems encountered in engineering practice were dealt with in a work by S. Timoshenko (1st edition 1928), while J. P. den Hartog's book was first published in 1934. The work of W. Ker Wilson appeared in 1942, that of Reisner in 1943, the latest edition of the works by Freberg and Kemler on mechanical vibrations appeared in 1955, Jacobsen and Ayre's book was published in 1958, the book of Norris et al. in 1959, and the handbook edited by Harris and Crede in 1961. Researches into wind- and earthquake effects are treated by Housner, Newmark, Davenport and many others. Further, about the dynamical influences on building structures, a book was edited by Koloušek et al. in 1969 and about the dynamics of structures in general, by Clough and Penzien in 1975. Similar questions especially regarding soil dynamics were treated, among others, by Andrews, Crockett, Hammond, Tschebotarioff, Ward, McAlpin, Pauw, Alpan, Eastwood, Rogers, Lorenz, Novak, Steffens, Hadjian, McNeill, Moore, Warburton and many others. These are dealt with in the corresponding chapters of the present book.

The introduction of the lumped parameter system in the book of Richart, Hall and Wood, published in 1970 was of importance; it also included the investigations of Whitman, Lysmer and others. Covering some significant studies in the field of soil dynamics a detailed report was published by Richart in 1975. In the thirties large-scale experiments were carried out by Hertwig, Früh and Lorenz on behalf of DEGEBO; these experiments were to determine the dynamic properties of soil.

A treatise was published in 1930 by Pavlyuk on foundation dynamics. In 1933 two other papers were published; one by Lurie, the other—somewhat later—, by Kondin. Both examined the vibration theory of elastically supported solid bodies. D. D. Barkan published his findings on dynamic effects on machine foundations in 1938. His basic work on the results of theoretical and experimental investigation in the field of machine foundations affected by dynamic action was published in 1948 (and translated into English in 1962). Shekhter's publication came out in the same period (in 1948), Makarichev studied chiefly the questions of disturbing forces induced by turbo-generators in 1951. On the basis of subsequent investigations the results were later modified and supplemented. Many works have since been published devoted to foundation dynamics in the USSR including those of Abashidze in 1963, and of Savinov in 1955 and 1964. Vibrations of materials and structures were, among others, investigated by Korchinski and by Sorokin in 1971.

A detailed guide for the dynamics of building structures edited by Korenev and Rabinovitch came out in 1972. Some further theoretical investigation results edited by Korenev, Rabinovich and Smirnov were published in 1975.

Further references and bibliographical data are given in the bibliography at the end of Volume Four. Data of the development of the theory of basic and other systems, of the different kinds of machine foundations, and of the other dynamical problems in civil engineering are to be found in the related volumes of the book.

Before considering basic definitions and proceeding to any detailed consideration of the various methods of computation and constructional solutions, it is mentioned here that in the practice of machine foundation design two general methods of calculation have been developed. Their basic principles may be outlined as follows. Until the present, it has been usual for the designer to begin his work by computing—following the principles of vibration theory—the natural frequencies of the foundation body. These natural frequencies are independent of the generating force and depend solely on the mass, shape and design of the foundation as well as on the mechanical properties of the soil which serves as a bed for it. According to this method the most important requirement is that the foundation should be out of tune, i.e. the foundation should be designed to ensure a natural frequency differing by about 20 to 50 per cent from the machine speed.

Another method is characterized by the fundamental requirement that the amplitude of the foundation vibration should not exceed a certain permissible value. Different permissible amplitudes are prescribed for different types of machinery.

Velocity and acceleration can also be of help in the calculations.

All these methods take into account the experiments carried out in recent decades to investigate the dynamic characteristics of the soil. These experiments furnish the designer of machine foundations with data on the dynamic properties of the soil and, being based on research and experiment, they are more reliable than the non-rational rules-of-thumb values previously used.

CHAPTER II

FUNDAMENTALS OF THE THEORY OF VIBRATION

The forces caused by moving periodic or impact loads acting on machine foundations are called dynamic loads, being thus distinguished from static ones.

Dynamic loads are usually characterized by their regular recurrence at certain intervals of time, whereas their magnitude changes rapidly with time.

Let us, for example, consider a pendulum which is, at a given moment displaced from its position of equilibrium (Fig. 1). The pendulum when released will swing in a vertical plane, returning, at certain intervals, to its initial position. The time interval which elapses between the start and the return of the pendulum to the same position is known as *the period*.

Subsequent considerations will be based on the assumption of undamped conditions, or of forces just sufficient to maintain uniform motion of the pendulum. The time interval required for the pendulum to return from any starting position to the same condition of motion and arriving from the same direction is referred to as *the full swinging period*. The projection of the pendulum's motion on a plane perpendicular to the plane of the swing is a straight line, its ends being the projection of the two "dead centres".

The motion of a body which after a certain interval returns to its former position and then repeats the displacement is called *periodic*. This kind of motion is described by periodic functions of time, e.g. circular functions. Periodic motions are frequently encountered both in nature and in the field of technology. For example, the motions of moving, vibrating and swinging engine parts, the motion of a weight suspended on a spring, the motion of any sound-producing body etc. are all periodic in character.

Periodic motion is closely related to the *wave motion* which takes place when a particle of an elastic medium begins to vibrate. Part of the kinetic energy of the oscillating particle is transmitted to its neighbours. This transmission, however, requires time because of the inertia of the neighbouring particles and, consequently, the other particles begin the motion later. In the case of wave motion, it is therefore not the material but rather the oscillation that is propagated in space. Points characterized by similar positions of vibrating bodies are known as points of *equal phase*. The distance between two such points is called the *wavelength*. When, on the one hand, the surface uniting all the points of equal phase is of spherical shape (as, for instance, in sound transmitting waves), we are dealing with *space waves*. When, on the other hand, the surface concerned is on a single plane (as, for instance, in waves on a water surface), we are dealing with *plane waves*. When the force producing the wave motion acts in the form of separate blows (as a collision or explosion), we are dealing with *impulse waves*.

Summing up the above it may be established that every body performing a motion which is repeated at regular intervals of time (i.e. moves periodically), is considered a *vibrating body*. When the vibration is propagated in space a *wave motion* is produced.

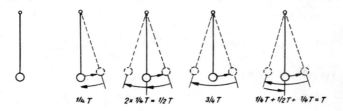

Fig. 1. Swinging of a pendulum

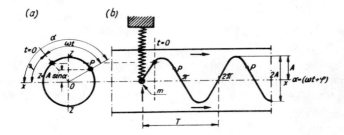

Fig. 2. Harmonic motion of a body suspended on a spring

The analysis of oscillations and waves is of fundamental importance in the design of machine foundations. Consequently, in order to treat more conveniently the problems encountered in the design of machine foundations, a brief review of the fundamentals of the theory of vibration is deemed necessary.

If the geometrical position of a mechanical system can be expressed at any instant by one number only, it is said to have one degree of freedom. Two rigid bodies connected by springs in such a manner that each body can move along a straight line and cannot rotate has, for example, two degrees of freedom. In the case of machine foundations generally one or two degrees of freedom systems occur in practice. More complicated systems are, for example, the frame structures of high speed machinery necessitating more complex systems with many degrees of freedom. The concept of vibration can be demonstrated conveniently by analysing the motion of a ball suspended on a helical spring (Fig. 2). A pencil fastened to the ball, in a direction perpendicular to the axis of the spring, will plot a sine curve against a paper strip which is moved with uniform velocity horizontally behind the spring. The sine curve corresponds to the up-and-down motion of the ball. The motion of any body which can be represented by a sine curve is known as *oscillation*. The time interval during which the spring pulls the ball upwards and subsequently pushes it back to its original position is called the *period* of vibration. Within one period a single *vibration cycle* takes place. Oscillations which can be described by a sine curve are termed *harmonic*. As will be demonstrated subsequently, a simple relationship exists between harmonic oscillations and rotation at uniform angular velocity.

1. Harmonic and other vibrations

A) GENERAL CONSIDERATIONS

Let point P in Fig. 2 move with uniform velocity on a circle whose radius is $A = \overline{OP}$. In order to define the motion let us assume the distance between point P and the centre O of the circle to remain unchanged throughout and angle α to increase with time t. Expressed in mathematical form

$$A = \text{constant}; \qquad \alpha = \omega t + \varphi$$

where ω is the angular velocity of circular motion, or, in other words, the circumferential velocity of a point moving on a circle whose radius is unity ($r = 1$). Angle φ is the magnitude of α measured at the beginning of the rotation, i.e. when $t = 0$.

Suppose now that the radius of the circle, the distance $\overline{OP} = A$, is projected on axis z. The projection will be $z = A \sin \alpha$. Since $\alpha = \omega t + \varphi$, this may be substituted to give

$$z = A \sin (\omega t + \varphi) \tag{1}$$

It will be perceived therefrom that if point P moves on a circle of radius A with uniform velocity, the projection of radius A on axis z can be described by a sine function of the angle $\alpha = \omega t + \varphi$. If this function is represented on the paper strip shown in Fig. 2, i.e. if the values of z are plotted against axis z, the corresponding $\alpha = \omega t + \varphi$ values on the horizontal axis x and the curve drawn, we obtain the path of the body of mass m, which is a sine curve. Equation (1) is thus the equation of vibratory motion.

The distance $OP = A$, viz. the radius of the circle described by point P, is called the amplitude of vibration. The increasing or reducing of the radius can be explained in other terms as using a stronger or weaker spring to set the ball in vibration.

The angular velocity ω is called the *circular frequency* of vibration; upon this depends the interval during which a full cycle of vibration is completed. Let t_1 be the instant when the vibration starts and t_2 when the body returns to its original position. Since point P moving on a circle travels the path 2π to describe a full sine curve it follows that

$$2\pi = \omega t_2 - \omega t_1$$

From this the time interval of one period

$$T = t_2 - t_1 = \frac{2\pi}{\omega} \tag{2}$$

where T is the duration of a full vibration cycle; the vibration process which takes place during this interval of time is called a *period*. The number of times the motion repeats itself per second is called the *frequency* and is denoted by n. Consequently,

$$n = \frac{1}{T} \tag{3}$$

Combining Eqs (2) and (3) we obtain

$$\omega = \frac{2\pi}{T} = 2\pi n \tag{4}$$

i.e. the circular frequency is 2π times the frequency. The number of cycles in a second, viz. the frequency, is measured in cps (cycles per second). In some publications various other symbols are used, e.g. Hz (Herz) found in German publications, or c/s, cyps and cycle/sec.

Substituting for ω in Eq. (1) the value given by Eq. (4):

$$z = \sin(\omega t + \varphi) = A \sin(2\pi n t + \varphi) = A \sin\left(2\pi \frac{t}{T} + \varphi\right) \tag{5}$$

where t denotes the time that has passed and T denotes the period of the vibration. The angle φ, indicating the phase difference at the moment $t = 0$, is known as the *phase angle*. It ranges from 0 to 2π, with the two limits denoting identical positions.

In general the motions of the vibrating body are rarely harmonic. Three types of motions are shown in Fig. 3: the periodic (a) similar to those described in Fig. 2; the random (b) where the displacement–time form does not repeat itself; and the transient (c) type of motion where some impulse type disturbance is present in a short-time interval.

If we superimpose two sinusoidal vibrations of different frequencies, for instance, in a ratio $n_2 : n_1 = 2 : 3$, then the *resulting vibratory motion* will no longer be sinusoidal; it remains, however, periodical (Fig. 4).

Such periodic vibratory motions, i.e. which repeat themselves after a certain interval of time (T), but cannot be described by a simple sine function and have, consequently, no harmonic character can, as is easy to verify, be expanded mathematically by means of a Fourier series into several harmonic motions. This is the so-called *harmonic analysis*.

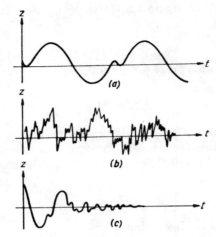

Fig. 3. (a) Periodic, (b) random, (c) transient motion

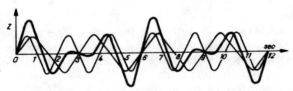

Fig. 4. Two sinusoidal oscillations of different frequency superimposed on periodical oscillation

If the periodical function $z = f(t)$ is known, then, according to Fourier's theorem, a series can be built up which is the sum of harmonic functions with fixed amplitude and phase, and whose frequencies are divisible by the so called basic frequency.

$$z = f(t) \cdot A_0 + A_1 \sin(\omega t + \varphi_1) + A_2 \sin(2\omega t + \varphi_2) +$$

$$+ A_3 \sin(3\omega t + \varphi_3) + \ldots + A_n \sin(n\omega t + \varphi_n)$$

(6)

where $\omega = 2\pi/T$ and $n = 1, 2, 3, \ldots$.

The vibrations of frequency $n \cdot 1/T$ are harmonics of the basic vibration. Thus, if the shape of the function $f(t)$ is known, the constant A_0, the amplitudes A_1, A_2, A_3, $\ldots$, A_n and the phases φ_1, φ_2, $\varphi_3, \ldots, \varphi_n$, of the single harmonic vibration taking part in the production of all the composite vibrations, $f(t)$ can be computed unambiguously by the aid of Fourier's formula. The resolving into Fourier series can be accomplished by means of instruments designed for the purpose.

It is illustrated in an example (Fig. 5) how a nonharmonic periodic motion can be "broken up" into a sum of harmonically related sinewaves. Two most important harmonic curves, the first and the second, represent here the "frequency spectrum" of the nonharmonic periodic motion.

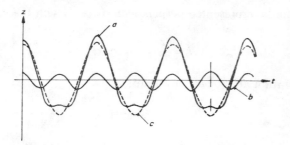

Fig. 5. Waveform "broken up" into a sum of harmonic sinewaves
a—nonharmonic periodic motion, b—first harmonic, c—second harmonic

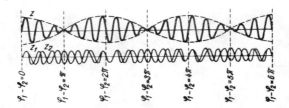

Fig. 6. Beating oscillation (periodical fluctuation of oscillation)

It may be noted here additionally that by superimposing two vibrations of nearly the same frequency—for instance: $n_1 : n_2 = 12 : 11$—and of the same amplitude, the so-called "*beating*" occurs (Fig. 6), the characteristic of which is the alternately increasing and decreasing vibrations. The frequency of the "beating", i.e. the beat frequency, is the difference between the frequencies of the component vibrations. The beating frequency is

$$n_b = n_1 - n_2 = 12 - 11 = 1 \text{ Hz},$$

and the corresponding time

$$T_b = \frac{T_1 T_2}{T_2 - T_1} = \frac{1}{n_b} = \frac{1}{1} = 1 \text{ sec}$$

The circular frequency is measured in rad/sec. To represent a motion of a vibrating particle we can use conveniently the vector method to represent the vibrations.

Let us rotate the vector with angular velocity ω in a counterclockwise direction (Fig. 7). Supposing that we start at $t = 0$ in the horizontal position of the vectors, the vertical projection of it will be

$$z = A \sin \omega t \qquad\qquad (7)$$

and the horizontal projection

$$x = A \cos \omega t \qquad\qquad (8)$$

The speed can be represented perpendicularly (90°) with the value of

$$\dot{z} = \frac{dz}{dt} = \omega A \cos \omega t \tag{9}$$

and the acceleration at 180° according to:

$$\ddot{z} = \frac{d^2 z}{dt^2} = A\omega^2 \sin \omega t . \tag{10}$$

From the first differential quotient of time (t) we get the speed and from the second the acceleration (Fig. 8).

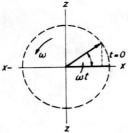

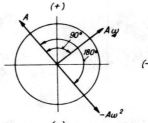

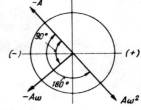

Fig. 7. Harmonic motion represented by a vector

Fig. 8. Vector representation of harmonic displacement, velocity and acceleration

In the horizontal sense the corresponding values are

$$\dot{x} = \frac{dx}{dt} = -A\,\omega \sin \omega t \tag{11}$$

and

$$\ddot{x} = \frac{d^2 x}{dt^2} = +A\omega^2 \cos \omega t \tag{12}$$

Sometimes the third differential quotient the "jerk" is used, e.g. in the z direction:

$$\dddot{z} = \frac{dz^3}{dt^3} = \omega^3 A \cos \omega t \tag{13}$$

For all these quantities in the case of harmonic motions, if one amplitude together with the frequency is given, then all other quantities are determined.

B) PEAK AVERAGE AND ROOT MEAN SQUARE (RMS) VALUES

For pure harmonic motions the values depending upon A are peak values A_{peak} and are useful only when more complex vibrations are of no interest. The average absolute value as shown in Fig. 9 takes into account the time history too:

$$A_{\text{average}} = \frac{1}{T} = \int\limits_0^T |z|\, dt \qquad (14)$$

As a descriptive quantity the most useful value is the RMS (root mean square) value:

$$A_{\text{RMS}} = \sqrt{\frac{1}{T}\int\limits_0^t z^2(t)\, dt} \qquad (15)$$

being in direct relationship with the energy content of the vibrations.

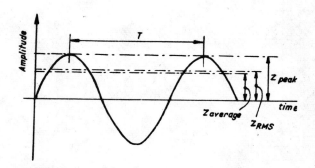

Fig. 9. Harmonic vibration signal with indication of the peak, the average and the RMS value

If one amplitude is given along with the frequency for the determination of all other quantities the nomograph of Fig. 10 is generally useful. In the RMS nomograph the values are given in m, m/sec, m/s^2 and cps.

In the case of random vibrations of Fig. 3/b which are also often encountered in civil engineering the vibration process is described by irregular motions. As it is impossible to measure such vibrations over infinite time, finite time values must be limited in practice. In dynamics in civil engineering there are many structural problems where the dynamic characteristics of the structure itself and the time dependent applied load are interrelated in such a way that the quasistatic approach may not be enough to achieve structural safety. This is so in the case of stormy winds, wind-induced waves and strong earthquakes. The non-deterministic nature of such effects necessitates the application of the random process theory in order to arrive at more realistic models. Safety problems to combat dynamic forces in the sense of the above mentioned problems are treated by Shinozuka [1141].

To describe the random vibrations, statistical parameters are used. Besides the earlier mentioned RMS values, the probability density, the autocorrelation function and the power spectral density are useful for describing a random function.

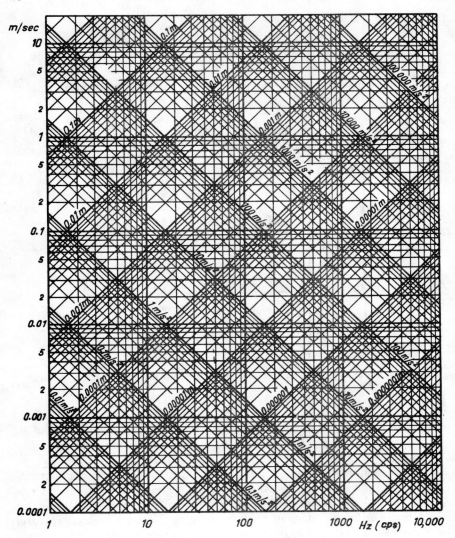

Fig. 10. Vibration monograph for frequency, acceleration, velocity and displacement for harmonic motion in RMS values

C) PROBABILITY DENSITY

For a stationary random function where the stationary process is an ensemble of signals where an average of of the values over the ensemble is at any time independent of time, it is convenient to use the concept of probability density— defined as a probability that the instantaneous amplitude value will be found within

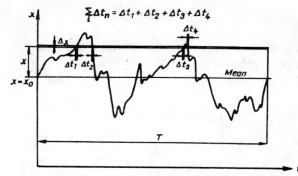

Fig. 11. Illustration of the concepts: probability and probability density

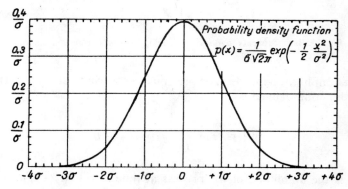

Fig. 12. Normalized Gaussian probability density curve

a certain Δx limited amplitude divided by the size of the interval. The probability denotes the chance of a particular event happening. If it is absolutely certain that the event in question will happen the probability of occurrence of the event is said to be 1. The occurrence is said to be 0 if the event will certainly not happen. Thus the probabilities are positive real numbers between 1 and 0.

The probability density is, as shown in Fig. 11 [130], mathematically expressed by

$$p(x) = \lim_{\Delta x \to 0} \frac{P(x) - P(x + \Delta x)}{\Delta x} \tag{16}$$

where the probability $P(x)$ is dimensionless.

The practical procedure involved in converting experimental or theoretical data into probability density data by ensuring that the area under the probability density curve is 1 is called normalization and the most common such curve, the normal Gaussian curve, is shown in Fig. 12 [142], where the relationship between the instantaneous amplitude values in Gaussian random vibration signal σ and the Gaussian probability curve is illustrated.

D) AUTOCORRELATION FUNCTION

In order to gain more information concerning the time history or frequency content of the process being studied statistical physicists introduced the autocorrelation function $\psi(\tau)$, which describes on the average how a particular in-

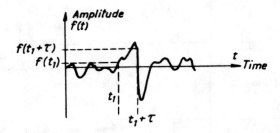

Fig. 13. Basic concepts involved in deriving the autocorrelation function

stantaneous amplitude depends upon previously occurring instantaneous values, as being that function defined by

$$\psi(\tau) = \lim_{T \to \infty} \frac{1}{T} \int_0^T f(t) f(t + \tau)\, dt \tag{17}$$

where $f(t)$ is the amplitude of the process at time t and $f(t_1 + \tau)$ designates the amplitude observed later at a time $(t_1 + \tau)$ as shown in Fig. 13 [142].

E) POWER SPECTRAL DENSITY

This function termed the mean spectral density function can be derived from the autocorrelation function mathematically by the exact definition [130]

$$w(f) = \lim_{\Delta f \to 0} \lim_{T \to \infty} \frac{1}{\Delta f\, T} \int_0^T f_{\Delta f}^2(t)\, dt \tag{18}$$

where $w(f)$ is the spectral density at frequency f, $f_{\Delta f}$ is the time function for that part of the vibration signal lying within the frequency band Δf and the integration time T.

By making an ordinary frequency analysis (see Chapter VIII) of the signal it can be shown that the following equation applies

$$w(f) = \frac{x_{\text{RMS}}^2(f, \Delta f)}{\Delta f} \tag{19}$$

in the case of small Δf bandwidth. Thus to determine, for example, the acceleration density, it is quite enough to measure the RMS value of the acceleration and divide by the bandwidth in Hz.

For the foregoing Sections A, B, and C see more details in Clough and Penzien [186].

2. Free vibrations without damping

Harmonic vibrations, which follow the laws explained previously, occur when force P acting on the body concerned is directly proportional to the displacement but acts in the opposite direction. A force of such character (say, in a spring) is termed *quasi-elastic*. Accordingly

$$P = -cz \tag{20}$$

where c is the constant of the quasi-elastic force, z the displacement.

To be more exact, constant c is identical with the magnitude of the spring force induced by unit displacement in the direction of vibration. When the value of c is great, the spring is said to be soft; when, on the contrary, it is small, the spring is stiff.

In accordance with Newton's second law (force = mass × acceleration)

$$P = m\ddot{z} \tag{21}$$

where m is the mass of the body, $\ddot{z}$ the acceleration.

Combining Eqs. (20) and (21) and rearranging terms we obtain

$$m\ddot{z} + cz = 0 \tag{22}$$

consequently, the inertial force and the spring force are always in equilibrium.

Equation (22) is a homogeneous linear differential equation of second order with constant coefficients whose general solution is

$$z = A \sin \sqrt{\frac{c}{m}} t + B \cos \sqrt{\frac{c}{m}} t \tag{23}$$

and one particular solution is

$$z = A \sin \sqrt{\frac{c}{m}} t \tag{24}$$

which resembles Eq. (1) and turns into the latter if

$$\omega_0 = 2\pi n_0 \sqrt{\frac{c}{m}} \tag{25}$$

As can be seen, the frequency of a body set in vibration by some given force is inversely proportional to the square root of the mass of the body. The motion which satisfies the corresponding differential equation is referred to as *undamped free vibration*.

Bodies of the same material and of identical structure possess one or more characteristic natural frequencies. If there occurs no change in the material and structural shape of the body, it maintains its characteristic natural frequency independently of the magnitude of the force acting on it and causing it to vibrate. The amplitude, however, has no definite value, its magnitude depends largely on the initial conditions characterizing the start of the motion. These conditions can be used to determine the constants involved in the solutions of the differential equations of free undamped vibration.

The relationship between the circular frequency (ω_0) and the number of revolutions per second (n) can be written as follows

$$n_0 = \frac{\omega_0}{2\pi}$$

whence the revolutions per minute

$$N = \frac{60\omega_0}{2\pi} = \frac{60}{2\pi} \cdot \sqrt{\frac{c}{m}} \tag{26}$$

where N is the number of revolutions per minute, ω_0 the circular frequency of the free vibration.

It can be seen that whereas a greater mass m causes a deceleration in the circular frequency of the free vibration, the increase in the spring constant c leads to its acceleration

With the help of the previous solution the natural frequency of variously loaded beams can be determined.

It has been shown that

$$\omega_0 = \sqrt{\frac{c}{m}}$$

and

$$P = cz$$

Writing the deflection δ of the beam caused by the above force P for the displacement z, we have

$$P = mg = cz = c\delta$$

$$c = \frac{mg}{\delta}$$

Substituting this value for c in the expression $\omega_0 = \sqrt{c/m}$, we obtain

$$\omega_0 = \sqrt{\frac{g}{\delta}}$$

On the other hand $\omega_0 = 2\pi \, N/60$, and consequently

$$\frac{2\pi N}{60} = \sqrt{\frac{g}{\delta}}$$

Let us substitute the value of g in 981 cm/sec^2) in the above expression

$$N = \frac{300}{\sqrt{\delta}} \, (\delta \text{ in cm}) \tag{27}$$

This expression gives the frequency per minute of the free vibration. For a rotating shaft supported at its two ends by bearings the speed of which equals the natural frequency is called the *critical speed* of the shaft. It can be seen from the equation that the free vibration is in a simple relationship with the deflection under static load. Deflections δ corresponding to a given load are compiled in Table 1. Natural frequencies may be computed readily by substituting these for δ in the simple formula given above. When using the table it should be remembered that the expressions indicated there are based on kg and cm units and in the case of springs i denotes the number of turns.

In general, a single degree of freedom system is represented by a single spring attached to a mass but it is also possible that an assemblage of springs is arranged in series, in parallel, or mixed as shown in Table 2, where the equivalent spring constants are also given.

TABLE 1

Deflections, spring constants and natural frequencies of girders

	δ	e	ω_0
	$\dfrac{l^3 Q}{3EI}$	$\dfrac{3EI}{l^2}$	$\sqrt{\dfrac{3gEI}{l^3 Q}}$
	$\dfrac{l^3 Q}{6EI}$	$\dfrac{6EI}{l^3}$	$\sqrt{\dfrac{6gEI}{l^3 Q}}$
	$\dfrac{a^2 a_1^2 Q}{3lEI}$	$\dfrac{3lEI}{a^3 a_1^2}$	$\sqrt{\dfrac{3glEI}{a^2 a_1^2 Q}}$

Table 1 cont.

	$\dfrac{7l^3Q}{96EI}$	$\dfrac{96EI}{7l^3}$	$\sqrt{\dfrac{96gEI}{7l^2Q}}$
	$\dfrac{l^3Q}{24EI}$	$\dfrac{24EI}{l^3}$	$\sqrt{\dfrac{24gEI}{l^3Q}}$
	$\dfrac{(l+a)a^2Q}{3EI}$	$\dfrac{3EI}{(l+a)a^2}$	$\sqrt{\dfrac{3gEI}{(l+a)a^2Q}}$

TABLE 2

Different assemblage of springs

	Arrangements		Spring constans
Series			$\dfrac{1}{c}=\dfrac{1}{c_1}+\dfrac{1}{c_2}$
Parallel			$c=c_1+c_2$
Mixed			$\dfrac{1}{c}=\dfrac{1}{c_1}+\dfrac{1}{c_2+c_3}$

3. Free vibrations with damping

In theory, a system which vibrates under the influence of a suddenly applied force with no other force acting upon it is a conservative system and would vibrate for an infinite length of time. In reality, however, there is always some kind of impeding force to decrease the amplitude of the free vibration with time thereby slowing it down and eventually stopping the motion of the body. This may be the resistance of the air or of a fluid which surrounds the body, it may be due to sliding friction, etc. In

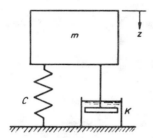

Fig. 14. Damped system with one degree of freedom

structures, this damping may be due to the internal molecular friction of the material (hysteresis) or the loss of energy due to the slippage of structural connections.

Such a damped system is commonly illustrated (Fig. 14) by a vibrating mass *m* connected to a piston which moves in a cylinder filled with oil. As the mass moves, the piston in the cylinder develops a viscous resistance causing a damping force in the body.

When there is *damping*, the differential equation (22) is supplemented by a new term expressing the direct relationship which exists between the damping force and velocity

$$m\ddot{z} + k\dot{z} + cz = 0 \tag{28}$$

where k is the constant of the linear damping force.

Supposing a particular solution of the above differential equation:

$$z = e^{\lambda t}$$

we obtain from Eq. (28):

$$e^{\lambda t}(m\lambda^2 + k\lambda + c) = 0 \tag{29}$$

As $e^{\lambda t}$ can never be zero the expression in parentheses must be equal to zero, and in consequence:

$$\lambda_{1,2} = -\frac{k}{2m} \pm \sqrt{\left(\frac{k}{2m}\right)^2 - \frac{c}{m}} \tag{30}$$

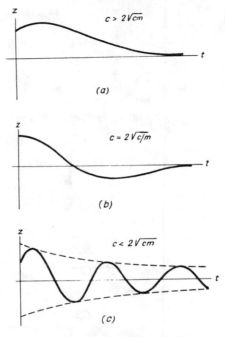

Fig. 15. Response curves for damped systems.
(a) overdamped, (b) critically damped, (c) underdamped

with the general solution:

$$z = Ae^{\lambda_1 t} + Be^{\lambda_2 t} \tag{31}$$

Depending upon whether the roots are real, complex, or equal, three possible cases must be considered:

(i)
$$\left(\frac{k}{2m}\right)^2 > \frac{c}{m} \quad \text{or} \quad k > \sqrt{cm}$$

In this case the expression under the square root sign is positive, the roots are real and z will decrease exponentially without change in sign. In consequence no vibration will occur, a non-periodic motion will result, the system is called overdamped. The displaced body approaches its equilibrium position smoothly as shown in Fig. 15a.

(ii)
$$\left(\frac{k}{2m}\right)^2 = \frac{c}{m} \quad \text{or} \quad k = 2\sqrt{cm}$$

and $\lambda_1 = \lambda_2 = -\dfrac{k}{2m}$

Here the sum of the two expressions under the square root sign in Eq. 30 is zero and we have critical damping which is the limiting case of the non-periodic motion. The motion is similar to the previous case (Fig. 15b).

(iii) $$\left(\frac{k}{2m}\right)^2 < \frac{c}{m} \quad \text{or} \quad k < 2\sqrt{cm}$$

Here the expression under the square root sign in Eq. 30 is negative and the roots of the characteristic equation become complex

$$\sqrt{\left(\frac{k}{2m}\right)^2 - \frac{c}{m}} = i\omega' \tag{32}$$

and introducing the following relation:

$$\frac{k}{2m} = \frac{\Delta}{T}$$

the general formula is

$$z = e^{-\frac{\Delta}{T}t}(Ae^{i\omega't} + Be^{i\omega't}) \tag{33}$$

With the aid of Euler's formula

$$e^{i\alpha t} = \cos\alpha + i\sin\alpha;$$

$$e^{-i\alpha t} = \cos\alpha - i\sin\alpha$$

formula (33) can be written:

$$z = e^{-\frac{\Delta}{T}t}(A\sin\omega't + B\cos\omega't \tag{34}$$

Taking into consideration the boundary constitions, one particular solution is

$$z = e^{-\frac{\Delta}{T}t}A\sin(\omega't + \varphi) \tag{35}$$

thereby

$$\omega' = \sqrt{\frac{c}{m} - \left(\frac{k}{2m}\right)^2} \quad \text{and} \quad \frac{\Delta}{T} = \frac{k}{2m}$$

where φ is the phase angle and the maximum amplitude is

$$A_1 = Ae^{-\Delta\frac{t}{T}} \tag{36}$$

the reciprocal of $k/2m$ is called the *relaxation time*. It is the time in which the amplitude "relaxes" to $1/e$ of its original value. The quantity Δ is termed the *logarithmic decrement* which is the logarithm to base e of the ratio of two successive amplitudes. Both characterize the damping of the vibration.

The equation

$$z = Ae^{-\Delta \frac{t}{T}} \sin(\omega' t + \varphi)$$

can be considered as a particular sine vibration whose amplitude is no longer constant, the frequency of the free vibrations is less than the undamped natural

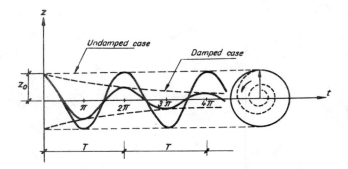

Fig. 16. Free vibration of one degree of freedom system with viscous damping

frequency, the frequency approaches zero according to Fig. 15/c and diminishes with the increase in time, since

$$e^{-\Delta \frac{t}{T}} = \frac{1}{e^{\Delta \frac{t}{T}}}$$

reduces continuously as the time t increases.

The underdamped case is also illustrated in Fig. 16, where the data of reduction for the damped case are shown by the envelope drawn in the figure which is identica¹ with the amplitude curve:

$$Ae^{-\Delta \frac{t}{T}}$$

The entire sine motion must remain within the limits marked by the two amplitude curves, the maximum value of the sine term included in Eq. (36) being ± 1.

When examined more closely, it can be seen that the greater the value of $k/2m$, the more rapid the approach of the amplitude curve to zero. If for instance $k/2m = 2$, after 1/2 sec the amplitude becomes $1/e = 0.37$; after 1 sec, $1/e^2 = 0.14$; after $1\frac{1}{2}$ sec $1/e^3 = 0.05$; and so on. Consequently, when time increases in an arithmetic progression, the amplitude curve approaches zero in a geometric progression. Since

$e^{0.7} = 2.014 \approx 2$, the 0.7 $2m/k$ value is called the *half-value time* because after this interval the amplitude is always reduced to half of its original value. The maximum displacements follow each other at regular intervals of time T. During this interval the amplitude curve drops from

$$e^{-\Delta \frac{t}{T}} \text{ to } e^{-\Delta \frac{t-T}{T}}$$

The ratio of two consecutive displacements, if their values are denoted by A_1, A_2 and A_3, is

$$\frac{A_1}{A_2} = \frac{A_2}{A_3} = \frac{A_3}{A_4} = \frac{e^{-\Delta \frac{t}{T}}}{e^{-\Delta \frac{t+T}{T}}} = e^{\Delta}$$

where

$$\Delta = \ln \frac{A_1}{A_2} \tag{37}$$

the value we have previously called the *logarithmic decrement*.

It can be seen that the circular frequency of the damped free vibrations is also subjected to a change. The square of the new circular frequency is

$$\omega'^2 = \omega_0^2 - \frac{k^2}{4m^2} \tag{38}$$

where ω_0 is the frequency of the corresponding free, undamped vibration, otherwise known as the natural frequency.

If $\omega_0 = k/2m$, that is, the relaxation time equals $1/\omega_2$, the vibration dies down within a single period to zero because $\omega' = 0$.

We obtain vibration only if k is less than the critical value $k_0 = 2\sqrt{cm}$, otherwise the vibration will be *aperiodical*.

Any vibration satisfying differential equation (28) is called *damped free vibration*.

Besides the above mentioned critical value for damping ($k_0 = 2\sqrt{cm}$) and the logarithmic decrement 'Δ', there are various other symbols for damping.

Such is the very often used D value, the damping factor, or ratio D, called sometimes "Lehr" damping; this relates the actual damping to the critical damping value, that is

$$D = k/k_0 = k/2\sqrt{cm} \tag{39}$$

and related to the logarithmic decrement:

$$\Delta = \frac{2\pi D}{\sqrt{1 - D^2}} .$$

When damping is small

$$\Delta \cong 2\pi D \tag{40}$$

The relation $\dfrac{\Delta}{\pi} = \gamma$ is called the solid damping factor and is for small damping $\gamma = 2D$, thus

$$\frac{\Delta}{\pi} = 2D \tag{41}$$

Sometimes the so-called loss factor obtained from the dynamic stress–strain relationship is used. This depends on the width of the hysteresis loop (see p. 231) with the value of $2D$ or $\dfrac{\Delta}{\pi}$.

The loss of energy per cycle expressed in percentage equivalent for 1 per cent loss per cycle equals a logarithmic decrement of about 0.005 and is also used to indicate damping in materials, thus, e.g. 5 per cent loss corresponds to $\Delta = 0.025$.

In the Soviet literature according to Kondin [615] and Savinov [1078] the value of $\dfrac{\Delta}{\pi} = \gamma$ is also expressed in the form

$$\frac{\Delta}{\pi} = \varphi\lambda \tag{42}$$

where λ is the natural frequency considered. (Values for soils are given in Table 37, Chapter XII, on p. 269.)

EXAMPLE

The mass–spring–dashpot system in Fig. 14 is subjected to an impulse. The amplitude of vibration after 5 cycles is 1/4 of the initial: $(A_5/A_0) = 1/4$. What is the logarithmic decrement of the system?

Since

$$\frac{A_0}{A_1} = \frac{A_1}{A_2}, \ldots, \frac{A_{n-1}}{A_n} = e^{\Delta},$$

then

$$\frac{A_0}{A_n} = \left(\frac{A_0}{A_1}\right)^n = e^{n\Delta}$$

Hence,

$$\Delta = \frac{1}{n}\ln\frac{A_0}{A_n} = \frac{1}{5}\ln 4 = 0.277.$$

4. Energy conditions of vibration

The energy of an undisturbed system vibrating freely consists of two parts: the *kinetic energy* $(mv^2/2)$ and the *potential energy*. Potential energy is, in fact, stored in the system as a result of work done against the constant force inducing the vibration (i.e. the quasi-elastic force). As examples we may mention the potential energy stored in a strained spring or in a displaced pendulum. Work performed is the product of displacement and force; in this case c denotes the spring constant and z the displacement, consequently, the *quasi-elastic* force equals cz. This force, however, is a function of the displacement and, accordingly, the work performed by it must be summarized with respect to each elementary portion dz of the displacement, which involves integration. This integration yields the potential energy of the system

$$\int_0^z c z \, dz = \frac{c z^2}{2} \tag{43}$$

The circular frequency of the free system was denoted by ω_0.

In the case considered, the kinetic energy of the system having mass m and vibrating in accordance with the function $z = A \sin \omega_0 t$ equals $mv^2/2$ and since $v = dz/dt$

$$\frac{mv^2}{2} = \frac{m}{2} (A \omega_0 \cos \omega_0 t)^2 = \frac{m}{2} A^2 \omega_0^2 \cos^2 \omega_0 t$$

Substituting for $\omega_0^2 = c/m$ we get

$$\frac{mv^2}{2} - \frac{c}{2} A^2 \cos^2 \omega_0 t \tag{44}$$

The *potential* energy of the vibrating system concerned is, according to Eq. (43), $cz^2/2$ and since $z = A \sin \omega_0 t$

$$\frac{cz^2}{2} = \frac{c}{2} A^2 \sin^2 \omega_0 t \tag{45}$$

From Eqs. (44) and (45) it can be seen that the kinetic and potential energies of the vibrating system are equal in their maximum values but reach these peaks at different instants. When passing through the central position where $z = 0$, the kinetic energy attains maximum and no potential energy is left, whereas in the extreme positions the potential energy reaches a maximum and the kinetic energy becomes zero. The sum of these two forms of energy is, at any instant

$$\frac{c}{2} A^2 (\sin^2 \omega_0 t + \cos^2 \omega_0 t) = \frac{c}{2} A^2$$

The sum of the kinetic and potential energy of the vibrating system is, at every instant, of equal magnitude and depends exclusively on the spring constant c and on the amplitude. This is obvious because the vibrating system in question is undisturbed, i.e. free of all external influences.

From the point of view of dynamics, such a vibrating system must therefore be regarded as a periodic interchange between the two forms of a certain amount of energy.

Multiplying differential equation (28) by $v = dz/dt$ and rearranging the terms we obtain—in the case of damping—the power equation of vibration

$$-\frac{dz}{dt}\left(\frac{mv^2}{2}+\frac{cz^2}{2}\right)=kv^2 \tag{46}$$

The above expression reveals that in the absence of damping, i.e. when $kv^2 = 0$, the total energy of vibration (viz. the kinetic energy $mv^2/2$ and the potential energy $cz^2/2$) undergoes no change with time and remains constant during a full cycle. When however, damping is present, the vibration energy diminishes with time in accordance with Eq. (46) at a rate indicated by the right-hand side of the equation. In this instance kv^2 expresses energy transformed into heat due to friction. On the other hand, vibration is no exception to the law of conservation of energy and thus the energy transformed into heat must equal the loss of energy which has occurred.

5. Forced vibrations

In the foregoing we have considered vibratory movement generated by a single momentary action of an external force, by an impulse taking place at the start of vibration. Similar vibrations are produced for example by a single blow of a hammer. Damping of some sort is always present in nature, therefore damped free vibrations are of the greatest practical significance. As mentioned before, when such vibrations are propagated in space, waves are produced in the medium concerned.

We shall now proceed to deal with vibrations which do not result from momentary action of some disturbance, but are produced by the continuous influence of an external periodic force. Such vibrations are called forced vibrations and are divided, like free vibrations, into two main groups: forced vibrations without and forced vibrations with damping, i.e. undamped and damped.

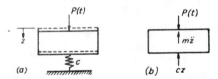

Fig. 17. Undamped harmonic loading

A) FORCED VIBRATIONS WITHOUT DAMPING

In undamped forced vibration the system is continuously balanced by three forces: the inertial force, the spring force, and the generating force (Fig. 17). The differential equation of motion can accordingly be written in the following form:

$$m\ddot{z}+cz=P(t) \tag{47}$$

The generating force is practically a harmonic function of time, consequently we shall confine ourselves to the examination of the equation

$$m\ddot{z} + cz = P_0 \sin \omega t \qquad (48)$$

The solution of Eq. (48) is obtained as the sum of the general solution of the homogeneous equation, and of particular solution of the inhomogeneous equation. The former was introduced when dealing with free vibrations, the latter can be computed by supposing that $z = z_0 \sin \omega t$. By substitution into the above equation we obtain

$$-m\omega^2 z_0 \sin \omega t + cz_0 \sin \omega t = P_0 \sin \omega t$$

whence, after dividing this equation by $\sin \omega t$, rearranging the terms and considering that, in accordance with Eq. (25),

$$\omega_0 = 2\pi n = \sqrt{\frac{c}{m}}$$

where ω_0 is the circular frequency of the undamped free vibration, we get

$$z_0 = \frac{P_0}{c} \frac{1}{1 - \left(\dfrac{\omega}{\omega_0}\right)^2} \qquad (49)$$

At this amplitude z_0 the supposed solution actually satisfies the equation concerned. The complete solution is thus,

$$z = A_1 \sin \omega_0 t + B_1 \cos \omega_0 t + \frac{P_0}{c} \frac{1}{1 - \left(\dfrac{\omega}{\omega_0}\right)^2} \sin \omega t \qquad (50)$$

It can be seen from the equation that in undamped forced vibrations the free vibration (the first two terms) and the forced vibration (the third term) are superimposed. Since in general $\omega \neq \omega_0$, the resultant vibration is not a harmonic motion; it is, in fact, not even a periodic one, if the ratio ω/ω_0 becomes irrational. Quantities A_1 and B_1 can be computed from the initial conditions. The amplitude of the resultant motion is influenced to the greatest extent by the third term. Here, obviously, the amplitude is affected considerably by any change in the ratio ω/ω_0.

Since P_0/c is the displacement due to the static force P_0, the relation

$$v = \frac{1}{1 - \left(\dfrac{\omega}{\omega_0}\right)^2}$$

can be regarded as a dynamic coefficient (usually called the magnification factor) because it shows how many times the displacement caused by a dynamic force P (acting at ω circular frequency) is greater than the displacement corresponding to the same static force.

Another common form of the dynamic coefficient (see note in Vol. II, p. 35), is

$$v = \frac{1}{1 - \left(\dfrac{\omega}{\omega_0}\right)^2} = \frac{\omega_0^2}{\omega_0^2 - \omega^2} = \frac{N_e^2}{N_e^2 - N_m^2} \tag{51}$$

where N denotes the rpm.

It is of interest to examine the implications of the above. If $\omega \ll \omega_0$, then $v \simeq 1$; and if $\omega \gg \omega_0$, then $v \simeq 0$. However, if $\omega \to \omega_0$ then $v \to \infty$ and the amplitude of vibration becomes infinitely large. In the design of machine foundations the examination of

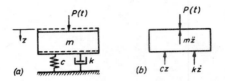

Fig. 18. Damped harmonic loading

resonance phenomena is of fundamental importance but since in practice there is always some damping present, this analysis will be undertaken in the section below dealing with damped forced vibrations.

B) DAMPED FORCED VIBRATIONS

In damped forced vibrations there are four forces continuously counter-balancing each other: the inertial force, the damping force, the spring force and the disturbing force (Fig. 18). Our assumptions are the same: the damping force is directly proportional to velocity, the spring force to displacement, and the generating force can be written as

$$P = P_0 \sin \omega t$$

The differential equation of the vibration can thus be written in the following form:

$$m\ddot{z} + k\dot{z} + cz = P_0 \sin \omega t \tag{52}$$

The solution here is the same as in the previous instance: the sum of the general solution of the equation with the right-hand size zero and of a particular solution of the complete equation. The former is known. As for the latter, let us assume that $z = z_0 \sin(\omega t - \varphi)$ is a solution. After substitution we obtain the following equation:

$$z_0 = \frac{P_0}{(c - \omega^2 m) + (\omega k)^2} \quad \text{and} \quad \tan \varphi = \frac{k\omega}{c - \omega^2 m} \tag{53}$$

The complete solution therefore becomes

$$
\begin{aligned}
z = e^{-\frac{k}{2m}t} \Bigg(& A_1 \sin \sqrt{\frac{c}{m} \div \frac{k^2}{4m^2}}\, t + \\
& + B_1 \cos \sqrt{\frac{c}{m} - \frac{k^2}{4m^2}}\, t \Bigg) + \\
& + \frac{P_0 \sin(\omega t - \varphi)}{\sqrt{(c - \omega^2 m)^2 + (\omega k)^2}}
\end{aligned}
\tag{54}
$$

The first term, representing the free vibration, quickly approaches zero (fading vibration), and the second term, representing the forced vibration (persistent vibration) becomes decisive.

We shall deal only with the second term and confine ourselves to the examination of the expression

$$
z = \frac{P_0 \sin(\omega t - \varphi)}{\sqrt{(c - \omega^2 m)^2 + (\omega k)^2}}
$$

The amplitude is obviously

$$
A = \frac{P_0}{\sqrt{(c - \omega^2 m)^2 + (\omega k)^2}}
\tag{55}
$$

If we substitute in this and the above expression $\omega_0 = \sqrt{c/m}$ for $\tan \varphi$ and introduce $\rho = \dfrac{\pi}{\Delta}$ (a value which will be discussed later) we obtain the expressions

$$
A = \frac{P_0}{c} \cdot \frac{\rho}{\sqrt{\left(\dfrac{\omega}{\omega_0}\right)^2 + \rho^2 \left[1 - \left(\dfrac{\omega}{\omega_0}\right)^2\right]^2}}
\tag{56}
$$

and

$$
\tan \varphi = \frac{\dfrac{\omega}{\omega_0}}{\rho \left[1 - \left(\dfrac{\omega}{\omega_0}\right)^2\right]}
\tag{57}
$$

As will be perceived from the equation for A the value P_0/c is the deflection caused by the static force P_0 and the second term can consequently be regarded as a dynamic magnification factor, thus

$$v = \frac{\rho}{\sqrt{\left(\frac{\omega}{\omega_0}\right)^2 + \rho^2 \left[1 - \left(\frac{\omega}{\omega_0}\right)^2\right]^2}}$$

(58)

or after transformation

$$v = \frac{\left(\frac{\omega_0}{\omega}\right)^2}{\sqrt{\left[\left(\frac{\omega_0}{\omega}\right)^2 - 1\right]^2 + \left(\frac{\Delta}{\pi}\right)^2 \left(\frac{\omega_0}{\omega}\right)^2}}$$

(59)

and putting, according to equation (41), $\dfrac{\Delta}{\pi} = 2D$,

$$v = \frac{1}{\sqrt{\left[1 - \left(\frac{\omega}{\omega_0}\right)^2\right]^2 + 4D^2 \left(\frac{\omega}{\omega_0}\right)^2}}$$

(60)

It will be seen from the equation for A that when the natural frequency $\omega_0 = \sqrt{c/m}$ equals the frequency of the vibrating system (ω), then $\omega/\omega_0 = 1$, and the amplitude A of forced vibration becomes ρ-times larger than P/c. This is true of resonance which occurs in practice when the natural frequency or frequencies (if a whole system is involved) of the mass corresponds to the frequency of the generating vibration. The amplitude has in this instance a definite value and the closer the frequency of the disturbing force to the natural frequency of the masses, the larger the amplitude. In the case of complete equality between the frequencies concerned, i.e. at resonance, and if the influence of damping is neglected, infinitely large amplitudes may theoretically be assumed to occur.

It is instructive to examine in a visual way the phenomenon of resonance.

Let us suspend a mass m from a pivot at point 0 (Fig. 19). Let the mass be displaced from the position of rest to a very small horizontal distance, say 1 mm, by spring a acting with force P on the mass. When released, mass m swings back 1 mm to the left (Fig. 20). The tensile force does not act on this length $a - b$. When acting again on length $b - c$, mass m swings to the right to a distance equal not only to the 1 mm due to swinging but to a total of 2 mm which includes the additional 1 mm due to the disturbing force. If this performance is continued the amplitude of the vibration will grow considerably, i.e. an external force applied periodically at the natural frequency of vibration can increase the amplitude to a magnitude which is many times greater than the amplitude due to a single action of the same external force.

Thus resonance which may develop between operating engines and their foundation may give rise to large amplitudes which cause great stresses in the material of the foundation. Violent vibrations may endanger not only the safe operation of the engine itself but, by propagation, also the safety of the surroundings.

Equation (51) concerning undamped free vibration reveals that resonance is impossible unless the circular frequency of the external period force ω is equal to the frequency of the free vibration that is, if

$$\omega = \omega_0 = \sqrt{\frac{c}{m}}$$

The amplitude cannot, however, increase infinitely since it changes continuously under the influence of damping forces. Eventually a steady state will ensue in which

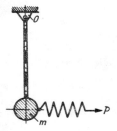

Fig. 19. Swinging mass acted on by a periodic force

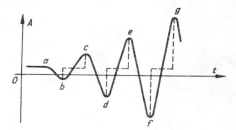

Fig. 20. Increase of the amplitude due to a periodic force

the growth of the amplitudes due to the periodic tensile force P is offset by the reduction of the same by damping. It has been established previously that the logarithmic decrement of the vibration was, for linear damping, Δ if

$$\frac{A_2}{A_1} = e^{-\Delta} \cong 1 - \Delta + \frac{\Delta^2}{2} - \cdots$$

or, expressed in another form

$$\frac{A_1 - A_2}{A_1} \approx \Delta$$

If say $\Delta = 0.01$ the amplitude diminishes in one cycle by one per cent. In our previous example such a decrement would permit a maximum amplitude of 200 mm provided spring force P causes, in accordance with our initial condition, an increase in amplitude of 2 mm per cycle. In other words, 1 per cent amplitude reduction equals precisely 2 mm when the amplitude is 200 mm. It can be seen, therefore, that a continuously acting small force P can, when no vibration whatever is present, displace mass m only by 1 mm from its position of equilibrium, whereas the same force can cause very great swings if the system is a vibrating one.

In general we may point out that when the logarithmic decrement is Δ the amplitude produced is $2/\Delta$ times as large as for a single action of the same force.

This explains, for instance, how a very small force applied against the teeth of the wheels regulating a pendulum clock is able to keep in continuous oscillation the relatively heavy pendulum.

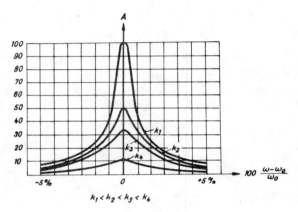

Fig. 21. Group of resonance curves

If mass m is subjected to the influence of not one but of two forces, the second, a tensile force, being applied from a direction opposite to the former, then the amplitude of vibration at a decrement of motion Δ will be $4/\Delta$. This value is denoted by ρ.

In the previous example the force of the springs was assumed to act momentarily, like single blows. If, however, the external periodic force applied follows, for example, a sine function, then the value of ρ will not equal $4/\Delta$ but

$$\rho = \frac{\pi}{\Delta}$$

The resonance curves in Fig. 21 show the values of amplitude A as functions of the relationship between the circular frequencies, i.e. tuning ratios

$$\frac{\omega - \omega_0}{\omega_0}$$

for various factors of resonance and damping coefficients (k). The curves show clearly that amplitude A dips downward sharply with the increase in the tuning ratio

$$\frac{\omega - \omega_0}{\omega_0}$$

The family of curves shows a very marked peak of resonance. It is seen that the smaller the value of k in a vibrating system, the more marked the resonance, and even a very small "getting out of tune" is sufficient to reduce the amplitude considerably. Since along the "resonance curves" marked resonance exists only at frequencies at which the resonance really occurs the curves are also called "response curves". Response is specifically termed to denote, e.g. the deflections produced by the dynamic load.

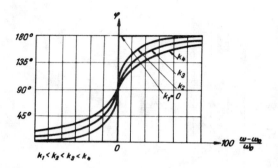

Fig. 22. Vibration of the phase angle φ

Figure 22 indicates how the phase angle between the amplitude (A) and the disturbing force (P) varies with changes in the tuning ratio

$$\frac{\omega - \omega_0}{\omega_0}$$

Other conditions are the same as in Fig. 21.

It can be seen that in the event of resonance $\dfrac{\omega - \omega_0}{\omega_0} = 0$ and $\varphi = 90$ degrees, that is, the work performed by the external disturbing force is the largest. Another conclusion to be drawn from Fig. 22 is that at low frequencies, i.e. if $\omega < \omega_0$, then $\varphi \approx 0$. In the case of very marked resonance peaks, when the tangent drawn to the curves at the point of inflexion is perpendicular to the abscissa, the transition through resonance may result in an abrupt change in phase of almost 180 degrees. For purposes of clarity, relationships applying to vibrating single-mass systems are given in Table 3.

C) VIBRATIONS EXCITED BY ROTATING MASSES

In the case of machine foundations for many systems the vibrations are excited by forces from unbalanced masses. When on a foundation mass m a mass m_e is rotating with the eccentricity of e according to Fig. 23, the exciting force is

$$P_0 = m_e e \omega^2 \tag{61}$$

TABLE 3

Characteristic relations	Type of vibration			
	Undamped		Damped	
	free	forced	free	forced
Arrangement		$P = P_0 \sin \omega t$		$P = P_0 \sin \omega t$
1 Circular frequency	$\omega_0 = \sqrt{\dfrac{c}{m}}$	$\omega = \text{const.}$	$\omega^2 = \omega_0^2 - \dfrac{k^2}{4m^2}$	$\omega = \text{const.}$
2 Vibrations per second (frequency) cps	$n = \dfrac{\omega_0}{2\pi}$	$n = \dfrac{\omega}{2\pi}$	$n = \dfrac{\omega'}{2\pi}$	$n = \dfrac{\omega}{2\pi}$
3 Vibrations per minute	$N = 60n = \dfrac{300}{\sqrt{\delta}}$	$N_m = 60n$	$N = 60n$	$N_m = 60n$
4 Duration of one period	$T = \dfrac{1}{n} = \dfrac{2\pi}{\omega_0}$	$T = \dfrac{2\pi}{\omega}$	$T = \dfrac{1}{n} = \dfrac{2\pi}{\omega'}$	$T = \dfrac{2\pi}{\omega}$

Instead of an exciting constant force of $P = P_0 \sin \omega t$, the value of P_0 can be replaced by Eq. (61), thus

$$P_e = m_e e \omega^2 \sin \omega t \tag{62}$$

In the case of a force generator as in Fig. 24, two counter-rotating unbalanced eccentric masses m_1 are present at the eccentricity of e. The phase relationship of

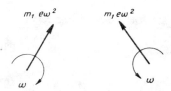

Fig. 23. Eccentric mass exciting a one degree of freedom damped system

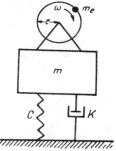

Fig. 24. Rotating mass excitation produced by two counter-rotating masses represented by force vectors

these masses is such that the addition of the two vertical components is assured, as the horizontal component is cancelled. The total eccentric mass is therefore the addition of the two masses $m_e = 2m_1$.

The exciting force is thus

$$P_e = m_e e \omega^2 \sin \omega t \tag{63}$$

Previously the constant force type excitation was discussed and it was found that according to Eq. (56) the amplitude depended on the constant force P_0:

$$A = \frac{P_0}{c} v$$

Instead of this value for a rotating type excitation the value of P_e (63) could be substituted giving an amplitude

$$A = \frac{m_e e \omega^2}{c} = \frac{m_e}{m} \cdot \frac{m}{c} e \omega^2$$

or since

$$\frac{m}{c}=\left(\frac{1}{\omega_0}\right)^2,$$

$$A=\frac{m_e e}{m}\left(\frac{\omega}{\omega_0}\right)^2 \tag{64}$$

which is the force amplitude for the rotating eccentric mass. The phase angle φ remains the same as in Eq. (57).

The corresponding response curves will be given in Chapter VI, p. 160, in Fig. 80.

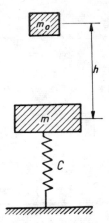

Fig. 25. Impact or collision effect for a one degree of freedom system

D) IMPACT OR COLLISION EFFECT

This effect is important in hammer foundations, where the dynamic loading on the structure is an interacting effect depending upon the motion of the structure and the striking mass.

We suppose, in the case of two masses, a centric load falling from a height h (Fig. 25). If the mass of the falling load is given by m_0 and the mass below is m we obtain, according to the law of impact after the shock:

$$mv' + m_0 v_0' = mv + m_0 v_0 \tag{65}$$

If the impact is not elastic at all

$$v = v_0 \tag{66}$$

Here v' is the velocity of the mass m, v_0' is the velocity of m_0 before the blow and v and v_0 are the velocities after the blow.

From (65) and (66) we obtain

$$v = \frac{mv' + m_0 v_0'}{m + m_0} \tag{67}$$

If v' is equal to zero before the impact, then

$$v = v_0' \frac{m_0}{m + m_0} \tag{68}$$

If the impact is completely elastic we get, according to the fact that the sum of the kinetic and potential energy of the system is at every instant equal,

$$\frac{1}{2}(mv'^2 + m_0 v_0'^2) = \frac{1}{2}(mv^2 + m_0 v_0^2) \tag{69}$$

For $v' = 0$,

$$v = v_0' \frac{2m_0}{m_0 + m}$$

If the collision of the bodies is plastic in character, for $v' = 0$ we get

$$v = v_0'(1 + k)\frac{m_0}{m_0 + m} \tag{70}$$

The values of $k = \dfrac{v_0' - v'}{v - v_0} = 0$ to 1 are called the coefficients of impact.

Supposing the weight falling from height h on a system of one degree of freedom composed of the mass m_0 falling on the mass $m = G/g$, supported by a spring of the spring-constant c, we get for the velocity of the mass m_0 just before the impact

$$v_0' = \sqrt{2gh}$$

The velocity of the mass m after the blow is to be obtained according to Eq. (70). The corresponding velocity is

$$\dot{v} = v_0 \omega_0 \cos(\omega_0 t + \varphi_0).$$

If we have the initial conditions: $v(0) = 0$; $\dot{v}_0 = v$; and $\varphi_0 = 0$:

$$v_0 = \frac{v}{\omega_0} = v\sqrt{\frac{G}{gC}} \tag{71}$$

The amplitude in the spring will be

$$A = v_0 C = v\sqrt{\frac{CG}{g}} \tag{72}$$

Similar impact effect problems will be treated in more detail in Vol. II Chapter II dealing with hammer foundations.

Different impulsive loading effects, where the dynamic loading is generally independent of the motion of the structure, will be treated in the next section.

E) IMPULSIVE DYNAMIC LOADING

Similar to the differential equation (47) setting up sinosoidal undamped dynamic effect, the expression for an impulsive load $P(t)$ is

$$m\ddot{z}(t) + cz(t) = P(t) \tag{73}$$

For conditions of $z(0) = 0$, $\dot{z} = 0$ for the values of $0 \leq t < \tau$, since $\omega_0 = \sqrt{c/m}$ and P_0/c is the static effect, and from the complete solution the first two terms could be neglected and the amplitude is influenced by the third term .

$$z = \frac{P_0}{c} v , \tag{74}$$

where v is the dynamic loading factor

$$v = \omega_0 \int_0^t f(t) \sin \omega_0 T(t - t') \, dt \tag{75}$$

where $\omega_0 = \dfrac{2\pi}{T_1}$, with T_1 being the fundamental period of the structure. Here t is the time which should be taken into consideration for the determination of the motion due to the impact form. For τ, the time of the force effect, the same formula as (75) is valid putting the value of τ in the formula instead of t.

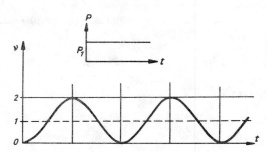

Fig. 26. Dynamic loading factor for a suddenly applied load

In the case of a suddenly applied load the dynamic loading factor will be $v = 1 - \cos \omega_o t$ and $v_{\max} = 2$. We see in Fig 26 that here twice the response of the static load is produced as the maximum dynamic load.

As in practice some damping is always present in the structure the term $\cos \omega_0 t$ does not exist and the dynamic factor remains close to 1. Without any damping the maximum dynamic effect of 2 will be obtained during the first cycle.

For six different pulse loads based on expression (75) solutions are given in the graphical representation of Fig. 27 after Sorokin [1167] and in [398] where the dynamic factor values symbolized by κ are plotted against the τ/T_1 rations. These pulse loads are rectangular (1), different kinds of triangular pulses (2), (3), (5), one half cycle sine pulse (4) and a full cycle versed sine pulse (6).

It is seen from the figure that as long as the value of τ/T_1 is less than $1/2T_1$, the shapes for all cases are quite similar. This is important, for example, for an isolation system, showing that when the duration of the shock pulse is short compared with the natural period of the system on which it acts, the severity of the shock is determined solely by the area of the shock pulse.

It should be mentioned that the difference in resonant frequency between damped and undamped resonances is generally small ($D \leq 1$). Damped shock curves are given in Fig. 28, e.g. for the half cycle sine pulse. Here instead of $\omega_0 = \sqrt{c/m}$, rather the value of $\omega_0 = \sqrt{c/m} \cdot \sqrt{1-D^2}$ is to be taken into consideration where $D = k/k_c = k/2\sqrt{cm}$. Owing to the small difference in resonant frequency in practice, the resonance shift may be neglected in the calculations.

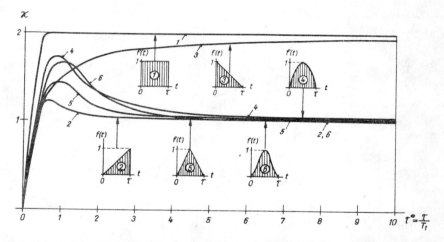

Fig. 27. Representation of the coefficient κ for six different pulse loads depending upon the $\tau = \tau/T_1$ ratios

For the different cases of explosive blasts or gusts due to wind, etc. a rectangular pulse load could be important.

Transforming formula (74) for the dynamical factor and putting instead of the maximum force P_0 the impulse force S as shown in Fig. 29 with the value

$$S = P_0 \int_0^\tau f(t)dt \tag{76}$$

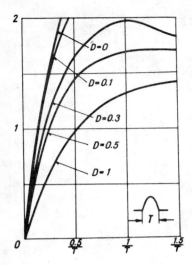

Fig. 28. Damped shock curves for the half
sine pulse

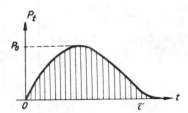

Fig. 29. Impulse force P_0 depending
upon t

and putting $T_1 = 2$, we obtain for the method based on the impulsive load after
[1167] for z_0:

$$z_0 = \varepsilon(\tau^*)\frac{s}{m\omega_0} \tag{77}$$

Here the value of $\varepsilon(\tau^*)$ is expressed by

$$\varepsilon(\tau^*) = \frac{\kappa(\tau^*)}{2\pi \int\limits_0^{\tau^*} f(t)dt} \tag{78}$$

For the six different pulse loads according to values from Eq. (76) for $\tau^* = \dfrac{\tau}{T_1}$ from 0.01 to 2.00, the coefficients ε [1167] are given in Table 4.

The $\varepsilon(\tau^*)$ values based on the impulsive force are plotted against the $\tau^* = \dfrac{\tau}{T_1}$ values in Fig. 30 [1167] for $\tau^* = \dfrac{\tau}{T_1}$ values from 0.01 to 10 with the corresponding values on the ordinate of 0.01 to 1. For the six different pulse loads for values between 0.01 to 2.0 the coefficients $\int\limits_0^{\tau} f(\tau)dt$ are given in Table 3. The shapes of the curves of Fig. 30 based on the impulse force are different from those of Fig. 27, showing monotonous downward tendencies and they are more suitable than the values of Fig. 27 based on the maximum force. For values $\tau^* = \dfrac{\tau}{T_1}$ from 2.5 until 20.0

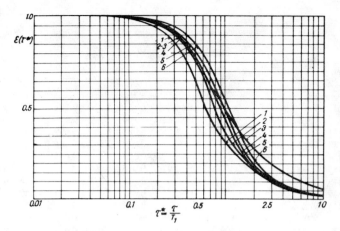

Fig. 30. Coefficients $\varepsilon(\tau^*)$ corresponding to the $\tau^* = \dfrac{\tau}{T_1}$ values for the six different pulse loads shown in *Fig. 26*

TABLE 4

Coefficients $z(\tau^*)$ for the six different pulsing loads according to $\int\limits_0^{\tau} f(\tau)dt$

$\tau^* = \dfrac{\tau}{T_1}$	Corresponding to the impulse cases of Fig. 26					
	1	2	3	4	5	6
0	1	1	1	1	1	1
0.01	1.000	1.000	1.000	1.000	1.000	1.000
0.05	0.996	0.999	0.999	0.999	0.999	0.998
0.10	0.983	0.990	0.990	0.991	0.994	0.993
0.15	0.963	0.974	0.974	0.979	0.981	0.985
0.20	0.936	0.958	0.958	0.963	0.968	0.974
0.25	0.900	0.933	0.933	0.943	0.950	0.960
0.30	0.858	0.905	0.905	0.917	0.930	0.943
0.35	0.810	0.872	0.872	0.890	0.902	0.923
0.40	0.757	0.835	0.835	0.858	0.875	0.901
0.45	0.697	0.797	0.800	0.823	0.844	0.876
0.50	0.637	0.755	0.761	0.785	0.811	0.849
0.60	0.530	0.664	0.692	0.705	0.739	0.788
0.70	0.455	0.569	0.631	0.625	0.667	0.724
0.80	0.398	0.477	0.579	0.552	0.559	0.661
0.90	0.354	0.416	0.533	0.489	0.537	0.599
1.0	0.318	0.369	0.494	0.433	0.480	0.543
1.2	0.265	0.301	0.429	0.344	0.383	0.444
1.4	0.227	0.253	0.379	0.277	0.306	0.365
1.6	0.199	0.219	0.340	0.227	0.244	0.301
1.8	0.177	0.192	0.307	0.192	0.208	0.252
2.0	0.159	0.172	0.280	0.167	0.184	0.212

TABLE 5

Values of the coefficients ε and κ according to the six pulsing loads

$\tau^* = \dfrac{\tau}{T_1}$	Corresponding to the impulse cases of Fig. 26											
	1		2		3		4		5		6	
	ε	κ	ε	κ	ε	κ	ε	κ	ε	κ	ε	κ
2.5	0.127	2.000	0.135	1.064	0.230	1.808	0.125	1.250	0.144	1.127	0.152	1.191
3.0	0.106	2.000	0.112	1.053	0.195	1.839	0.104	1.200	0.117	1.106	0.119	1.125
3.5	0.091	2.000	0.095	1.045	0.169	1.861	0.083	1.167	0.099	1.091	0.099	1.089
4.0	0.080	2.000	0.083	1.040	0.149	1.878	0.071	1.143	0.086	1.080	0.085	1.067
5.0	0.064	2.000	0.066	1.032	0.121	1.900	0.056	1.111	0.068	1.064	0.066	1.042
6.0	0.053	2.000	0.054	1.027	0.102	1.916	0.045	1.091	0.056	1.053	0.055	1.029
7.0	0.045	2.000	0.046	1.023	0.088	1.928	0.038	1.076	0.048	1.046	0.046	1.021
8.0	0.040	2.000	0.041	1.020	0.077	1.938	0.033	1.066	0.041	1.040	0.040	1.016
9.0	0.035	2.000	0.036	1.018	0.069	1.944	0.029	1.059	0.037	1.035	0.035	1.012
10.0	0.032	2.000	0.032	1.016	0.062	1.950	0.026	1.053	0.033	1.032	0.032	1.010
15.0	0.021	2.000	0.021	1.010	0.042	1.966	0.017	1.035	0.021	1.021	0.021	1.004
20.0	0.016	2.000	0.016	1.008	0.031	1.975	0.013	1.025	0.016	1.016	0.016	1.002

the corresponding values of ε and κ are given for the six cases in Table 5. The Soviet recommendations for the method of the coefficient of impact are based on the principles given above.

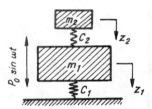

Fig. 31. Two-mass two degree of freedom system

F) FORCED VIBRATION OF A TWO-DEGREE OF FREEDOM SYSTEM

We have seen the single degree of freedom system where the geometrical system was expressed at any instant by one number only. Two rigid bodies connected by springs in such a manner that each body can move along a straight line and cannot rotate has two degrees of freedom. Such systems are often applied in machine foundations. Vibration elimination can also be achieved by similar arrangements. In Fig. 31 two masses m_1 and m_2 are connected by springs c_1 and c_2. The system will vibrate excited by a harmonic force $P = P_0 \sin \omega t$ in the vertical direction. The displacement of the system is characterized by the coordinates z_1 and z_2 and the related differential equations are

$$m_1 z_1 + c_1 z_1 + c_2(z_1 - z_2) = P_0 \sin \omega t$$

$$m_2 z_2 + c_2(z_2 - z_1) = 0 \tag{79}$$

As the free vibrations due to damping quickly approach zero the forced vibrations become decisive and therefore the related displacements are

$$z_1 = z_{01} \sin \omega t$$

$$z_2 = z_{02} \sin \omega t \tag{80}$$

Substituting the values of (80) into the expressions (79) and eliminating $\sin \omega t$, we obtain

$$(-\omega^2 m_1 + c_1 + c_2)z_{01} - c_2 z_{02} = P_0 \tag{81}$$

$$-c_1 z_{01} + (-m_2 \omega^2 + c_2)z_{02} = 0 \tag{82}$$

Introducing the following symbols:

$\delta_0 = \dfrac{P_0}{c_1}$ the displacement of m_1 caused by the static force P_0,

$\omega_{01} = \sqrt{\dfrac{c_1}{m_1}}$ the natural frequency of the system (m_1, c_1),

$\omega_{02} = \sqrt{\dfrac{c^2}{m^2}}$ the natural frequency of the system (m_2, c_2).

Substituting these values into (79) we get

$$\left(1 + \frac{c_2}{c_1} - \frac{\omega^2}{\omega_{01}^2}\right)z_{01} - \frac{c_2}{c_1}z_{02} = \delta_0 \tag{83}$$

$$z_{01} = z_{02}\left(1 - \frac{\omega^2}{\omega_{02}^2}\right) \tag{84}$$

Solving Eq. 84 for z_{01} and z_{02} we get

$$\left.\begin{aligned}
\frac{z_{01}}{\delta_0} &= \frac{1 - \dfrac{\omega^2}{\omega_{02}^2}}{\left(1 - \dfrac{\omega^2}{\omega_{02}^2}\right)\left(1 + \dfrac{c_2}{c_1} - \dfrac{\omega^2}{\omega_{01}^2}\right) - \dfrac{c_2}{c_1}} \\[4ex]
\frac{z_{02}}{\delta_0} &= \frac{1}{\left(1 - \dfrac{\omega^2}{\omega_{02}^2}\right)\left(1 + \dfrac{c_2}{c_1} - \dfrac{\omega^2}{\omega_{01}^2}\right) - \dfrac{c_2}{c_1}}
\end{aligned}\right\} \tag{85}$$

It is interesting to realize here that in the case of $\omega = \omega_{02}$, the amplitude of the vibration of mass m_1, $z_{01} = 0$, i. e. the mass m_1 remains at rest and the equation for the vibration of the mass m_2 will be

$$z_{02} = \frac{P_0}{c_2} \sin \omega t$$

To make sure that the mass m_1 remains at rest even though there is an exciting force acting on the system, we arrive at a suitable solution by connecting it with a mass m_2 thereby ensuring the condition

$$\omega = \omega_{02}^2 = \frac{c_2}{m_2}.$$

With such an arrangement, vibration isolation or a considerable damping effect can be obtained.

Cases for three degrees of freedom systems will be treated in section 7, and mentioned in Vol II Chapter II on hammer foundations.

6. Forced vibrations of machine foundations

Operating machines transmit, through the foundation, forced vibrations to the soil. Considerations are generally related to an implicit fundamental theory according to which the vibrating body is assumed to obey Hooke's law $\varepsilon = \sigma/E$. According to this law the elastic deformation of the body under load is linear, obviously only up to the elastic limit. The graphic representation of Hooke's law is a straight line, as seen in Fig. 32 (dashed line). Vibrations at which the quasi-elastic force is not directly proportional to the displacement, i.e. vibrations which do not follow Hooke's law, are known as pseudoharmonic vibrations. In Fig. 32 the resonance curve is distorted towards the right and is related to the superlinear characteristic curve, at which, as against linear vibrations (dashed line) stiffness increases together with amplitude. In the opposite case, when the resonance curves diverge to the left, the vibrations are termed sublinear, where stiffness decreases with increasing amplitude (Fig. 33).

The soil is commonly assumed to have elastic properties consequently, its vibratory resistance is regarded as being proportional to the displacement characterized by the bedding coefficients according to the deformation of the soils: C_z for uniform compression, C_φ for nonuniform compression, C_x for uniform displacement and C_ψ for nonuniform displacement used in this part in Chapter VI and treated in detail in Chapter IX. Pseudoharmonic vibrations of rigid bodies and related computation methods are further treated in Chapters X–XII.

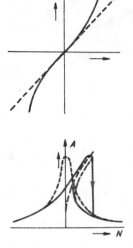

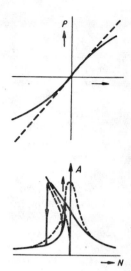

Fig. 32. Resonance curve at superlinear vibration

Fig. 33. Resonance curve at sublinear vibration

7. Multi-degree of freedom systems

Basic systems are simplified systems to which vibrations of complex machine foundations are reduced.

It is to be noted that there are numerous theoretical exact methods and approximate practical ones for the calculation of natural frequencies of different basic systems.

Thus Föppl in 1931 gave exact mathematical methods of vibration theory; Bleich in 1932–33 dealt with the theory and approximate solution for the vibration of beams; Hohenemser and Prager solved the problem of vibrations of beams by an approximate method in 1933 and made an estimate of the nodal points. Timoshenko in 1937, Firestone in 1938, Den Hartog in 1947, Freberg and Kemler in 1949, Hetényi in 1950, Söchting in 1951, Goldenblat and Sizov in 1952, Koloušek in 1953 and 1962, Snitko in 1953, all suggested solutions and equations for beams, frames, plates, etc. Bauer's work in 1953 contained a collection of formulae relying on the fundamental principles of the theory of vibration; Nesitka in 1955 gave differential equations in systems with several degrees of freedom; Jacobsen and Ayre in 1958 provided numerical and graphical theoretical methods and numerous approximate solutions of vibration problems, as well as an extended bibliography. The books of Norris et al. (1959), Klotter (1960), and Lorenz (1960)—with nomograms facilitating the practical application of the exact methods—should be mentioned. Using electronic computers the finite element method treated by

Clough in 1960, by Zienkiewicz et al. in 1966, by Lysmer and others in 1968 and the application of the transfer matrix method detailed in the work of Pestel and Leckie in 1963 also deserve mention. Tables for the natural frequencies of plates are given by Bareš in 1969; the works edited in 1970 by Korenev and in 1972 by Korenev and Rabinovitch discuss the related problems; the analysis of plates was also treated by Szilárd, in 1974.

Actually every elastic body consists of an infinite number of uniformly distributed mass points, and has infinitely many natural frequencies. Therefore the number of degrees of freedom is infinite. Degree of freedom is denoted by the number of coordinates characterizing the configuration of the system at any instant of the motion. The motion of a mass point in one direction can be characterized by a single coordinate therefore the system possesses one degree of freedom.

The motion of a system possessing one degree of freedom can be expressed mathematically by a simple differential equation; a finite system possessing several degrees of freedom, by a set consisting of a corresponding number of simple differential equations; a system of infinite degrees of freedom, by a partial differential equation or a set of such equations.

In the present study the following cases of natural frequencies of basic systems will be treated, taking into special consideration the practice of machine foundations:

  A. Accurate solution of systems with several degrees of freedom.
  B. Straight-line vibrations of multi-mass systems.
  C. Transverse vibrations of one- and two-mass systems.
  D. Vibrations of systems with infinite degrees of freedom.
  E. Approximate solutions.

A) ACCURATE SOLUTION OF SYSTEMS WITH SEVERAL DEGREES
      OF FREEDOM*

Calculation of Natural Frequencies. If the masses of an elastic multi-mass system are separated from each other, they can be displaced or rotated in n directions. The possibility of n displacements or rotations represents n degrees of freedom.

In the course of the following deduction, the following notations will be used for direction i:

> displacement (rotation) x_i
> mass (mass moment of inertia) m_i (Θ_i)
> force of inertia $m_i \ddot{x}_i$
> supporting force (moment) P_i

According to Maxwell, elasticity is characterized by influence factors a_{ik} in a manner that $a_{ik} = a_{ki}$ where a_{ik} denotes the displacement of mass i due to unit force at k and a_{ki} the displacement of mass k due to unit force at i. If, as according to Nesitka,

* After Nesitka [868].

we use the dual values P_{ik} instead of the influence factors, the values being generally known from the static computations, we obtain the following:

Let us suppose that the masses are restrained as regards their direction of motion. If the mass at point k is released and displaced by unity, then at various points, force P_{ik} arises. The force at point k itself is P_{kk} if the displacements x_i at points 1 to n are assumed by replacing supporting forces by inertial forces; when damping is disregarded, the equation of equilibrium at point k is:

$$x_1 P_{k1} + x_2 P_{k2} + \ldots + x_i P_{ki} + \ldots + x_k P_{kk} + \ldots + x_n P_{kn} = -m_k \ddot{x}_k \qquad (86)$$

For undamped conditions

$$x_i = \bar{x}_i \cos \omega t \qquad \text{and } \ddot{x}_i = \omega^2 \bar{x}_i \cos \omega t \qquad (87)$$

After transformation the differential equation assumes the form:

$$\bar{x}_1 P_{k1} + \bar{x}_2 P_{k2} + \ldots + \bar{x}_i P_{ki} + \ldots \bar{x}_k (P_{kk} - m_k \omega^2) + \ldots \bar{x}_n P_{kn} = 0 \qquad (88)$$

The n equations for vibrational amplitudes form a homogeneous set giving natural frequencies and modes of vibration. When the determinant formed from the coefficients of the set of equations is equal to zero, the equation of natural frequencies (ω) is obtained. For the frequencies ω we get n real solutions.

Coupled Vibrations. Should individual vibrations be coupled, a smaller degree of freedom results. The displacements under consideration being small, relations of a linear character can be assumed to exist between them:

$$x_k = c x_i$$

Owing to the positive coupling, only the components in direction x_i of forces acting upon individual masses are entered into the equation describing equilibrium conditions. The ith equation will become

$$x_i P_{i1} + \ldots = -Z_i \cos \alpha_i$$

while the kth equation must be added to the ith equation multiplied by c.

For example, by substituting into a set of equations with four degrees of freedom $x_4 = c x_3$ we obtain

$$
\begin{aligned}
&P_{11} - m_1 \omega^2 \quad P_{12} \qquad\qquad (P_{13} + c P_{14}) \\
&P_{21} \qquad\qquad P_{22} - m_2 \omega^2 \ (P_{23} + c P_{24}) \\
&(P_{31} + c P_{41}) P_{32} + c P_{42} \ (P_{33} + c P_{34}) + c(P_{43} + c P_{44}) - (m_3 + c^2 m_4)\omega^2
\end{aligned}
\qquad (89)
$$

The solution hereafter is identical with that of a system having three degrees of freedom (see Vol. II, p. 43).

Construction of Natural Modes of Vibration. If the natural frequencies obtained are introduced successively into the set of Eqs. (86), n homogeneous sets of equations are obtained. The solution of the equation can be written in the following form:

$$\bar{x}_1 : \bar{x}_2 : \ldots : \bar{x}_k : \ldots : \bar{x}_n = (-1)^{i+1}\frac{D_{i1}}{\sqrt{m_1}} : (-1)^{i+2}\frac{D_{i2}}{\sqrt{m_2}} : \ldots$$

$$: \ldots : (-1)^{i+k}\frac{D_{ik}}{\sqrt{m_k}} : \ldots : (-1)^{i+n} \cdot \frac{D_{in}}{\sqrt{m_n}} \tag{90}$$

where D_{ik} is the subdeterminant belonging to the ikth member. Vibrations are perpendicular to each other, i.e.

$$\sum_{i=1}^{n} m_i \bar{x}_{ki} \bar{x}_{li} = 0 \tag{91}$$

Forced Vibrations. If the vibrating system is subjected to an impulse, i.e. set into motion by a single impact, the system vibrates—according to its natural mode of vibration—with its natural frequency. In the case of periodic impulses, however, the system assumes the frequency of the disturbing force. The modes of forced vibrations and the magnitudes of amplitudes are given by the solution of the set of equations (see following equation 93). It is assumed, however, that damping is negligibly small except in the proximity of resonance, where it must be taken into consideration.

If a periodic force acts at the ith point in direction x_i, then

$$Q_i(t) = Q_i \cos \omega t \tag{92}$$

$$\bar{x}_1(P_{11} - m_1\omega^2) + \bar{x}_2 P_{12} + \bar{x}_i P_{1i} + \ldots + \bar{x}_n P_{1n} = 0$$
$$\bar{x}_1 P_{21} \qquad\qquad + \bar{x}_2(P_{22} - m_2\omega^2) + x_i P_{2i} + \ldots x_n P_{2n} = 0$$

$$\begin{matrix} \cdot & & \cdot & & \cdot \\ \cdot & & \cdot & & \cdot \\ \cdot & & \cdot & & \cdot \end{matrix}$$

$$\bar{x}_1 P_{i1} \qquad\qquad + x_2 P_{i2} + \ldots \bar{x}_i(P_{ii} - m_i\omega^2) + \bar{x}_n P_{in} = Q_i$$

$$\begin{matrix} \cdot & & \cdot & & \cdot \\ \cdot & & \cdot & & \cdot \\ \cdot & & \cdot & & \cdot \end{matrix}$$

$$\bar{x}_1 P_{n1} + \bar{x}_2 P_{n2} + \ldots \bar{x}_i P_{ni} + \ldots \bar{x}_n(P_{nn} - m_n\omega^2) = 0 \tag{93}$$

The solution of the equation is

$$x_k = Q_i(-1)^{i+k}\bar{D}_{ik})\bar{D} \tag{94}$$

where $\bar{D}_{ik}$ represents the subdeterminant of the set of equations belonging to the ikth member.

Introducing

$$\frac{P_{ik}}{\sqrt{m_i m_k}} = (ik),$$

Eq. (94) assumes the form:

$$x_k = \frac{Q_i(-1)^{i+k}\bar{D}_{ik}}{\sqrt{m_i m_k D}}$$ (95)

It follows from Eq. (95) that the value of x_k becomes infinitely large if the disturbing frequency ω is identical with one of the natural frequencies, and that $x_k = 0$ if the determinant of the numerator equals zero, and if $k = i$, the system has a nodal point in i. Natural frequency is identical with the frequency of forced vibration, the mass itself remaining motionless.

Systems having two, three and four degrees of freedom are treated here according to the requirements of practice with the remark that systems of three (formula (106)), four (formula (109)) and more degrees of freedom are easily solved by means of electronic computers using well-known algebraic operations.

(a) Systems having two degrees of freedom

The coefficient determinant of the frequency equation is in this case:

$$\begin{vmatrix} P_{11} - m_1\omega^2 & P_{12} \\ P_{21} & P_{22} - m_2\omega^2 \end{vmatrix} = 0$$ (96)

For the sake of symmetry and uniform dimensions the ith row and the ith column are divided by $\sqrt{m_i}$. With the notations:

$$\frac{P_{ik}}{\sqrt{m_i m_1}} = (ik) \quad \text{and} \quad \omega^2 = \lambda$$

Eq. (96) becomes:

$$\begin{vmatrix} (11) - \lambda & (12) \\ (21) & (22) - \lambda \end{vmatrix} = 0$$ (97)

or developed according to the powers of λ:

$$\lambda^2 - \lambda \Lambda_1 + \Lambda_2^2 = 0$$ (98)

where

$$\Lambda_1 = (11) + (22)$$

$$\Lambda_2^2 = \begin{vmatrix} (11) & (12) \\ (21) & (22) \end{vmatrix}$$ (99)

Introducing the coefficients:

$$\kappa = \frac{\lambda}{\Lambda_1} \quad \text{and} \quad \alpha = \frac{\Lambda_2^2}{\Lambda_1^2}$$

we obtain

$$\kappa^2 - \kappa + \alpha = 0 \tag{100}$$

The solution of this equation is

$$\kappa_{12} = \frac{1}{2} \pm \sqrt{\frac{1}{4} - \alpha} \tag{101}$$

The roots are real and positive, if

$$0 \leqq \alpha \leqq \frac{1}{4}$$

(b) Systems having three degrees of freedom

The coefficient determinant of the frequency equation is in this case

$$\begin{vmatrix} P_{11} - m_1\omega^2 & P_{12} & P_{13} \\ P_{21} & P_{22} - m_2\omega^2 & P_{23} \\ P_{31} & P_{32} & P_{33} - m_3\omega^2 \end{vmatrix} = 0 \tag{102}$$

Simplified in the same manner as Eq. (97), it assumes the form

$$\begin{vmatrix} (11) - \lambda & (12) & (13) \\ (21) & (22) - \lambda & (23) \\ (31) & (32) & (33) - \lambda \end{vmatrix} = 0 \tag{103}$$

or developed according to the powers of λ we have

$$-\lambda^3 + \lambda^2 \Lambda_1 - \lambda \Lambda_2^2 + \Lambda_3^3 = 0 \tag{104}$$

where

$$\Lambda_1 = (11) + (22) + (33)$$

$$\Lambda_2^2 = \begin{vmatrix} (11) & (12) \\ (21) & (22) \end{vmatrix} + \begin{vmatrix} (11) & (13) \\ (31) & (33) \end{vmatrix} + \begin{vmatrix} (22) & (23) \\ (32) & (33) \end{vmatrix} \tag{105}$$

$$\Lambda_3^3 = \begin{vmatrix} (11) & (12) & (13) \\ (21) & (22) & (23) \\ (31) & (32) & (33) \end{vmatrix}$$

Introducing the coefficients

$$\kappa = \frac{\lambda}{\Lambda_1} ; \quad \alpha = \frac{\Lambda_2^2}{\Lambda_1^2} ; \quad \beta = \frac{\Lambda_3^3}{\Lambda_1^3}$$

the equation becomes:

$$-\kappa^3 + \kappa^2 = \alpha\kappa - \beta \qquad (106)$$

If

$$0 \leq \alpha \leq \frac{1}{3}$$

$$0 \leq \beta \leq \frac{1}{27}$$

three real roots are obtained.

(c) Systems having four degrees of freedom

The coefficient determinant of the frequency equation is

$$\begin{vmatrix} P_{11} - m_1\omega^2 & P_{12} & P_{13} & P_{14} \\ P_{21} & P_{22} - m_2\omega^2 & P_{23} & P_{24} \\ P_{31} & P_{32} & P_{33} - m_3\omega^2 & P_{34} \\ P_{41} & P_{42} & P_{43} & P_{44} - m_4\omega^2 \end{vmatrix} = 0 \qquad (107)$$

In general $P_{ik} = P_{ki}$. For the sake of symmetry and of uniform dimensions the *i*th column is divided by $\sqrt{m_i}$. With the notations

$$P_{ik}\sqrt{m_i m_k} = (ik) ; \qquad \omega^2 = \lambda$$

Eq. (107) assumes the form:

$$\begin{vmatrix} (11) - \lambda & (12) & (13) & (14) \\ (21) & (22) - \lambda & (23) & (24) \\ (31) & (32) & (33) - \lambda & (34) \\ (41) & (42) & (43) & (44) - \lambda \end{vmatrix} = 0 \qquad (108)$$

Developed according to the powers of λ, we have

$$\lambda^4 - \lambda^3 \Lambda_1 + \lambda^2 \Lambda_2^2 - \lambda \Lambda_3^3 + \Lambda_4^4 = 0 \qquad (109)$$

where

$$\Lambda_1 = (11) + (22) + (33) + (44)$$

$$\Lambda_2^2 = \begin{vmatrix} (11) & (12) \\ (21) & (22) \end{vmatrix} + \begin{vmatrix} (11) & (13) \\ (31) & (33) \end{vmatrix} + \begin{vmatrix} (11) & (14) \\ (41) & (44) \end{vmatrix} +$$

$$+ \begin{vmatrix} (22) & (23) \\ (32) & (33) \end{vmatrix} + \begin{vmatrix} (22) & (24) \\ (42) & (44) \end{vmatrix} + \begin{vmatrix} (33) & (34) \\ (43) & (44) \end{vmatrix} ;$$

$$\Lambda_3^3 = \begin{vmatrix} (11) & (12) & (13) \\ (21) & (22) & (23) \\ (31) & (32) & (33) \end{vmatrix} + \begin{vmatrix} (11) & (12) & (14) \\ (21) & (22) & (24) \\ (41) & (42) & (44) \end{vmatrix} + \begin{vmatrix} (11) & (13) & (14) \\ (31) & (33) & (34) \\ (41) & (43) & (44) \end{vmatrix} +$$

$$+ \begin{vmatrix} (22) & (23) & (24) \\ (32) & (33) & (34) \\ (42) & (43) & (44) \end{vmatrix} \tag{110}$$

$$\Lambda_4^4 = \begin{vmatrix} (11) & (12) & (13) & (14) \\ (21) & (22) & (23) & (24) \\ (31) & (32) & (33) & (34) \\ (41) & (42) & (43) & (44) \end{vmatrix}$$

In the course of computing work the following checks on correctness are available (see Biezeno and Grammel, [98] Vol. I, p. 161).

$$\sum_{i=1}^{n} (ii) = \sum_{l=1}^{n} \lambda_1$$

and

$$\sum_{i=1}^{n} \sum_{k=1}^{n} (ik)^2 = \sum_{l-1}^{n} \lambda_1^2 \tag{111}$$

If the notations

$$\kappa = \frac{\lambda}{\Lambda_1}; \quad \alpha = \frac{\Lambda_2^2}{\Lambda_1^2}; \quad \beta = \frac{\Lambda_3^3}{\Lambda_1^3}; \quad \gamma = \frac{\Lambda_4^4}{\Lambda_1^4} \tag{112}$$

are introduced the equation becomes

$$\kappa^4 - \kappa^3 + \alpha \kappa^2 = \beta \kappa - \gamma \tag{113}$$

The criteria for the existence of four real roots are

$$0 \leq \alpha \leq \frac{3}{8}$$

$$0 \leq \beta \leq \frac{1}{16}$$

$$0 \leq \gamma \leq \frac{1}{256}$$

An example for the use of the method is given in Vol. II. pp. 143–144 for a system with two degrees of freedom.

(d) Systems having six degrees of freedom

For such cases an eccentrically springing foundation [77], [739], [496] is shown as an example in Fig. 34. Here the centre of gravity is S with coordinates x, y and z and the centre of elasticity is 0 with the coordinates ξ, η and ζ and with the moments of inertia I'_x I'_y and I'_z relating to the coordinate-system x, y and z and with the mass moments Θ_x, Θ_y Θ_z relating to the axes ξ, η and ζ.

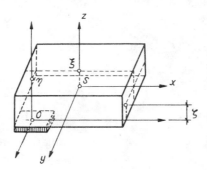

Fig. 34. Excentrically springing foundation as an example of a six degree of freedom system

Computation of the natural frequencies. A base surface F and the soil coefficients C_x, C_y, C_ϕ and C_ψ (see Chapter IX. Sec. 2) are supposed.

For the six degrees of freedom system the corresponding equations are:

$$m\ddot{x} + C_xF\,(x - \zeta\varphi_y - \eta\varphi_z) = 0$$
$$m\ddot{y} + C_xF\,(y - \zeta\varphi_x - \xi\varphi_z) = 0$$
$$m\ddot{z} + C_zF\,(z - \eta\varphi_x - \xi\varphi_y) = 0$$

$$\Theta_x\ddot{\varphi}_x + C_\varphi I'_x\varphi_x - \eta C_zF\,(z - \eta\varphi_x - \xi\varphi_y) - \zeta C_xF\,(y - \zeta\varphi_x - \xi\varphi_z) = 0$$
$$\Theta_y\ddot{\varphi}_y + C_\varphi I'_y\varphi_y - \xi C_zF\,(z - \eta\varphi_x - \xi\varphi_y) - \zeta C_xF\,(x - \zeta\varphi_y - \eta\varphi_z) = 0$$
$$\Theta_z\ddot{\varphi}_z + C_\psi I'_z\varphi_z - \xi C_xF\,(y - \zeta\varphi_x - \xi\varphi_z) - \eta C_xF\,(x - \zeta\varphi_y - \xi\varphi_z) = 0$$

(114)

Supposing the following conditions

$$x = A_x \sin \omega t, \qquad y = A_y \sin \omega t, \qquad z = A_z \sin \omega t$$

$$\varphi_x = \alpha_x \sin \omega t, \qquad \varphi_y = \alpha_y \sin \omega t, \qquad \varphi_z = \alpha_z \sin \omega t$$

(115)

and reducing by $\sin \omega t$ we obtain for the corresponding accelerations

$$\ddot{x} = -A\omega^2, \qquad \ddot{y} = -A_y\omega^2, \qquad \ddot{z} = -A_z\omega^2$$

$$\ddot{\varphi}_x = -\alpha_x\omega^2, \qquad \ddot{\varphi}_y = -\alpha_y\omega^2, \qquad \ddot{\varphi}_z = -\alpha_z\omega^2$$

(116)

Putting Eqs. (115) and (116) into Eq. (114) and by rearranging according to A_x, A_y, A_z, α_x, α_y and α_z we obtain the following equations

$$A_x(C_xF - m\omega^2) - \alpha_y\zeta C_xF - \alpha_z\eta C_xF = 0$$

$$A_y(C_xF - m\omega^2) - \alpha_x\zeta C_xF - \alpha_z\xi C_xF = 0$$

$$A_z(C_zF - m\omega^2) - \alpha_x\eta C_zF - \alpha_y\xi C_zF = 0$$

$$-A_y\zeta C_xF - A_z\eta C_zF + \alpha_x(\eta^2 C_zF + \zeta^2 C_xF -$$

$$-\Theta_x\omega^2 + C_\varphi I'_x) + \alpha_y\xi\eta C_zF + \alpha_z\xi\zeta C_xF = 0 \qquad (117)$$

$$-A_x\zeta C_xF - A_z\xi C_zF + \alpha_x\xi\eta C_zF + \alpha_y(C_\phi I'_y +$$

$$+\zeta^2 C_xF + \xi^2 C_zF - \Theta_y\omega^2) + \alpha_z\eta\zeta C_xF = 0$$

$$-A_x\eta C_xF - A_y\xi C_xF + \alpha_x\xi\zeta C_xF + \alpha_y\eta\zeta CF +$$

$$+\alpha_z(C_\psi I'_z + \xi^2 C_xF + \eta^2 C_xF - \Theta_z\omega^2) = 0$$

The natural frequencies are gained by putting the determinant D (composed by the coefficients A_x, A_y, A_z α_x, α_y, α_z) equal to zero. Thus

$$D = \begin{vmatrix}
C_xF - m\omega^2 & 0 & 0 & 0 & -\zeta C_xF & -\eta C_xF \\
0 & C_xF - m\omega^2 & 0 & -\zeta C_xF & 0 & \xi C_xF \\
0 & 0 & C_zF - m\omega^2 & -\eta C_zF & -\xi C_zF & 0 \\
0 & -\zeta C_xF & -\eta C_zF & \begin{aligned}&C_\phi I'_x + \\ &+\zeta^2 C_xF + \\ &+\eta^2 C_zF - \\ &-\Theta_x\omega^2\end{aligned} & \xi\eta C_zF & \xi\zeta C_xF \\
-\zeta C_xF & 0 & -\xi C_zF & \xi\eta C_zF & \begin{aligned}&C_\phi I'_y + \\ &+\zeta^2 C_xF + \\ &+\xi^2 C_zF \\ &-\Theta_y\omega^2\end{aligned} & \eta\zeta C_xF \\
-\eta C_xF & -\xi C_xF & 0 & \xi\zeta C_xF & \xi\zeta C_xF & \begin{aligned}&C_\psi I'_z + \\ &+\xi^2 C_xF + \\ &+\eta^2 C_xF - \\ &-\Theta_z\omega^2\end{aligned}
\end{vmatrix} = 0 \qquad (118)$$

Computation of the amplitudes. For a supposed force P and the related moments the components P_x, P_y, P_z and M_x, M_y and M_z are maximum values of the excitation. Using matrix notations

$$\bar{\bar{A}} \cdot \bar{a} = \bar{b}, \tag{119}$$

where the elements of the matrix $\bar{\bar{A}}$ are the same as the elements of the determinant D, we obtain

$$\bar{a} = \begin{matrix} A_x \\ A_y \\ A_z \\ x \\ y \\ z \end{matrix} \tag{120}$$

and

$$\bar{b} = \begin{matrix} P_x \\ P_y \\ P_z \\ M_x \\ M_y \\ M_z \end{matrix} \tag{121}$$

The solutions are easily obtained by electronic computer using the relation

$$\bar{a} = \bar{\bar{A}}^{-1} \cdot \bar{b} \tag{122}$$

It is clear that the method can be simplified for a smaller number of freedom systems.

B) STRAIGHT-LINE VIBRATIONS OF MULTI-MASS SYSTEMS

The examples in this chapter relate to several masses, linked with springs, and to the determination of their natural frequencies. Naturally they can be applied to straight-line vibrations of one- and two-mass systems as well.

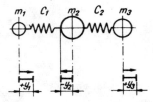

Fig. 35. Three-mass oscillating system

The following considerations are based on a three-mass system (Fig. 35).

If any of the masses of the system is displaced and afterwards released, then if no damping occurs the three masses will start vibrating with amplitudes y_1, y_2 and y_3, respectively.

The equations of motion are

(i) $m_1\ddot{y}_1 = -(y_1 - y_2)c_1$

(ii) $m_2\ddot{y}_2 = (y_1 - y_2)c_1 - (y_2 - y_3)c_2$ (123)

(iii) $m_3\ddot{y}_3 = (y_2 - y_3)c_2$

where on the right side of the equation are the restoring spring forces, and on the left side the inertial forces.

When combined, the equations yield the expression:

$$m_1 + m_2 + m_3 - \left[\frac{m_1 m_2}{c_1} + m_1 m_3 \left(\frac{1}{c_1} + \frac{1}{c_2}\right) + \frac{m_2 m_3}{c_2}\right]\lambda^2 +$$

$$+ m_1 m_2 m_3 \left(\frac{1}{c_1} \times \frac{1}{c_2}\right)\lambda^4 = 0$$

(124)

The two roots $(\lambda_1 \lambda_2)$ of the equation give the two angular frequencies with which the three-mass system can vibrate.

Two of the three masses vibrate in one direction, the third vibrates in the opposite direction, the maximum amplitude being reached by every mass at the same instant. The reduced equation for a three-mass system, Eq. (124), can be generalized for systems with any number of masses.

The terms of the equation are then as follows:

   (i) the first term is formed by the sum of masses;

   (ii) the second term comprises the quotients formed by the products of the permutation of any two masses and by the sum of the spring constants of the springs connecting them. The sign of the entire term is negative;

   (iii) the third term is the quotient of the products of the permutation of any three masses and of the products of the spring constants connecting them, etc.

For every system of masses the number of roots is one less than the number of masses.

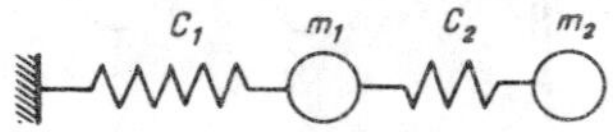

Fig. 36. Two-mass oscillating system fixed to the ground

If the swinging system is fixed by springs at one or both ends to a mass which is very large in comparison with the others, e.g. to the ground, then this mass should be regarded as infinitely large and $m = \infty$ should be substituted in the equation. Therefore a system fixed to the soil has as many roots as masses.

For instance, by replacing one mass of a three-mass system by the soil (Fig. 36) and considering its mass as infinitely large, further by dividing every member of the equation by m_3 and assuming the limit transition $m_3 \to \infty$, the following equation results:

$$1 - \lambda^2 \left[\frac{m_1}{c_1} + m_2 \left(\frac{1}{c_1} + \frac{1}{c_2} \right) \right] + \lambda^4 \frac{m_1 m_2}{c_1 c_2} = 0$$

The amplitude of the masses is obtained as the solution of the equations of moment:

$$\left. \begin{array}{l} y_1 = A_1 \sin (\lambda t + \varphi) \\ y_2 = A_2 \sin (\lambda t + \varphi) \\ y_3 = A_3 \sin (\lambda t + \varphi) \end{array} \right\} \tag{125}$$

Differentiating Eqs. (125) twice and substituting them in the equations of motion we get

$$\left. \begin{array}{l} -\lambda^2 m_1 A_1 = -(A_1 - A_2) c_1 \\ -\lambda^2 m_2 A_2 = (A_1 - A_2) c_1 - (A_2 - A_3) c_2 \\ -\lambda^2 m_3 A_3 = (A_2 - A_3) c_2 \end{array} \right\} \tag{126}$$

The addition of the equations yields

$$\Sigma m_i A_i = m_1 A_1 + m_2 A_2 + m_3 A_3 = 0 \tag{127}$$

indicating that the system has a single centre of gravity which does not suffer displacement in the course of vibration. The graphical determination of the mode of vibration is based on this consideration.

(a) Graphical determination of the mode of vibration

In determining natural frequency it is not the amplitudes of the masses, but the ratio of the amplitudes to each other which is of interest. Therefore, assuming for any amplitude (e.g. of a three-mass system), the arbitrary value A_1, we have

$$A_2 = A_1 \frac{\lambda^2 m_1 A_1}{c_1} \quad \text{and} \quad A_3 = A_2 - \frac{2(m_1 A_1 + m_2 A_2)}{c_2}$$

With these, if λ is known, the mode of vibration can be drawn. The ratio of the amplitudes is often known as a result of the symmetry of masses and spring constants. In similar cases the mode of vibration can be plotted by assuming the masses at distances corresponding to the spring constants, and by entering the amplitudes on the verticals of the masses. The line connecting the ordinates of the amplitudes intersects the axis at the nodal points. The system containing several masses can be reduced to the left and to the right of the nodal points to one-mass systems, the frequencies of which give the unknown roots of vibration. Once the spring constants are determined by measurement, the natural frequencies are obtained from the equation

$$\lambda = \sqrt{c/m}$$

In the case of the above three-mass system, the spring constants are plotted horizontally, whereas amplitudes are plotted in their original direction, i.e. vertically.

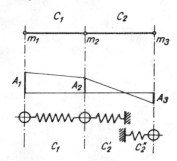

Fig. 37. First mode of vibration of a three-mass system (one nodal point)

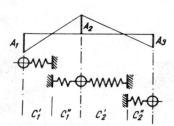

Fig. 38. Second mode of vibration of a three-mass system (two nodal points)

One mode of vibration is seen in Fig. 37. The intersection of the axis and of the line connecting the ordinates defines a nodal point. The system can be reduced to one-mass and two-mass systems of the same angular frequency, therefore:

$$\lambda_1 = \sqrt{\frac{c_2''}{m_3}}$$

The diagram of the second mode of vibration is shown in Fig. 38. The line connecting the amplitudes A_1, A_2, A_3 obtained with the help of λ_1 intersects the axis at nodal points; the system can thus be reduced to three one-mass systems. Consequently

$$\lambda_2 = \sqrt{\frac{c_1'}{m_1}} = \sqrt{\frac{c_2''}{m_3}}$$

There is always a fixed point at the point of attachment in a system fixed to the soil provided that the latter is considered a rigid body.

(b) Dunkerley's approximating method

This method can be used to determine the lowest so-called basic vibration of a system containing several masses arranged along a straight line (Fig. 39).

The system is reduced theoretically into three, each consisting of a single mass and all springs lying in the direction of the point of attachment. The natural frequencies of these systems are:

$$\lambda_I; \quad \lambda_{II}; \quad \lambda_{III}$$

where

$$\frac{1}{\lambda_T^2} = \frac{m_1}{c_1}; \quad \frac{1}{\lambda_{II}^2} = m_2 \left(\frac{1}{c_1} + \frac{1}{c_2} \right);$$

$$\frac{1}{\lambda_{III}^2} = m_3 \left(\frac{1}{c_1} + \frac{1}{c_2} + \frac{1}{c_3} \right)$$

and the approximate natural frequency of basic vibration is

$$\frac{1}{\lambda^2} = \frac{1}{\lambda_I^2} + \frac{1}{\lambda_{II}^2} \frac{1}{\lambda_{III}^2} \tag{128}$$

Natural frequencies computed by this approximating method are 5 to 10 per cent lower than the actual ones.

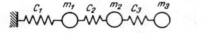

Fig. 39. Three-mass vibrating system
fixed to the ground

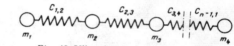

Fig. 40. Vibrating system with n masses

(c) Holzer's method

The approximating method developed by Holzer [469] lends itself to the determination of the natural frequency of multi-mass systems either without damping or with damping that can be neglected. In order to explain the essential features of this method reference is made to the n-mass system shown in Fig. 40.

Assume the system to vibrate with an angular frequency ω_1 which can be no natural frequency, if any external generating force is present. Assume further mass m_1 to move with an amplitude of unity, that is, 1 cm. Thus the equation of motion for mass m_1 is $x_1 = 1 \cdot \sin \omega_1 t$. Hence the greatest compression of the spring 1, 2, will be

$$x_{1,2} = \frac{m_1 \omega_1^2}{c_{1,2}} \tag{129}$$

Inasmuch as the displacement of mass m_1 is 1, and the compression of the spring is given by the above value, the displacement of mass m_2 is obtained as

$$x_2 = x_1 - x_{1,2} = 1 - \frac{m_1 \omega_1^2}{c_{1,2}} \tag{130}$$

Hence the maximum value of the force acting on mass m_2 is

$$P_2 = m_2 \omega_1^2 \left(1 - \frac{m_1 \omega_1^2}{c_{1,2}} \right) \tag{131}$$

and the compression of the spring

$$x_{2,3} = \frac{m_2 \omega_1^2 \left(1 - \dfrac{m_1 \omega_1^2}{c_{1,2}} \right)}{c_{2,3}} \tag{132}$$

Proceeding logically we reach the nth mass which cannot move unless acted upon by a force P_n. With free vibration, however, $P_n = 0$, and thus the necessary equation for computing the value of ω_1 is given.

The above approximating computation can be expediently carried out in the tabulated form shown in Table 6.

TABLE 6

ith natural frequency $\omega ij = \ldots \omega_{ij}^2 = \ldots j$th approximation

Mass no.	m_k (1)	$m_k \omega_i^2$ (2)	x_k (3)	$m_k \omega_{ij}^2 x_k$ (4)	$\sum_1^n m_k \omega_i^2 x_k$ (5)	$c_{k,k+1}$ (6)	$\dfrac{\sum_1^n m_k \omega_{ij}^2 x_k}{c_{k,k+1}}$ (7)
1							
2							
3							
n							

The numbers representing the magnitude of the individual masses are in the first column; the same values multiplied by the square of the assumed ω_{ij} are in the second. In the first line of the third column we must put 1, and in the other lines we enter the difference between the third and seventh columns of the preceding line. The fourth column is the product obtained by multiplying the second column by the third one, and the fifth column is the sum of the values of column 4. Columns 6 and 7 need no further explanation.

If the assumed value ω_{ij} is correct, the last line of column 5 will yield a value equal to 0. If not, the procedure must be repeated using a new value ω_{ij+1} until the correct value is found. This value of ω_{ij} is one of the natural frequencies of the system. If there is no reversal of sign in column 5, we obtain the first natural frequency, if there is only one reversal, we obtain the second natural frequency. In general, when k sign reversals take place we get the $(k+1)$th natural frequency of the system being studied. For the second, third, etc. approximating assumptions the following rule will provide guidance: with a positive remainder when looking for the first, third, etc. natural frequencies, we must try a higher value of ω; when looking for the second, fourth, etc. natural frequencies, we must try a lower value of ω. With a negative remainder we must proceed in the opposite way.

C) TRANSVERSE VIBRATIONS OF ONE- AND TWO-MASS SYSTEMS

This subsection is devoted to the investigation of vibrations of concentrated masses on rods, of which the mass can be neglected (Fig. 41).

The restoring elastic force developed by a rod displaced at the position of the mass by the distance y can be expressed as

$$P = \frac{y}{\eta} \qquad (133)$$

where η represents the displacement of the rod at the position of the mass, due to unit force.

The corresponding equation of motion is

$$m\ddot{y} = -P = -\frac{\eta}{y} \qquad (134)$$

(inertial force $= -$ spring force);

$$\ddot{y} + \lambda^2 y = 0$$

whence the angular frequency of the natural vibration is

$$\lambda^2 = \frac{1}{m\eta} \qquad (135)$$

The natural frequency per minute is obtained from the expression

$$N = \frac{300}{\sqrt{\delta}} \qquad (\delta \text{ in cm}) \qquad (136)$$

where δ is the deflection of the rod (cm) under the influence of mass m and at that position.

If there are two masses on a rod (Fig. 42), they may vibrate in two different ways: in the same direction or in opposite directions.

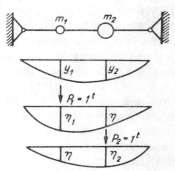

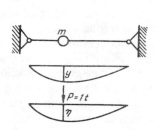

Fig. 41. Vibration of point-like mass on a rod of negligible mass

Fig. 42. Vibration of two point-like masses on a rod of negligible mass

Two natural frequencies, the first of them being the basic vibration, correspond to the above vibrations. When loaded simultaneously by masses m_1 and m_2, the deflections of the rod at the corresponding points will be denoted by y_1 and y_2, respectively; η_1 is the deflection of the rod at position m_1 when the rod is acted upon by the force $P_1 = 1$; η_2 is the deflection of the rod at the position of the other mass when $P = 1$ acts at the position of the first mass. According to Maxwell's theorem this value is the same in both cases.

$$y_1 = P_1\eta_1 + P_2\eta$$

$$y_2 = P_1\eta + P_2\eta_2$$

(137)

whence

$$P_1 = \frac{y_1\eta_2 - y_2\eta}{\eta_1\eta_2 - \eta^2} ; \qquad P_2 = \frac{y_2\eta_1 - y_1}{\eta_1\eta_2\eta^2}\eta$$

(138)

Since

$$-P_1 = m_1\ddot{y}_1 \qquad \text{and} \qquad -P_2 = m_2\ddot{y}_2$$

the equations of motion will be

$$m_1(\eta_1\eta_2 - \eta^2)\ddot{y}_1 + y_1\eta_2 - y_2\eta = 0$$

$$m_2(\eta_1\eta_2 - \eta^2)\ddot{y}_2 + y_2\eta_1 - y_1\eta = 0$$

(139)

The solution of the above set of equations is the expression:

$$m_1 m_2 (\eta_1\eta_2 - \eta^2) \lambda^4 - (m_1\eta_1 + m_2\eta_2) \lambda^2 + 1 = 0$$

(140)

The two roots of this expression yield the two natural frequencies.

D) VIBRATIONS OF SYSTEMS WITH INFINITE DEGREES OF FREEDOM

The neglect of the mass of the spring usually results in a rather high degree of inaccuracy. If the mass of the column carrying the masses of the horizontal shaft and the vibrating mass is to be taken into consideration, these must be regarded as a series of masses of infinite number, elastically coupled to one another. Consequently the vibrations of this system of masses will have an infinite number of different modes and, accordingly, an infinite number of natural frequencies.

Below we shall deal with (a) the natural transverse frequencies of beams with a continuous mass distribution subject to transverse vibrations, (b) the natural transverse frequencies of plates. Approximate solutions will be given in Section 7E.

The infinite number of masses of the above systems can be replaced with good approximation by a great but finite number of masses, yet even then we face a problem the solution of which is, for practical purposes, best suited to the electronic computer which is a routine and necessary tool in the theory and practice of most of the problems in the dynamics of civil engineering. About the use of computers for machine foundations, see more details in Vol. II, Chapter IV. Sec. 2; Vol. III, Chapter II. Sec. 2; further for building structures in Vol. IV, Chapter I. Sec. 5.

Several methods of computation can be found in the technical literature. Such a method is the phase plane method, a graphical method mentioned in Section D/c. The usefulness of the finite element method is mentioned in Section D/d especially in connection with soil dynamics. Because the details of this method are treated elsewhere, only basic principles with the relevant literature will be given here. Finally the transfer matrix method mentioned in Section D/e will be shown in more detail by examples in Volume III. The simple approximative solutions discussed in Section E remain familiar since the electronic computer is a popular tool in the applications. The accurate solution by means of successive approximations is given in (a) for small, finite numbers (two to four). Several methods are widely used giving quite satisfactory solutions for practical purposes. We shall consider one of these methods in Section 7Ea and, for others, reference will be made to the literature. A commonly used method of successive approximations will be described in (b).

(a) *Natural frequencies of prismatic structures with continuous mass distribution and constant cross-section*

We shall discuss transverse vibrations which are very important for prismatic structures.

To determine the transverse vibrations of a prismatic beam it should be noted that one mode of vibration $y(x)$ pertains in general to every natural frequency. The differential equation of the mode of vibration is

$$EI\frac{d^4y(x)}{dx^4} = \mu\lambda^2 y(x) \tag{141}$$

where E = Young's modulus of elasticity
     I = moment of inertia of the cross-section of the beam
     x = co-ordinate in the direction of the axis of the beam
     μ = mass per unit length
     λ = (provisionally unknown) natural transverse frequency of the beam.

Introducing the notation

$$b = \sqrt[4]{\frac{\mu\lambda^2}{EI}} \tag{142}$$

the solution will be

$$y(x) = C_1 \sinh bx + C_2 \cosh bx + C_3 \sin bx + C_4 \cos bx \tag{143}$$

The ratio of the unknown constants $C_1, \ldots, C_4$ can be computed from the conditions of the support of the beam. For the values of the constants C, four linear equations can be found. The determinant of this set of equations must be equated to zero in order to obtain a result other than zero. A transcendental expression, i.e. an

TABLE 7

Natural frequencies of transverse vibrations for beams

$$N(1/\text{Min}) = 9.55 \zeta_i \sqrt{\frac{EI}{\mu l^4}}$$

E = modulus of elasticity
I = moment of inertia of beam cross-section
μ = mass per unit length of the beam
l = length between the supports

	Fundamental mode	Second	Third	Fourth
		Natural mode of vibration		
Cantilever	$\zeta_1 = 3.52$	$\zeta_2 = 22.4$	$\zeta_3 = 61.7$	$\zeta_4 = 121.0$
Simply supported beam	$\zeta_1 = \pi^2 = 9.87$	$\zeta_2 = (2\pi)^2 = 39.5$	$\zeta_3 = (3\pi)^2 = 88.9$	$\zeta_4 = (4\pi)^2 = 158.0$
Fixed beam	$\zeta_1 = 22.4$	$\zeta_2 = 61.7$	$\zeta_3 = 121.0$	$\zeta_4 = 200.0$
Beam with one end simply supported, the other fixed	$\zeta_1 = 15.4$	$\zeta_2 = 50.0$	$\zeta_3 = 104.0$	$\zeta_4 = 178.0$
Beam simply supported on three supports	$\zeta_1 = 9.87$	$\zeta_2 = 15.4$	$\zeta_3 = 39.5$	$\zeta_4 = 50.0$

infinite number of natural frequencies, is thus obtained for λ. Various ratios of the constants C, corresponding to different values of λ, can readily be computed. These constants define the functions describing the various natural frequencies. The first four natural frequencies together with the corresponding modes of vibration have been compiled in Table 7 for some of the more important cases.

With modes of vibration of higher order, the beams are dimensioned for simply supported end conditions, and the span is taken as the distance between two adjacent nodal points. The amplitude is the deflection of this beam under the dynamic force (see Vols II and III), divided by the factor of fatigue (see Vols II and III).

(b) *Natural frequencies of transverse vibrations for slabs*

For determining the natural frequencies of transverse vibrations for slabs, reference is made to the works of Söchting [1158] and Timoshenko [1251]. Natural frequencies in the most important cases are given in Table 8.

(c) *Phase plane method*

This graphical method makes use of rotating vectors (Fig. 43). The terms of z and $\dot{z}/\omega_0$ are plotted graphically and the curve obtained thereby is the phase plane trajectory.

Considering a single degree of freedom system, the corresponding differential equation can be described by

$$m\ddot{z} + cz = P(t) \tag{144}$$

For $P = 0$ the solution of the free vibration system has the form

$$z = A \cos \omega_0 t + B \sin \omega_0 t \tag{145}$$

where $\omega_0 = \sqrt{c/m}$ and the equation describing the velocity of the mass will be

$$\frac{\dot{z}}{\omega_0} = -A \sin \omega_0 t + B \cos \omega_0 t \tag{146}$$

On squaring and adding Eqs. (145) and (146) we get

$$z^2 + \left(\frac{\dot{z}}{\omega_0}\right)^2 = A^2 + B^2 = R^2 \tag{147}$$

This is an equation of a circle with the coordinates of z and $\dot{z}/\omega_0$ and the radius is (Fig. 44)

$$R = \sqrt{A^2 + B^2} \tag{148}$$

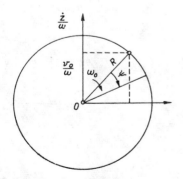

Fig. 43. Phase plan element for
$P = 0$

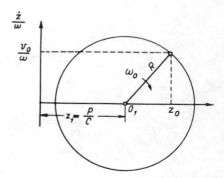

Fig. 44. Phase plan element for $P \neq 0$

TABLE 8

Natural frequencies of transverse vibrations for slabs

1. Fixed circular slabs

$$N(1/\text{min})=9.55\zeta\sqrt{\frac{Eh^3}{\mu R^4 : 12(1-v^2)}}$$

$E=$ modulus of elasticity
$h=$ thickness of slab
$\mu=$ mass per unit area of slab
$v=$ Poissons's number (steel: 0.3; reinforced concrete: 0.2)

Values of ζ

Number of nodal circles	Number of nodal diameters 0	1	2	3
0	10.21	21.26	34.87	51.02
1	39.77	60.83	84.53	111.00
2	89.10	120.10		

(Points of nodal circles and of nodal diameters retain their original position during vibrations of the circular slab.)

2. Rectangular slabs

$$N(1/\text{min})=9.55\lambda\sqrt{\frac{Eh^3}{\mu 12(1-v)}}$$

Values of λ for different conditions of support

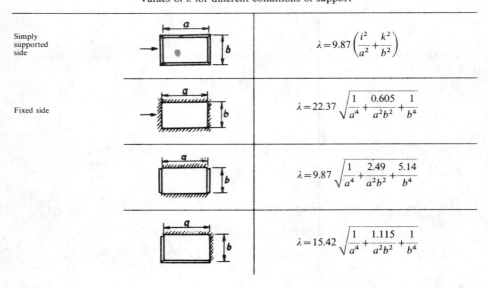

Simply supported side		$\lambda=9.87\left(\frac{i^2}{a^2}+\frac{k^2}{b^2}\right)$
Fixed side		$\lambda=22.37\sqrt{\frac{1}{a^4}+\frac{0.605}{a^2b^2}+\frac{1}{b^4}}$
		$\lambda=9.87\sqrt{\frac{1}{a^4}+\frac{2.49}{a^2b^2}+\frac{5.14}{b^4}}$
		$\lambda=15.42\sqrt{\frac{1}{a^4}+\frac{1.115}{a^2b^2}+\frac{1}{b^4}}$

Table 8. cont.

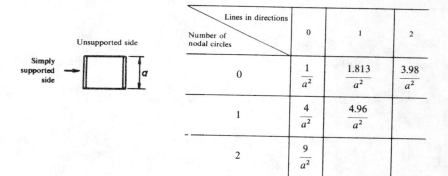	$\lambda = 9.87 \sqrt{\dfrac{1}{a^4} + \dfrac{2.33}{a^2 b^2} + \dfrac{2.44}{b^4}}$
	$\lambda = 22.37 \sqrt{\dfrac{1}{a^4} + \dfrac{0.566}{a^2 b^2} + \dfrac{0.475}{b^4}}$

Here i and k denote the number of half-wave lengths parallel to sides a and b respectively. For $i = 1, 2, 3 \ldots$, and $k = 1, 2, 3, \ldots$, respectively, the basic and harmonic frequencies are obtained.

Number of nodal circles \ Lines in directions	0	1	2
0	$\dfrac{1}{a^2}$	$\dfrac{1.813}{a^2}$	$\dfrac{3.98}{a^2}$
1	$\dfrac{4}{a^2}$	$\dfrac{4.96}{a^2}$	
2	$\dfrac{9}{a^2}$		

Tabulated values of λ apply to the case
$v = 0 \ (a = b)$

Fundamental and harmonic modes of vibration of quadratic slabs fixed at four sides

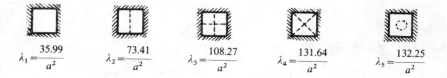

$$\lambda_1 = \frac{35.99}{a^2} \qquad \lambda_2 = \frac{73.41}{a^2} \qquad \lambda_3 = \frac{108.27}{a^2} \qquad \lambda_4 = \frac{131.64}{a^2} \qquad \lambda_5 = \frac{132.25}{a^2}$$

If the values of A and B from Eqs. (145) and (146) are evaluated at $t = 0$,

and

$$A = z_0 \tag{149}$$

$$B = \frac{v_0}{\omega_0} \tag{150}$$

where z_0 is the initial displacement and v_0 the initial velocity condition.

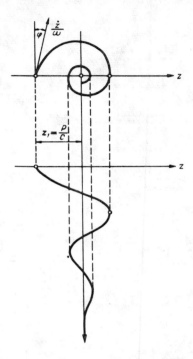

Fig. 45. Phase plan representation of damped vibration

Graphically, according to Fig. 42, the radius of $R = z_0^2 + (v_0/\omega_0)^2$ rotates clockwise with an angular velocity ω_0. Any arc ψ represents an interval in time by the relation $\psi = \omega_0 t$. If $P \neq 0$ but is constant we obtain:

$$A = z_0 - \frac{P}{C} \; ; \qquad B = \frac{v_0}{\omega_0} .$$

thus, Eq. (147) is modified into

$$\left(z - \frac{P}{c}\right)^2 + \left(\frac{\dot{z}}{\omega_0}\right)^2 = A^2 + B^2 = \left(z_0 - \frac{P}{c}\right)^2 + \left(\frac{v_0}{\omega_0}\right)^2 \tag{151}$$

which still represents a circle but with a displaced centre by P/c along the z axis. This is shown graphically in Fig. 45. When force P is not constant time, the force — time diagram may be taken approximately by a series of step pulses. Thus, at the end of each interval we get the initial conditions for the next one.

For viscously damped systems oblique coordinates are to be applied. The velocity coordinate $\dot{z}/\omega$ is measured after Jacobsen and Ayre [519] at an angle φ taken clockwise from the ordinate. The axis 90° is rotated in such a manner that the abscissa represents the displacement z. The angle φ is a measure of the damping of the system

$$\sin \varphi = k/K_c = D \tag{152}$$

As is well known the critical value

$$K_c = 2\sqrt{c/m}, \tag{153}$$

and according to the method of oblique coordinates by the relation

$$R = R_0 e^{-D\psi/\sqrt{1-D^2}} = R_0 e^{-\psi \tan \varphi} \tag{154}$$

the rotating radius R and the damped angular frequency ω_D are functions of the damping ratio D; furthermore:

$$\omega_D = \omega_0 \sqrt{1-D^2} = \sqrt{1-D^2} \sqrt{c/m} \tag{154a}$$

By Eqs. (152) and (153) a log spiral template can be established. As the angular movement ψ increases the radius decreases because of the spiral line in the phase plane, and the corresponding time will be

$$t = \frac{\psi}{\omega_0 \sqrt{1-D^2}} = \frac{\psi}{\omega_{0D}} \tag{155}$$

supposing for $z = \dot{z} = 0$, represented by the 0 point of the origin of the coordinates on Fig. 44. Thus the initial radius will be $R_0 = z_1$ and the corresponding static displacement $z_1 = P/c$. In the figure we see the path described by the log spiral. By increasing time the displacement will approach z_1, the static displacement.

The method can be applied for impact or transient motions and for systems of nonlinear properties, nonlinear spring forces, etc. The phase plane method is described in detail by Jacobsen and Ayre [519] for engineering vibrations. The further adoption of the system is shown by Drnevich et al. [277] and by Richart et al. [1024] and an example for a large impact machine foundation taking into account nonharmonic analysis is given by McNeill [818]. The graphical method is useful for visualization of the procedures.

(d) Finite element method

The finite element method (FEM) is based upon breaking down a structure or one part of a structure into small and simple components. The elements are in the simplest way triangular. After having subdivided the structure into sections, the mathematical descriptions of the behaviour of the individual segments are derived and then these descriptions are pieced together to form a mathematical description of the whole structure. In practice these calculations are performed by computer. A large number of FEM programs with the related documentation are available to interested users from universities, research institutes or private companies. (These have sometimes been developed through the use of public funds.) Such a group is, for example, PAFEC (Program for Automatic Finite Element Calculations) published by the University of Nottingham in the U.K. [919]. (One of the contributors being G. B. Warburton.) A simple example is shown in Fig. 46 for a thin square plate

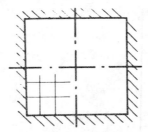

Fig. 46. Example for clamped thin square plate

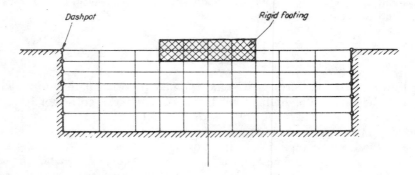

Fig. 47. Schematic arrangement for a finite element solution in soil dynamics

clamped along all four edges. When nine elements are used to model one quarter of the problem, the first natural frequency is calculated to an accuracy of 1.24 per cent. Another example shown in Fig. 47 illustrates, after Woods, the schematic arrangement for a finite element solution in soil dynamics presented at the series of lectures held under the chairmanship of F. E. Richart in Ann Arbor in 1968.

This general numerical method for solving field problems may also be applied to plain stress problems as an application of the displacement method of structural mechanics to continuum mechanics.

The continuum is to be parted into a finite number of elements and nodal points. For the crosspoints the load vector is $\{P\}$ and the displacement $\{U\}$. The linear relationship with the stiffness matrix $[C]$ is

$$[C]\{U\} = \{P\} \tag{156}$$

If adopted for dynamic stress analysis supposing $[M]$ as mass and $[K]$ as the damping matrix, the relationship becomes

$$[M]\{\ddot{U}\}_t + [K]\{\dot{U}\}_t + [C]\{U\}_t = \{P\}_t \tag{157}$$

With regard to further applications of the finite element method see Vol. IV. Chapter I.

(e) Transfer matrix method

This method, based on the publication of Pestel and Leckie [943], is a good tool for dynamic analysis, especially for framed foundations. To solve complex problems in structural dynamics the method involves successive matrix multiplications which can easily be carried out on a digital computer. Remarks on the popularity of the method and further solutions of linear equations are to be found in Vol. III on pp. 170 ff. Details of the transfer matrix method adopted also with suitable numerical examples are given in Vol. III, pp. 246 ff.

E) APPROXIMATE SOLUTIONS

(a) Rayleigh's method

It is a well known fact that the natural frequency consists essentially of a change in the kinetic and potential energies the sum of which is constant, if no damping is taken into consideration. Thus

$$E_k + E_p = \text{const.}$$

At maximum displacement $E_k = 0$, and at the moment when the spring is relaxed $E_p = 0$. Hence

$$E_{k\max} = E_{p\max}$$

When the displacement is $y = A \sin \lambda t$, the velocity $v = \dot{y} = A\lambda \cos \lambda t$ and the restoring force $P = Ac$, then

$$E_{k\,\max} = \frac{mv_{\max}^2}{2} = \frac{1}{2} m\lambda^2 A^2$$

and

$$E_{p\,\max} = \frac{1}{2} PA = \frac{1}{2} A^2 c$$

Consequently

$$\frac{1}{2} m\lambda^2 A^2 = \frac{1}{2} A^2 c$$

and the natural frequency is

$$\lambda^2 = \frac{c}{m}$$

This applies to every element of the mass, and for the entire system the following equation must be true:

$$\int_0^1 E_{k\max} = \int_0^1 E_{p\,\max} \tag{158}$$

If we succeed in finding the mode of the vibrations of the beam or column, and the kinetic and potential energies of each mass element then, on the basis of the natural frequencies of these elements, the natural frequency of the entire system can be determined. If a mode of vibration is chosen in which all mass elements vibrate in the same direction, we obtain the fundamental vibration. In the case of transverse vibrations Rayleigh assumes that at the maximum amplitude of the fundamental vibration the form of the beam will resemble that assumed by the beam when it is deflected under a static load. Accurate computation has proved the correctness of this assumption

The investigation of vibrations perpendicular to the axis yields the expression:

$$\Sigma E_{k\,\max} = \sum_{i=1}^n \int_0^{li} \frac{1}{2}\lambda^2 y^2 dm = \sum_{i=1}^n \int_0^{li} \frac{1}{2}\mu\lambda^2 y^2 dx \tag{159}$$

The second equality applies to the case where the load is uniformly distributed, μ represents the mass per unit length and y denotes the maximum amplitude of the mass element, i.e. the deflection due to static load.

$$\Sigma E_p^0 = \sum_{i=1}^n \int_0^{li} \frac{M^2}{2IE} dx = \sum_{i=1}^n \int_0^{li} \frac{1}{2EI} \frac{d_0^2 y^2}{dx^2} dx \tag{160}$$

where $\Sigma E_p =$ the work performed by the mass elements, obtained as the product of the increasing spring force and the amplitude

$M =$ the bending moment which is at the same time proportional to the second differential quotient of the deflected beam axis

$M/IE =$ the reciprocal of the radius of curvature.

The symbol $\sum_{i=1}^n$ indicates that the summation must be extended to all members comprising the system. If the line of deflection can be expressed by a function, the integration can be performed. Otherwise the component members must be resolved into elements and the results summarized. Finally

$$\lambda_1^2 = \frac{\sum_{i=1}^n \int_0^{li} EI\, y^2 dx}{\sum_{i=1}^n \int_0^{li} \mu y^2 dx} \tag{161}$$

gives the natural frequency of the basic vibration.

These considerations apply to the case where exclusively transverse vibrations take place in a system consisting of several members. The natural frequency of columns can be determined on the same principle with the difference, however, that the work performed during the compression of the column must be determined from the force acting upon the elements of the column and from the displacements suffered by the centres of gravity of the elements owing to compression.

This approximate method gives somewhat higher values than accurate computation. The reason is that the beam was rendered "stiff" by the arbitrary assumption of the mode of vibration and thus its vibrations were accelerated.

Rayleigh's formula was simplified by Morley in 1909 which is equally well known as Kull's formula from 1918 or Kayser's formula of 1929. A gradual improvement of the results obtained by this formula resulted from the work by Hohenemser and Prager in 1933. The theorem that nature chooses from among all possible modes of vibration needing the smallest quantity of energy for the continuous change of knetic–potential–kinetic is used in Ritz's method in 1911 quoted also by Biezeno and Grammel in 1953. The method of Galerkin discussed in Goldenblatt–Sisow's book published in 1952, Chapter II, page 62, is also approximating in character.

(b) The method of successive approximation

This method for calculating natural frequencies is based on the following principle: in natural vibration the inertial force of every elementary mass is in equilibrium with the spring force acting upon it. The maximum value of kinetic energy of the mass is further equal to the maximum of its potential energy. Consequently, when the weight of the oscillating element is taken into consideration—provided this is not negligibly small—and if any, even non-uniformly distributed, loads act on the vibrating beam, then the spring force arising at the displacement of the beam is always of the same magnitude as the one caused by the forces of inertia of the beam at the time of displacement.

If we can find the mode of displacement at which the displacement due to the inertial force equals the displacement assumed, we have found the state of equilibrium from which the natural frequency of the system can be determined. The inertial force is calculated from the given values of corresponding masses and displacements. For an arbitrary system (e.g. a continuous beam, or frame, etc.) the differential equations of a beam under inertial force are:

$$I \frac{d^4 y}{dx^4} - m \frac{\lambda^2}{E} v = 0$$

$$F \frac{d^2 u}{dx^2} + m \frac{\lambda^2}{E} u = 0$$

(162)

The above differential equations describe the deformation of a beam under a load $m\lambda^2 v/E$, respectively $m\lambda^2 u/E$ where v and u denote the displacements perpendicular and parallel to the axis, respectively.

Though exact mathematical solutions are available for these differential equations, the procedure involved is a lengthy one requiring much time even in simple cases when only transverse vibrations are taken into account. When in addition, axial and shear forces are considered, the effect of normal and shear forces must not be neglected particularly when designing turbine foundations with reinforced-concrete frames, and the amount of calculation required is enormous. Thus the adoption of a mathematical solution can hardly be justified. Moreover, taking into account the fact that our assumptions concerning the length of the members and the conditions of support still involve appreciable uncertainties, we are bound to come to the conclusion that the mathematical exactness in the analysis of machine foundations should not be overemphasized. For these reasons the above difficulties should preferably be overcome by a method which produces the solution of the differential equations by successive approximations and with the desired degree of accuracy. The time required for mathematical work is governed by the latter. The procedure of this method—preferably using electronic computers—consists of the following steps:

1. The beam (simply supported, fixed, continuous, grid, plane or space frame, etc.) which, in addition to the dead weight, carries various concentrated and uniformly distributed loads, is divided into small sections, according to the accuracy required. These sections can be regarded as individual elements each having a constant moment of inertia. The load carried by each can be assumed to be uniformly distributed and to act at the centre of gravity of each element as a concentrated force.

2. Arbitrary deflection and displacement curves are assumed to be perpendicular and parallel to the axis of the beam element. Displacements perpendicular to the axis are denoted by v and those parallel with the axis by u. Though the shape of the curve can be chosen freely, it should be underlined that the volume of subsequent mathematical work depends on the agreement between the curve adopted for the first trial and the actual curve. For this reason it is advisable to determine, at the first assumption, the curve of static deflection corresponding to the actual loading, this being similar to the mode of vibration.

3. From the v and u values chosen for the first trial, the corresponding inertial forces can be determined.

For beams of homogeneous material, it is advisable to introduce the notation:

$$v^2 = \frac{\lambda^2}{Eg}$$

The inertial force reduced by E can thus be obtained with the value

$$\frac{m\lambda^2 v}{E} = Pv^2 v \quad \text{and} \quad \frac{m\lambda^2 u}{E} = Pv^2 u$$

where P represents the weight of the beam element.

In the first trial we start with values $v = 1$, and $E = 1$.

4. With the assumed values $v^2 = 1$ and $E = 1$, we proceed by determining the deflection curve of the beam. It is assumed that the forces of inertia act on each element both along the axis of the beam and perpendicular to it. These two forces of inertia are naturally different, their magnitude is, however, proportional to the assumed displacement.

5. The v' and u' displacements obtained in this way are used for the determination of the Pv' and Pu' values with respect to every element. Hence, determining the $(Pv')^2$ and $(Pu')^2$ values and summarizing them, we obtain at the second trial the approximate value:

$$v'^2 = \frac{1}{\sqrt{\Sigma(Pv')^2 + (Pu')^2}} \tag{163}$$

which is proportional to λ.

6. As part of the second trial we next determine inertial forces with the corresponding v', u' and v' values in the way described above.

The proportional values obtained by substitution of the inertial forces are:

$$Pv'\gamma'^2 \text{ and } Pu'\gamma'^2$$

7. Now these inertial forces are applied again to the beam and the resulting displacements v' and u' are calculated once more.

8. Then the values of Pv''/Pu'', $(Pv'')^2$ and $(Pu'')^2$ are again determined and with these

$$\gamma''^2 = \frac{1}{\sqrt{\Sigma(Pu'')^2 + (Pv'')^2}} \tag{164}$$

This procedure is continued until the successive values obtained are approximately equal. Here, then, we have found the value which corresponds to the state of equilibrium. The final natural frequencies can now be obtained by using the following formulae:

$$\lambda = \gamma^{(n)}\sqrt{Eg}$$

$$n = \frac{\gamma^{(n)}}{2\pi}\sqrt{Eg} \tag{165}$$

$$N = \frac{60\gamma^{(n)}}{2\pi}\sqrt{Eg}$$

The third trial usually produces the required result. Slower rates of convergence may often occur with frames where the displacements due to axial and shear forces must also be considered. In such cases it is advisable to select the most characteristic points of each bar (the central point of a beam and the top of a column) and to proceed by examining how the displacement of the points concerned varies. By doing this we shall obtain the probable final values of the displacements by estimation or by forming a geometrical progression. With the quotient of these final values and the displacement of the point chosen for the last trial we multiply the values applying to the other points. The product gained in this way is to be regarded as the first approximation and the procedure should be repeated until the correct final result is obtained.

The method discussed above enables us to obtain not only the natural frequencies related to the fundamental vibrations but also the higher harmonics thereof provided the discrepancy between the assumed and actual modes of vibration is not significant.

When dealing with these major harmonics the modes of oscillation must be located. For this purpose the inertial force determined in the first trial on the basis of an arbitrary choice of the node is compared with the spring force and if these two values are not equal, the position of the node is modified by progressive trial and error until it proves to be correct, the inertial forces equalling the spring forces at that point.

This method is highly suitable for the determination of natural frequencies of any degree and can be applied to oscillating systems of any configuartion having several degrees of freedom and composed of a number of elements.

It should be remarked here that in general the solutions by means of iteration techniques owe a great deal to the computer. High speed digital computers have enabled new areas for structural theory to be developed for solving linear equations. The state of the art for such solutions was treated by Ch. Meyer [829], it was followed by discussions of Kar [549], of Williams et al. [1330], and Th. H. Johnsen and J. R. Ray [531], and closed by the author [829] with a great many references. If the problem ensures fast convergence, iterative techniques remain useful especially if, in cases of small loads, the estimate of a solution is close to the exact solution. A more complete state of the art paper was published by Meyer [830] on special problems related to linear solvers with many references of a general nature, details of direct methods, of band solutions, of the partitioning methods, of frontal and other direct methods, as well as iteration methods treating also numerical problems. About theory and computation of rod structures including dynamic problems see also Szabó and Roller [1218]. For optimum structural design by dynamic programming see Ray and Durrant [986a].

Finally it should be mentioned that a detailed treatise of the theory concerning the dynamics of structures including the analysis of nonlinear systems, distributed parameter systems and of random vibrations is presented by Clough and Penzien [285].

The following examples are easily solved for different structural and force situations with the aid of computers, giving results which are convenient in practice.

EXAMPLE 1

Determination of the natural frequency of a simply supported beam. The determination of the natural frequency of a beam under any conditions of loading will be exemplified by the calculations for a simply supported beam. Let the *I*-beam

EXAMPLE 1   NATURAL FREQUENCY OF A SIMPLY SUPPORTED BEAM   111

600 mm high with $I = 139.000$ cm^4 shown in Fig. 48a support a concentrated load of 12 t and a uniformly distributed load of $q = 2$ t/m.

The calculation can be carried out by successive approximation (Table 9) in tabulated form.

1. Let the beam be divided into six equal parts and let the uniformly distributed load be concentrated at the points of division. Naturally at point 2 the concentrated load of 12 t also exerts its effect (Fig. 48b).

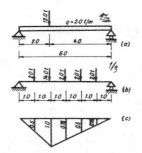

Fig. 48. Simply supported beam.

a—loading of beams, b—loads concentrated at dividing points, c—deflection
line assumed as first approximation

2. Let us assume that the deflection of the beam is approximately linear, so that the maximum deflection—the value of which is assumed to be 1—takes place below the concentrated load of 14 t (see Fig. 48c.)

3. Let us now determine the values Pvy^2 at the different points. Let us assume as a first approximation that $\gamma^2 = 1$, since initially, only the ratio of the deflections is of interest.

TABLE 9

First approximation

Position of the point	1	2	3	4	5	6	7	8
	P t	v cm	$Pv\gamma^2$	M	w	v'	Pv'	$(Pv')^2$
0	0	0	0	0	0	0	0	0
1	2.0	0.50	1.0	1 133	0.803	261.6	523	$27.0 \cdot 10^4$
2	14	1.00	14.00	2 166	1.388	442.9	6 201	$3\,845.0 \cdot 10^4$
3	2.0	0.75	1.50	1 800	1.277	485.2	971	$94.0 \cdot 10^4$
4	2.0	0.50	1.00	1 282	0.911	400.2	800	$64.0 \cdot 10^4$
5	2.0	0.25	0.50	666	0.474	223.9	448	$20.0 \cdot 10^4$
6	0	0	0	0	0	0	0	0

$$\Sigma(Pv')^2 = 4050 \cdot 10^4$$

4. The values Pvy^2 should be regarded as loads and the moments occurring at the different points of division should be determined.

5. The area of the surfaces limited by the moment diagram will give the angular displacement occurring at the individual points of division.

$$\omega_k = \frac{xx}{6I}(M_{k-1} + 4M_k + M_{k+1})$$

where a denotes the distance between the points; M_{k-1}, M_k and M_{k+1} are the moments at points $k-1$, k and $k+2$, respectively.

The above expressions are the values of the angular displacements multiplied by E.

6. Let the angular displacements w_k act as a load on the beam; the moment line will then give the deflection line too.

7. Let us determine the values Pv' and

8. the values $(Pv')^2$

Knowing $\Sigma(Pv')^2$ the value of γ'^2 can be determined according to Eq. (163)

$$\gamma'^2 = \frac{1}{\sqrt{\Sigma(Pv')^2}} = \frac{1}{\sqrt{4{,}050 \cdot 10^4}} = 0.000157\,(0.116 \cdot 10^{-10})$$

For the second approximation we calculate using the value $Pv'\gamma'^2$ and obtain the value of $\Sigma(Pv'')^2$ by means of the method of calculation used for the first approximation (Table 10).

The value γ''^2 is obtained according to Eq. (164) as

$$\gamma''^2 = \frac{1}{\sqrt{\Sigma Pv'')^2}} = \frac{1}{\sqrt{239{,}300}} = 0.002044$$

TABLE 10

Second approximation

1	2	3	4	5	6	7	8
Position of the point	P t	$Pv'\gamma'^2$	M	w	v''	Pv''	$(Pv'')^2$
0	0	0	0	0	0	0	0
1	2.0	0.0821	84.7	0.0600	20.02	40.04	1 600
2	14.0	0.9735	161.2	0.1043	34.02	476.28	226,900
3	2.0	0.1525	140.4	0.0992	37.61	75.22	5 700
4	2.0	0.1256	104.3	0.0735	31.28	62.56	3 900
5	2.0	0.0703	55.7	0.0392	17.60	35.20	1 200
6	0	0	0	0	0	0	0

$$\Sigma(Pv'')^2 = 239{,}300$$

EXAMPLE 1   NATURAL FREQUENCY OF A SIMPLY SUPPORTED BEAM   113

. After repeating the procedure of calculation we shall obtain 0.00204 as the value of γ'''^2, which is very near to γ''^2. Accepting the value of γ'''^2 as correct, we obtain:

$$\gamma''' = \sqrt{0.00204} = 0.04511 \ (0.604 \cdot 10^{-3}).$$

The natural frequency of the beam is thus

$$N = \frac{60}{2\pi} \gamma''' \sqrt{Eg} = \frac{60 \cdot 0.04511}{6.283} \sqrt{2.100 \cdot 981} = 618 \text{ cpm.}$$

The result should be checked according to Herrmann (Ref. [452] (p. 38)), and Jänich [524] (p. 73).

With the loads $q = 2.0$ t/m; $P = 12.0$ t we obtain according to Herrmann's Eq. (137)

$$\delta_{mq} = \frac{20}{384.21 \times 10^6 \times 1.39 \times 10^{-3}} (5 \times 6.0^4 + 24 \times 1.0^2 \times 6.0^2 + 16 \times 1.0^2) = 0.00102 \text{ m,}$$

and Herrmann's Eq. (138),

$$\delta_{mp} = \frac{12.0}{3.21 \times 10^6 \times 1.39 \times 10^{-3}} \cdot \frac{2.0^2 \times 4.0^2}{6.0} = 0.00146 \text{ m,}$$

$$\delta_m = 0.00102 + 0.00146 = 0.00248 \text{ m} = 0.248 \text{ cm}$$

Excluding the shear force, the natural frequency is

$$N = \frac{300}{\sqrt{0.248}} = 605/\text{min}$$

Herrmann's Eq. (138) yields:

$$\delta_{aq} = 0.3 \frac{2.0}{21 \times 10^6 \times 2.54 \times 10^{-2}} = 0.00000362 \text{ m}$$

and from Herrmann's Eq. (137):

$$\delta_{aq} = 2.4 \frac{12.0 \times 2.0 \times 4.0}{6.0 \times 21 \times 10^6 \times 2.54 \times 10^{-2}} = 0.0000073 \text{ m}$$

$$\delta_Q = 0.00000362 + 0.0000073 = 0.0000109 \text{ m} = 0.00109 \text{ cm}$$

$$\delta = 0.248 + 0.00109 = \sim 0.249 \text{ cm}$$

Including the shear force, for the natural frequency we obtain

$$N = \frac{300}{\sqrt{0.249}} = 600/\text{min.}$$

According to Jänich, [504] (on p. 73).

$$N = 13.5 \times 10^5 \sqrt{\Sigma I_i / l_i : \Sigma l_i^3 (p_i + 2\Sigma P_i f_i^2 / l_i)}$$

and transformed to a single-span beam

$$N = 13.5 \times 10^5 \sqrt{\frac{I}{l^4 (q + 2Pf^2 / l)}} =$$

$$= 13.5 \times 10^5 \sqrt{\frac{1.39 \times 10^{-3}}{6.04(2.0 + 2 \times 12.0 \times 0.724/6.0)}} = 630/\text{min}$$

This expression was derived by Jänich (after [270]). In its basic forms it is to be found also in Goldenblatt and Sisov [383].

In connection with Jänich's formula it should be mentioned that it has been derived for continuous beams on the basis of Rayleigh's method. Identical angular displacements are assumed in the formula over every support so that the effect of continuity is not completely allowed for.

EXAMPLE 2

Determination of the natural frequency of a system of beams. Below, the natural frequency of a system of floor beams will be determined. The arrangement of the beams is shown in Fig. 49. Both beams are divided into six equal parts, and the uniformly distributed loads are assumed to act at the points of division.

Loads:

Concentrated load acting at points 12 and $12' = 2 \times 3.0$ t
Uniformly distributed load:
Longitudinal beam A of cross-section 0.40×0.9 0.90 t/m

Longitudinal beam B of cross-section 0.40×0.8 0.80 t/m

Transverse beam C of cross-section 0.30×0.6 0.45 t/m
The cross-section and the moments of inertia of the beams are:
Longitudinal beam A
I_A 2,430,000 cm^4
F_A 3600 cm^2
Longitudinal beam B
I_B 1,710,000 cm^4
F_B 3200 cm^2
Transverse beam C
I_C 540,000 cm^4
F_C 1800 cm^2

EXAMPLE 2 NATURAL FREQUENCY OF A SYSTEM OF BEAMS 115

When calculating the natural frequency the longitudinal beams should be assumed as being fully fixed. The vertical displacement (i.e. compression) of the supporting structure is neglected. Considering the torsional stiffness of the longitudinal beam a 50 per cent fixity can be assumed for the transverse beam. The loads acting at the points of division are:

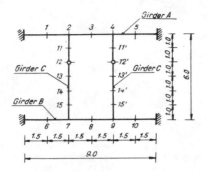

Fig. 49. System of floor beams showing points examined

Point 1: 0.9×1.5 $= 1.35$ t

Point 2: $0.9 \times 1.5 + \dfrac{0.45}{2}$ $= 1.57$ t

Point 3: $= 1.35$ t
Point 4: $= 1.57$ t
Point 5: $= 1.35$ t
Point 6: 0.8×1.5 $= 1.20$ t

Point 7: $0.8 \times 1.5 + \dfrac{0.45}{2}$ $= 1.42$ t

Point 8: $= 1.20$ t
Point 9: $= 1.42$ t
Point 10: $= 1.20$ t
Point 11: 0.45×1.0 $= 0.45$ t
Point 12: $0.45 \times 1.0 + 3.0$ $= 3.45$ t
Point 13: $= 0.45$ t
Point 14: $= 0.45$ t
Point 15: $= 0.45$ t

The deflections can be determined by means of the influence diagrams of deflection and initially their ordinates must be defined (Table 11). The deflections at sections i and k of the single-span simply supported beam due to the effect of a moving load $P = 1$, multiplied by EI can be obtained from the following expressions (Fig. 50):

$$\eta_i = \frac{l^3}{6} \beta\delta(1 - \beta^2 - \delta^2)$$

TABLE 11

*Ordinates of the influence diagram for the longitudinal beam A
and the transverse beam C*

Longitudinal beam A

Cross-section at	Ordinates of the influence diagram (η)				
	1	2	3	4	5
Point 1	4.68	7.10	7.33	5.85	3.18
Point 2	7.10	12.00	12.95	10.60	5.85
Point 3	7.33	12.95	15.20	12.95	7.33
Point 4	5.85	10.60	12.95	12.00	7.10
Point 5	3.18	5.85	7.33	7.10	4.68

Transverse beam C

Cross-section at	Ordinates of the influence diagram (η)				
	11	12	13	14	15
Point 11	1.38	2.10	2.17	1.73	0.94
Point 12	2.10	3.57	3.84	3.14	1.73
Point 13	2.17	3.84	4.50	3.84	2.17
Point 14	1.73	3.14	3.84	3.57	2.10
Point 15	0.94	1.73	2.17	2.10	1.38

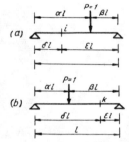

Fig. 50. Examination of cross-sections i and k under the effect of moving load $P=1$

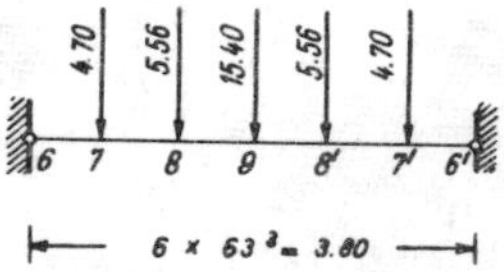

Fig. 51. Loads $Pv\gamma^2$ acting on beam C (partial fixity)

and

$$\eta_k = \frac{l^3}{6} a\varepsilon (1 - a^2 - \varepsilon^2)$$

For the longitudinal beam B the values of the influence diagram are the same as for the longitudinal beam A.

As regards the deflections of the beams under the load $Pv\gamma^2$ the following conditions should be investigated:

(i) Deflection of the Transverse Beam C (Fig. 51). First the deflection of a beam freely supported at two points should be determined and from the values so obtained the vertical displacements due to fixity should be subtracted.

EXAMPLE 2   NATURAL FREQUENCY OF A SYSTEM OF BEAMS   117

The vertical displacement at point 11 is the product of the ordinate of the influence diagram (η) and of the load acting at the point in question:

Loads:
$1.38 \times \quad 9.4 = \quad 13.0$
$2.10 \times 107.0 = 225.0$
$2.17 \times \quad 11.7 = \quad 25.4$
$1.73 \times \quad 9.5 = \quad 16.4$
$0.94 \times \quad 7.2 = \quad 6.8$
$\qquad e_{11} = \overline{286.6}$

Similarly,

the vertical displacement of point 12: $e'_{12} = 489.0$

the vertical displacement of point 13: $e'_{13} = 536.0$

the vertical displacement of point 14: $e'_{14} = 446.0$

the vertical displacement of point 15: $e'_{15} = 249.0$

With a fully fixed beam the moments due to the above load are

$$M_A = 116.45; \qquad M_B = 71.15$$

With partial fixity only half of the moments M_A and M_B are taken into account. The deflection of the beam C due to the fixity moment is

$$e'' = -\frac{l^2}{2}(M_A \mu_B - M_B \mu_A)$$

where $\mu_A = \delta - \delta^3$ and $\mu_B = \varepsilon - \varepsilon^3$

$$e''_{11} = -\frac{6.0^2}{6}(58.2 \times 0.2547 + 35.6 \times 0.162) \quad = -183.0$$

$$e''_{12} = -\frac{6.0^2}{6}(58.2 \times 0.3704 + 35.6 \times 0.2963) \quad = -192.5$$

$$e''_{13} = -\frac{6.0^2}{6}(58.2 \times 0.375 + 35.6 \times 0.375) \quad = -211.0$$

$$e''_{14} = -\frac{6.0^2}{6}(58.2 \times 0.2963 + 35.6 \times 0.3704) \quad = -183.0$$

$$e''_{15} = -\frac{6.0^2}{6}(58.2 \times 0.162 + 35.6 \times 0.2547) = -111.0$$

Adding the deflections e' and e'', the deflections of the beam C are:

$$e_{11} = 286.6 - 123.0 = 163.6$$

$$e_{12} = 489.0 - 192.5 = 296.5$$

$$e_{13} = 536.0 - 211.0 = 325.0$$

$$e_{14} = 446.0 - 183.0 = 263.0$$

$$e_{15} = 249.0 - 111.0 = 138.0$$

(ii) Deflection of the Longitudinal Beam A. As well as the loads $Pv\gamma^2$ acting directly on the longitudinal beam, the loads transmitted by the transverse beam must also be considered (Fig. 52).

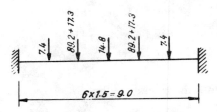

Fig. 52. Loads $Pv\gamma^2$ acting on beam A

The reaction of the transverse beam:

$$\frac{9 \cdot 4.5 \rightarrow 107 \cdot 0.4 + 11 \cdot 7.3 + 9 \cdot 5.2 + 7 \cdot 2.1}{6} \quad 89.2$$

the deflections of a simply supported beam are:

the vertical displacement at point 1: $e'_1 = 1546.6$

the vertical displacement at point 2: $e'_2 = 2695.8$

the vertical displacement at point 3: $e'_3 = 3093.0$

the vertical displacement at point 4: $e'_4 = 2695.8$

the vertical displacement at point 5: $e'_5 = 1546.6$

When the beam is fully fixed:

$$M_b = \pm 240.33$$

The deflection of the longitudinal beam A due to the fixing moment:

$$e'' = -\frac{l^2}{6} M_b (\mu_A + \mu_B)$$

EXAMPLE 2   NATURAL FREQUENCY OF A SYSTEM OF BEAMS   119

$$e_1'' = -\frac{9.0^2}{6} \times 240.33 \times 0.4167 = -1352.0$$

$$e_2'' = -\frac{9.0^2}{6} \times 240.33 \times 0.667 \ = -2163.0$$

$$e_3'' = -\frac{9.0^2}{6} \times 240.33 \times 0.75 \ \ = -2433.0$$

$$e_4'' = \qquad\qquad\qquad\quad\ = -2163.0$$

$$e_5'' = \qquad\qquad\qquad\quad\ = -1352.0$$

By adding the deflections e' and e'' the deflections of the beam A will be obtained:

$e_1 = 1546.6 - 1352.0 = 194.6$

$e_2 = 2695.8 - 2163.0 = 532.0$

$e_3 = 3093.0 - 2433.0 = 660.0$

$e_4 = \qquad\qquad\quad = \ \ 532.8$

$e_5 = \qquad\qquad\quad = \ \ 194.6$

The deflections of the beam B can be obtained in a similar way:

$e_6 = \qquad\qquad = 142.0$

$e_7 = \qquad\qquad = 363.0$

$e_8 = \qquad\qquad = 446.0$

$e_9 = \qquad\qquad = 363.0$

$e_{10} = \qquad\qquad = 142.0$

Since for computing the deflections, the spans are given in metres, the values obtained must be multiplied by 10^6 and then divided by the moment of inertia of the beams in order to obtain the deflections in cm. In Table 12 (see page 120) the deflections multiplied by 10^6 (I) are given. The mean values of the deflections at points 2, 4, 7, and 9 have been added to the deflections of the beam C.
Knowing the value $\Sigma(Pv')^2$ the value γ'^2 can be determined:

$$\gamma'^2 = \frac{1}{\sqrt{\Sigma(Pv')^2}} = \frac{1}{\sqrt{1537.61 \cdot 10^4}} = 0.000255$$

In the second approximation the value $Pv''\gamma'^2$ is used and the value of $\Sigma(Pv'')^2$ is obtained by the method used for the first approximation:

$$\Sigma(Pv'')^2 = 660.98$$

TABLE 12

First approximation

Position of the point	P t	v cm	$Pv\gamma^2$	v'	Pv'	$(Pv')^2$
1	1.35	5.5	7.4	80.0	108.0	$1.16 \cdot 10^4$
2	1.57	11.0	17.3	219.0	344.0	$11.80 \cdot 10^4$
3	1.35	11.0	14.8	273.0	368.0	$13.50 \cdot 10^4$
4	1.57	11.0	17.3	219.0	344.0	$11.80 \cdot 10^4$
5	1.35	5.5	7.4	80.0	108.0	$1.16 \cdot 10^4$
6	1.20	5.5	6.6	83.0	100.0	$1.00 \cdot 10^4$
7	1.42	11.0	15.6	212.0	301.0	$9.05 \cdot 10^4$
8	1.20	11.0	13.2	261.0	313.0	$9.80 \cdot 10^4$
9	1.42	11.0	15.6	212.0	301.0	$9.05 \cdot 10^4$
10	1.20	5.5	6.6	83.0	100.0	$1.00 \cdot 10^4$
11	0.45	21.0	9.4	519.5	234.0	$5.50 \cdot 10^4$
12	3.45	31.0	107.0	766.5	2 640.0	$696.00 \cdot 10^4$
13	0.45	26.0	11.7	818.5	369.0	$13.60 \cdot 10^4$
14	0.45	21.0	9.5	703.5	316.0	$10.00 \cdot 10^4$
15	0.45	16.0	7.2	472.5	213.0	$4.53 \cdot 10^4$
11'	0.45	21.0	9.4	519.5	234.0	$5.50 \cdot 10^4$
12'	3.45	31.0	107.0	766.5	2 640.0	$696.00 \cdot 10^4$
13'	0.45	26.0	11.7	818.5	369.0	$13.60 \cdot 10^4$
14'	0.45	21.0	9.5	703.5	316.0	$10.00 \cdot 10^4$
15'	0.45	16.0	7.2	472.5	213.0	$4.13 \cdot 10^4$

$$\Sigma(Pv')^2 = 1537.61 \cdot 10^4$$

and can be determined as

$$\gamma''^2 = \frac{1}{\sqrt{\Sigma(Pv'')^2}} = \frac{1}{\sqrt{660.98}} = 0.0389$$

Since the values of $Pv''\gamma''^2$ given in the last column of Table 13 (see page 121) correspond almost exactly to the values $Pv'\gamma'^2$, the value γ''^2 can be regarded as correct and the natural frequency of the system of beams can be determined as

$$\gamma'' = \sqrt{0.0389} = 0.197$$

and

$$N = \frac{60}{2\pi} \gamma'' \sqrt{Eg} = \frac{60 \cdot 0.197}{6.283} \sqrt{300 \cdot 981} = 1.020 \text{ cpm.}$$

EXAMPLE 3

Determination of the natural frequency of a two-legged, fixed frame. Below, the natural frequency of a cross-frame in a turbo-generator foundation will be determined. The frame is fully fixed at the bottom and its dimensions are given in Fig. 53. The beam and the columns have been divided into six equal parts and the

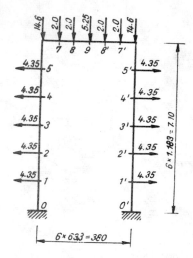

Fig. 53. Schematic arrangement of frame showing weights concentrated at dividing points

TABLE 13

Second approximation

Position of the point	P t	$Pv'\gamma^2$	v''	Pv''	$(Pv'')^2$	$Pv''\gamma^2$
1	1.35	$2.85 \cdot 10^{-2}$	0.528	0.713	0.51	$2.77 \cdot 10^{-2}$
2	1.57	$8.77 \cdot 10^{-2}$	1.410	2.210	4.88	$8.60 \cdot 10^{-2}$
3	1.35	$9.37 \cdot 10^{-2}$	1.750	2.360	5.55	$9.18 \cdot 10^{-2}$
4	1.57	$8.77 \cdot 10^{-2}$	1.410	2.210	4.88	$8.60 \cdot 10^{-2}$
5	1.35	$2.85 \cdot 10^{-2}$	0.528	0.713	0.51	$2.77 \cdot 10^{-2}$
6	1.20	$2.55 \cdot 10^{-2}$	0.527	0.632	0.40	$2.46 \cdot 10^{-2}$
7	1.42	$7.68 \cdot 10^{-2}$	1.400	1.980	3.92	$7.70 \cdot 10^{-2}$
8	1.20	$7.98 \cdot 10^{-2}$	1.755	2.100	4.41	$8.16 \cdot 10^{-2}$
9	1.42	$7.68 \cdot 10^{-2}$	1.400	1.980	3.92	$7.70 \cdot 10^{-2}$
10	1.20	$2.55 \cdot 10^{-2}$	0.527	0.632	0.40	$2.46 \cdot 10^{-2}$
11	0.45	$5.96 \cdot 10^{-2}$	3.400	1.530	2.34	$5.95 \cdot 10^{-2}$
12	3.45	$67.30 \cdot 10^{-2}$	5.030	17.360	301.00	$67.50 \cdot 10^{-2}$
13	0.45	$9.40 \cdot 10^{-2}$	5.450	2.450	6.00	$9.53 \cdot 10^{-2}$
14	0.45	$8.05 \cdot 10^{-2}$	4.700	2.120	4.50	$8.25 \cdot 10^{-2}$
15	0.45	$5.43 \cdot 10^{-2}$	3.120	1.400	1.96	$5.45 \cdot 10^{-2}$
11'	0.45	$5.96 \cdot 10^{-2}$	3.400	1.530	2.34	$5.95 \cdot 10^{-2}$
11'	3.45	$67.30 \cdot 10^{-2}$	5.030	17.360	301.00	$67.50 \cdot 10^{-2}$
13'	0.45	$9.40 \cdot 10^{-2}$	5.450	2.450	6.00	$9.35 \cdot 10^{-2}$
14'	0.45	$8.05 \cdot 10^{-2}$	4.070	2.120	4.50	$8.25 \cdot 10^{-2}$
15'	0.45	$5.43 \cdot 10^{-2}$	3.120	1.400	1.96	$5.45 \cdot 10^{-2}$

$$\Sigma(Pv'')^2 = 660.98$$

dead weights of the elements are assumed to be concentrated at the points of division. The loads are as follows:

Column: at points 1, 2, 3, 4, 5, 1′, 2′, 3′, 4′, 5′: 4.35 t

at point 6:   14.6 t

Beam: at points 7, 8, 7′, 8′:   2.00 t

at point 9:   5.25 t

Data concerning the frame:

Moment of inertia of the beam: $I_b = 0.176$ m^4

Cross-section of the beam: $F_b = 1.15$ m^2

Moment of inertia of the column: $I_c = 0.134$ m^4

Cross section of the column: $F_c = 1.32$ m^2

The deflections can be determined by the method used in the previous example. The ordinates of the deflections at the individual points are determined first and they yield the deflections multiplied by EI.

The ordinates of the influence diagram of the column considered as a beam on two supports are compiled in Table 14.

Table 15 contains the ordinates of the influence line for the frame beam assumed to be simply supported.

For the first approximation the displacements of the frame are given by the ordinates of the deflection, and horizontal displacement diagrams assumed for the beam and columns. The displacements are entered in the third column of Table 16 (Fig. 53).

In the fourth column the value $Pv\gamma^2$ is based on the assumption that $\gamma = 1$. The displacements of the frame due to the load $Pv\gamma^2$ are calculated by means of the influence diagram. The loads $Pv\gamma$ are shown in Figs. 54 and 55.

(i) The horizontal displacements at the dividing lines on the column, assumed to be simply supported at the two ends. As an example we shall determine the displacement at point 1:

$$2.30 \times 2.92 = 6.70$$
$$3.50 \times 8.70 = 30.50$$
$$3.58 \times 12.40 = 44.40$$
$$2.86 \times 12.00 = 34.30$$
$$\underline{1.56 \times 6.80 = 10.60}$$
$$e_1 = 126.50$$

EXAMPLE 3   NATURAL FREQUENCY OF A TWO-LEGGED FRAME   123

TABLE 14

Ordinates of the influence diagram of columns

Cross-section at	Ordinates of the influence diagram (η)				
	1	2	3	4	5
Point 1	2.30	3.50	3.58	2.86	1.56
Point 2	3.50	5.90	6.35	5.20	2.86
Point 3	3.58	6.35	7.45	6.35	3.58
Point 4	2.86	5.20	6.35	5.90	3.50
Point 5	1.56	2.86	3.58	3.50	2.30

TABLE 15

Ordinates of the influence diagram of beams

Cross-section at	Ordinates of the influence diagram (η)				
	1	2	3	4	5
Point 1	0.353	0.536	0.550	0.440	0.240
Point 2	0.536	0.910	0.976	0.800	0.440
Point 3	0.550	0.976	1.140	0.976	0.550
Point 4	0.440	0.800	0.976	0.910	0.536
Point 5	0.240	0.440	0.550	1.136	0.353

TABLE 16

First approximation

	Position of the point	$\dfrac{P}{t}$	$\dfrac{v}{cm}$	$Pv\gamma^2$	v'	Pv'	$(Pv')^2$	
Horizontal displacement of the column	1	4.35	0.67	2.92	1.68	7.31	53.5	
	2	4.35	2.00	8.70	4.72	20.50	420.0	
	3	4.35	2.85	12.40	6.78	29.50	870.0	
	4	4.35	2.75	12.00	6.41	27.90	780.0	
	5	4.35	1.57	6.80	3.66	15.90	253.0	
							$2376.5 \times 2 = 4753.0$	
Vertical displacement of the beam	7	2.00	2.35	4.70	4.56	9.12	83.0	
	8	2.00	2.78	5.56	5.68	11.36	129.0	
	9	5.25	2.94	15.40	6.08	32.00	1025.0	
	8'	2.00	2.78	5.56	5.68	11.36	129.0	
	7'	2.00	2.35	4.70	4.56	9.12	83.0	
							1449.0	1449.0
Vertical displacement of the column	1	4.35	0.28	1.22	0.55	2.39	5.7	
	2	4.35	0.56	2.45	1.085	4.72	22.3	
	3	4.35	0.84	3.65	1.598	6.95	48.3	
	4	4.35	1.13	4.90	2.08	9.05	82.0	
	5	4.35	1.41	6.15	2.12	10.95	120.0	
	6	14.60	1.70	24.80	2.90	42.30	1785.0	
							$2063.3 \times 2 = 4126.6$	

$$\Sigma (Pv')^2 = 10{,}328.6$$

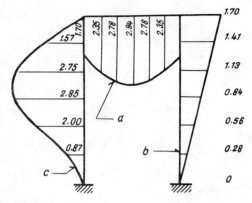

Fig. 54. Displacements v of frame due to loads

a—vertical displacement of frame beam b—vertical displacement of column, c—horizontal displacement of column

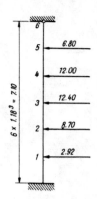

Fig. 55. Loads $Pv\gamma^2$ acting on the column (full fixity at bottom)

The horizontal displacement at point 2: $e'_2 = 222.1$

The horizontal displacement at point 3: $e'_3 = 258.65$

The horizontal displacement at point 4: $e'_4 = 226.85$

The horizontal displacement at point 5: $e'_5 = 131.45$

The horizontal displacements due to the moments

$$e''_1 - \frac{7.1^2}{6}(41.0 \cdot 0.2547 + 12.40 \cdot 0.162) = -104.0$$

$$e''_2 - \frac{7.1^2}{6}(41.0 \cdot 0.3704 + 12.40 \cdot 0.2963) = -159.0$$

$$e''_3 - \frac{7.1^2}{6}(41.0 \cdot 0.3750 + 12.40 \cdot 0.375) = -168.0$$

$$e''_4 - \frac{7.1^2}{6}(41.0 \cdot 0.2963 + 12.40 \cdot 0.3704) = -141.0$$

$$e''_5 - \frac{7.1^2}{6}(41.0 \cdot 0.1620 + 12.40 \cdot 0.2547) = -82.4$$

The sum of the values e and e'' yields the horizontal displacements of the column:

$$e_1 = 126.5 - 104.0 = 22.5$$

$$e_2 = 222.1 - 159.0 = 63.1$$

$$e_3 = 258.65 - 168.0 = 90.65$$

$$e_4 = 226.85 - 141.0 = 85.95$$

$$e_5 = 131.45 - 82.4 = 49.05$$

(ii) The vertical deflections of the frame beam, if it is assumed to be simply supported:

$$e'_7 = 16.70$$

$$e'_8 = 29.09$$

$$e'_9 = 33.55$$

The vertical displacements due to the fixity:

$$e''_7 = +\frac{12.40 \times 3.8^2}{6} \, 0.4167 = +12.45$$

$$e''_8 = +\frac{12.40 \times 3.8^2}{6} \, 0.6667 = +19.90$$

$$e''_9 = -\frac{12.40 \times 3.8^2}{6} \, 0.7500 = +22.40$$

The vertical displacements of the beam are obtained by addition of the displacements e' and e'', and are

$$e_7 = 16.70 + 12.45 = 29.15$$

$$e_8 = 29.09 + 19.90 = 48.99$$

$$e_9 = 33.55 + 22.40 = 55.95$$

When calculating the deflections the spans were in m, the values so obtained must be multiplied by 10^6, and then divided by the moment of inertia in order to obtain the deflections in cm. The compression of the columns determined from the sum of all loads on the column must be added to the deflections of the beam.

$$\Sigma P_c = 7.70 + 5.56 + 4.70 + 24.80 + 6.15 + 4.90 + 3.65 + 2.45 + 1.22 = 61.13$$

the vertical displacement at point 1:

$$e'' = \frac{61.13 \times 118}{13,200} = 0.550$$

the vertical displacement at point 2: $0.55 + 59.91 \times 0.009 = 1.085$

the vertical displacement at point 3: $1.085 + 57,46 \times 0.009 = 1.598$

the vertical displacement at point 4: $1.598 + 13.81 \times 0.009 = 2.080$

the vertical displacement at point 5: $2.080 + 48.91 \times 0.009 = 2.520$

the vertical displacement at point 6: $2.520 + 42.76 \times 0.009 = 2.900$

Accordingly the displacement at point 6 must be added to the displacement of the beam. Hereafter $\Sigma(Pv')^2$ (Table 16) should be determined.

Knowing the value of $\Sigma(Pv')^2$, the value γ^2 can be determined as

$$\gamma'^2 = \frac{1}{\sqrt{\Sigma(Pv')^2}} = \frac{1}{\sqrt{10,328.6}} = 0.00985$$

At the second approximation $Pv'\gamma'^2$ is used and $\Sigma(Pv'')^2$ is obtained as in the first approximation (Table 17). The value of γ''^2

$$\gamma''^2 = \frac{1}{\sqrt{\Sigma(Pv')^2}} = \frac{1}{\sqrt{4.66}} = 0.463(0.827 \times 10^{-4}) \quad \text{and} \quad \gamma'' = 0.681$$

The natural frequency is

$$N'' = \frac{60}{2\pi} \gamma'' \sqrt{Eg} = \frac{60}{6283} 0.681 \sqrt{300 \times 981} = 3530 \text{ cpm}$$

The calculation should be repeated since the values $Pv''\gamma''^2$ in the last column of Table 17 differ appreciably from $Pv'\gamma'^2$. For this reason at the third approximation the deflections due to the load $Pv''\gamma''^2$ and the sum $\Sigma(Pv'')^2$ will be determined (Table 18).

TABLE 17

Second approximation

Position of the point	P_t	$Pv'\gamma'^2$	v''	Pv''	$(Pv'')^2$		$Pv''\gamma''^2$
1	4.35	0.072	0.0412	0.1790	320×10^{-4}		0.083
2	4.35	0.202	0.1165	0.507	$2,580 \times 10^{-4}$		0.235
3	4.35	0.291	0.1605	0.7	$4,900 \times 10^{-4}$		0.314
4	4.35	0.275	0.151	0.657	$4,310 \times 10^{-4}$		0.304
5	4.35	0.157	0.086	0.374	$1,400 \times 10^{-4}$		0.173
					$13,510 \times 10^{-4} \times 2 = 27,020 \times 10^{-4}$		
7	2.0	0.09	0.0895	0.179	320×10^{-4}		0.083
8	2.0	0.112	0.1145	0.229	525×10^{-4}		0.106
9	5.25	0.315	0.123	0.645	170×10^{-4}		0.299
8'	2.0	0.112	0.1145	0.229	525×10^{-4}		0.106
7'	2.0	0.09	0.0895	0.179	320×10^{-4}		0.083
					$5,860 \times 10^{-4}$	$5,860 \times 10^{-4}$	
1	4.35	0.024	0.01	0.0435	19×10^{-4}		0.0202
2	4.35	0.047	0.0198	0.0863	75×10^{-4}		0.04
3	4.35	0.069	0.0292	0.127	161×10^{-4}		0.059
4	4.35	0.089	0.0379	0.165	272×10^{-4}		0.0765
5	4.35	0.108	0.0458	0.200	400×10^{-4}		0.0925
6	14.60	0.416	0.0528	0.77	$5,940 \times 10^{-4}$		0.356
					$6,867 \times 10^{-4} \times 2 = 13,734 \times 10^{-4}$		

$$\Sigma(Pv'')^2 = 46,614 \times 10^{-4}$$

EXAMPLE 3   NATURAL FREQUENCY OF A TWO-LEGGED FRAME   127

TABLE 18

Third approximation

Position of the point	$\dfrac{P}{t}$	$Pv''\gamma''^2$	v'''	Pv'''	$(Pv''')^2$		$Pv'''\gamma'''^2$
1	4.35	0.083	0.04630	0.2010	404.0×10^{-4}		0.0908
2	4.35	0.235	0.127	0.553	$3,050.0 \times 10^{-4}$		0.25
3	4.35	0.314	0.175	0.761	$5,800.0 \times 10^{-4}$		0.344
4	4.35	0.304	0.1655	0.72	$5,200.0 \times 10^{-4}$		0.326
5	4.35	0.173	0.0935	0.407	$1,660.0 \times 10^{-4}$		0.184
					$16,114.0 \times 10^{-4} \times 2 = 32,228.0 \times 10^{-4}$		
7	2.00	0.083	0.0863	0.173	300.0×10^{-4}		0.078
8	2.00	0.106	0.1125	0.226	510.0×10^{-4}		0.102
9	5.25	0.299	0.1215	0.638	$4,070.0 \times 10^{-4}$		0.289
8'	2.00	0.106	0.1125	0.226	510.0×10^{-4}		0.102
7'	2.00	0.083	0.0863	0.173	300.0×10^{-4}		0.078
					$5,690.0 \times 10^{-4}$	$5,690.0 \times 10^{-4}$	
1	4.35	0.0202	0.00885	0.0385	15.0×10^{-4}		0.0175
2	4.35	0.04	0.0175	0.076	58.0×10^{-4}		0.0344
3	4.35	0.059	0.02582	0.112	125.0×10^{-4}		0.051
4	4.35	0.0765	0.0336	0.146	213.0×10^{-4}		0.066
5	4.35	0.0925	0.0407	0.177	313.0×10^{-4}		0.080
6	14.60	0.356	0.04693	0.685	$4,680.0 \times 10^{-4}$		0.310
					$5,404.0 \times 10^{-4} \times 2 = 10,808.0 \times 10^{-4}$		

$$\Sigma(Pv''')^2 = 48,726.0 \times 10^{-4}$$

The value of γ'''^2 is

$$\gamma'''^2 = \frac{1}{\sqrt{\Sigma(Pv''')^2}} = \frac{1}{\sqrt{4.87}} = 0.453; \quad \gamma''' = 0.673$$

The natural frequency

$$N''' = \frac{60}{2\pi} \gamma''' \sqrt{Eg} = \frac{60}{6283} \, 0.673\sqrt{300 \times 981} = 3490 \text{ cpm}$$

The difference between $Pv'''\gamma'''^2$ and $Pv''\gamma''^2$ being from about 5 to 10 per cent only, the computation will not be continued and the natural frequency will be accepted as $N = 3490$ cpm (Fig. 56).

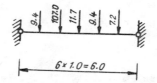

Fig 56. The loads $Pv\gamma^2$ acting on the frame beam (partial fixity)

8. Experimental determination of natural frequencies

As can be seen in the foregoing chapter, natural frequencies of structural elements can be determined both by exact theoretical treatment and by simplified calculations, the latter, however, giving only approximate results. Natural frequencies, as is known, are experienced in practice together with their harmonics. The calculation of these latter and particularly the calculation of the higher harmonics is a tedious and complicated process. The results gained by the theoretical analysis of natural frequencies can be considered reliable for structures as, for instance, those assembled from prefabricated elements where the joints can be regarded as freely rotating or only partially fixed. Here there is practically no constraint between adjoining elements and, consequently, we have only to determine the natural frequencies of each element, taking into account the periodical effect transmitted to the supporting structures by the elements subject to vibration. Vibration intensity at the points of transmission will depend on the value of the transmission factor

$$\frac{1}{1-\left(\dfrac{\omega}{\omega_n}\right)^2}$$

where ω is the angular frequency of the motion of the point of support, and ω_n is that of the motion of the supporting element.

With buildings, where vibrations of the most varied kinds occur in consequence of the junctions of walls, roofs etc., the theoretical determination of natural frequencies is very complicated and the result cannot be accepted as entirely satisfactory for practical purposes.

As is known, the natural frequency of a simply supported beam is considerably lower than that of a fully fixed one. A prerequisite for any theoretical analysis of the natural frequency of beams is an exact knowledge of the degree of fixity thereof. What we actually know is that if, e.g., the natural frequency of a simply supported beam is say 100 per min, an identical but fully fixed beam will have a natural frequency of 222 per min*.

---

* In Vol. II. Chapter V, on p. 217 the natural frequency of a simply supported floor joist with one laterally movable support is given as

$$n_1 = 1.17 \times 30 \sqrt{\frac{3 \times 10^6 \times 384}{5} \times \frac{I}{q l^4}} = 5.31 \times 10^5 \sqrt{\frac{I}{q l^4}}$$

that of a joist fixed at both ends js

$$n_2 = 1.14 \times 30 \sqrt{3 \times 10^6 \times 384 \times \frac{I}{q l^4}} = 11.7 \times 10^5 \sqrt{\frac{I}{q l^4}}$$

Thus for $E = 3,000,000$ (t/m^2) the ratio becomes $11.7/5.31 = 2.22$. This result agrees fairly well with the value $100 \times 2.22 = 222 \cong 227$ (see the observed value on p. 129).

It should be stressed that natural frequency depends on the actual degrees of fixity, but the theoretical determination of the latter is usually difficult.

The experimental determination of natural frequencies is a suitable way of eliminating the above inaccuracies. Thus, if it is possible to determine experimentally the natural frequency of a partially fixed beam, the difference between the natural frequencies of the partially fixed beam and the simply supported beam on the one hand, and between the partially fixed beam and the entirely fixed cantilever on the other, can easily be calculated. Conclusions can be drawn in this way as to the degree of fixity.

For experimental tests, to be discussed in more detail later, a vibrator with variable speed has been used to generate vibrations. Another method for inducing vibrations consists in the application of static load until the beam is deformed. The load is then suddenly released. In practice the most suitable and the simplest method is to set individual elements vibrating by dropping a weight on them. The exact determination of the absolute values of the amplitudes thus generated is of no importance for computing natural frequencies. Considering further that the amplitudes depend on the energy of the blow and the factors characterizing the shock intensity, it will suffice to drop a piece of concrete of about 10 to 15 kg from a height of say, 40 to 50 cm on the element selected for examination. A similar method can be adopted to determine the natural frequency in the horizontal plane. For this a similar weight should be brought into collision with the element in question using the weight as a pendulum and dealing a blow at the body in the horizontal plane. The experimentally determined natural frequency can be compared with that obtained by calculation.

In an example of vibration analysis performed at a Hungarian power plant, a supporting element of the boiler house, considered as a simply supported beam, had an original natural frequency of 11 cps. When mounted in the structure, a value of 25 cps could be measured. The ratio of the two values is $25/11 = 2.27$. Thus the beam actually behaved as a fixed beam after installation, inasmuch as the ratio of the natural frequencies of the fixed and simply supported beam had been derived previously as 2.22, that is, almost the above value. In other instances examined, the coefficient of fixity was $18/14 = 1.29$ and $25/14 = 1.79$. In the former case we had to deal with a partial fixity of approximately 25 per cent, whereas in the latter, the fixity is 60 per cent.

Conclusions as to the character of support may also be drawn by measuring the amplitudes at several points of the beam and plotting the curve of amplitudes, characterizing the deformation produced by vibration.

By analysing experimentally the propagation of waves to other elements of the building, we may also draw conclusions as to the way in which the elements concerned affect each other.

Hence vibration analysis enables us to explain actual static conditions and, though indirectly, to check the quality of the construction.

CHAPTER III

CLASSIFICATION OF MACHINE FOUNDATIONS AND MACHINES

Machine foundations can be divided into the following ma..n groups, according to their constructional features.

1. Simple or block foundations

These are either in a single mass or contain openings up to 50 per cent of their volume (Fig. 57/1 and e.g. Fig. 46 in Vol. II p. 85).

2. Complex foundations

These may be divided into the following three groups:

(i) Wall-like foundations, which usually consist of two walls parallel to each other, supporting the machine (Fig. 57/2a or e.g. Fig. 46 in Vol. III on p. 48).

(ii) Caisson foundations, with which the necessary rigidity can be attained by the appropriate arrangement of material-saving elements (see Fig. 57/2b or e.g. Fig. 38 in Vol II p. 78).

(iii) Framed foundations, which have a structure of vertical columns and horizontal frame beams braced together by means of longitudinal beams; frame girders and longitudinal beams constitute a horizontal raft (Fig. 57/2c or e.g. Figs. 18 and 51 in Vol. III on pp. 28 and 51).

(iv) Horizontally framed upper table supported by vibration isolating springs with slender columns on foundation slabs practically free from dynamic effects (see Fig. 57/2d or e.g. Fig. 67 in Vol. III on p. 59).

The above types are frequently combined in practice.

Machines are classified according to their operating speed and may be divided into the following groups:

a. Machines generating shock-like forces such as steam hammers. Block foundations with only a few openings are usually provided for machines of this type. In order to protect the environment, similar machines should be founded on elastic shock or vibration absorbers. Low-speed machines operate at 60 to 80 rpm; high-speed ones attain 150 rpm or more.

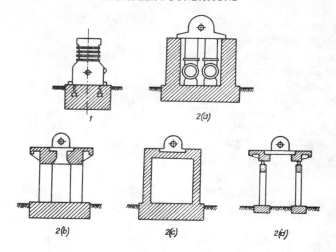

Fig. 57. Basic types of machines with dynamic action.

1. massive (block) foundation; 2. complex foundations: (a) wall-like foundation; (b) framed foundation; (c) caisson type foundation; (d) horizontally framed upper table supported by vibration isolating springs with slender columns on foundations practically free from dynamic effects

b. Low-speed machines of about 50 rpm, such as machines of the paper industry, printing machines, steam mills, produce no dangerous amplitudes. They are supported by raft foundations, without elastic layers.

c. Low-speed machines of about 10 cps. These machines operating at a maximum speed of 600 rpm are supported either by block foundations or foundations of a complex type, and may or may not be provided with elastic pads.

d. Machines of a moderate speed of 10 to 25 cps. For supporting such machines having operating speeds of 600 to 1500 rpm, many kinds of foundations may be used; they are usually provided with elastic pads. Adequate precautions must be taken to prevent the occurrence of excessive amplitudes.

e. Machines with high operating speeds of 25 cps or more. The foundations constructed for this type of machines—among them compressors and turbines—are usually set directly on the ground, and are mostly of the complex type, consisting of frames. Operating speeds are around 3000 rpm but speeds of 10,000 rpm or more may be attained.

In connection with the above classification it should be noted that machines with small inertial forces, i.e. low kinetic energy, can be placed without any special foundations, on the ground or on a floor, either directly or with the insertion of elastic layers since the amplitudes produced are but hardly or not at all observable.

When designing the foundations for these machines the small dynamic forces can be neglected. Only the static loads need to be taken into account and, as regards the supporting structure, care must be taken that the smaller dynamic forces which may occur should be transmitted, after being strongly damped, to the soil or to the floor.

Such machines are, for example, driving motors of the smaller type, pumps, machine tools, spinning machines, looms, etc.

For design calculations the following classification—corresponding to the current specifications—can be accepted:

1. Foundations for machines producing shock forces. Hammer foundations belong to this group (see Vol. II Chapters I–II).

2. Foundations for machines producing periodical forces. Reciprocating machines (discussed in Vol. II Chapters III–IV) belong to this group.

3. Turbine foundations. Foundations for machines of high operating speeds are (discussed in Vol. III Chapters I–II).

4. Other machines. Foundations for machines with special drives—such as rolling mills, forging presses, crushing mills, flour mills and machine tools—are discussed in Vol. II Chapter V.

CHAPTER IV

FUNDAMENTAL PRINCIPLES FOR THE DESIGN OF MACHINE FOUNDATIONS

Dynamic forces of machines should be transmitted to the soil through the foundation in such a way that, by the correct selection of the foundation mass or by the use of vibration damping, all kinds of harmful effects are eliminated. The corresponding specifications of several countries have been drawn up essentially on the basis of the above principle. Some ideas common to most of them are given in the following Sections.

The level of the ground water table is significant to the design of machine foundations. Where for example, the water table level is near the bottom plane of the mat foundation, it is advisable to clear the water level by a depth equal to or greater than 1/3 of the foundation width (Fig. 58). This is necessary since ground water transmits vibrations to a great distance without damping. On the other hand, in cohesive soils such as clay and loam, considerable damping may take place. Yet the soil may become plastic and this, in turn, may result in the transmission of harmful vibrations to the environment. In both cases the problems presented cannot usually be solved by means of raft foundations, and—depending on the soil characteristics—special solutions (pile foundations, open caissons, or soil consolidation) must be resorted to if elastic pads are insufficient for reducing the transmitted dynamic forces.

Care must generally be taken to ensure that the frequency of the machine itself is not in tune with that of the machine–foundation system, neither should there be acceleration in the soil which is greater than 0.2 g. In addition, the actual soil pressure should not exceed that permissible for dynamic loading and the amplitudes of the machine foundation should not exceed those permissible for the type of machine being used.

In the foundations of fine-machine tools erected close to each other it is of the greatest importance that no vibrations—not even the slightest—should be transmitted to the surroundings. For this purpose special vibration-damping layers (cork or wood plates, helical springs, rubber padding, etc.) are used.

The foundations of hammers, crushers, etc.—especially when the soil is loose and non-cohesive—may bring about a high degree of consolidation in the subsoil. Inasmuch as the transmittance of vibrations cannot be reduced by the proper design of the foundation to a tolerable degree, vibration absorbers will again be necessary.

The mechanical engineer's aim is to balance correctly the alternating or rotating masses of the machine (see Vol. II Chapter VI).

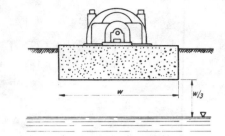

Fig. 58. Relationship of groundwater to machine foundation

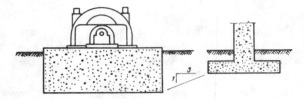

Fig. 59. Relationship of adjoining building foundation

The most suitable material for machine foundations is reinforced concrete. Foundations constructed of plain concrete or masonry are used for machines transmitting mainly static loads.Care should be taken that the common centre of gravity of the foundation and the machine is in the vertical of the centre of gravity of the foundation plane, or close to it. It is advisable to separate, usually by means of expansion joints, machine foundations from adjacent buildings and underground structures. With foundations of low-capacity machines or where the occurrence of harmful reactions between machine foundations and the adjacent structures is unlikely, separation is not necessary.

The length of the anchor bolts can be shortened by means of special anchoring facilities, hooks, or hammerhead bolts, but the continuity of forces, between machine and foundation, must not be affected. All this should be done, of course, in consultation with the mechanical engineer. Various conduits and pipes embedded in the foundation (steam supply pipes, pressure pipes, etc.) must be arranged for the most economical foundation design without infringing the mechanical require-ments. Steam supply pipes and hot-air lines must be properly isolated and sealed.

The foundation must be protected against machine oil by means of acid-proof paint, acid-resistant coating, silicate treatment or by a cover of acid-resistant tiles.

Building foundations in the vicinity of the machine foundations can be constructed at a level higher than that of the latter, however, the possible decrease in the angle of internal friction of the soil due to dynamic forces should he examined (Fig. 59). Slopes of 1 : 3 could generally be accepted. If the distance between the two foundations is very slight, these should preferably be constructed at the same elevation.

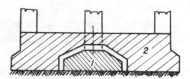

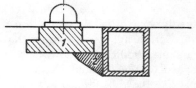

Fig. 60. Machine foundation (1) placed over a building foundation (2)

Fig. 61. Solution of a machine foundation (1) by replacing the soil with poor concrete (2)

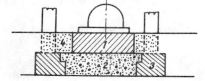

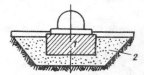

Fig. 62. In cases of poor soil conditions densified sand (2) can replace the bad layer with earthfilling (4) around the foundation (1)

Fig. 63. Solution for a separate foundation (1) with densified sand layer (2) below the foundation.

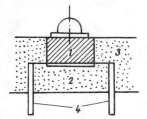

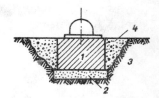

Fig. 64. To ensure a better effect of the sand layer (2) below the foundation (1) sheet piles (4) can be helpful. The foundation is surrounded by sand (3)

Fig. 65. In cases of rocky soil (3), a relatively small sheet of stamped sand (2) could act below the foundation (1)—surrounded by earthfilling (4)—as a damping layer against strong impact forces

Special arrangements for machine foundations are shown in the following examples based also on Polish practise (see also [697]). In Fig. 60 a machine foundation is placed over a building foundation. It is possible to replace the soil by lean concrete as shown in Fig. 61. In the case of poor subsoil conditions, densified sand could replace the bad layer between the building foundations with earth filling around the foundation. The densified layer as shown in Fig. 62 are stamped in 20–25 cm sheets by stamping devices. This solution is shown for a separate foundation in Fig. 63. To ensure that the sand layer has a better effect, sheet piles can be helpful, as shown in Fig. 64. For rocky soils a relatively small sheet of stamped sand could also act as a damping layer against strong impact forces (Fig. 65).

In order to eliminate harmful vibrations of the foundations that may un-expectedly occur after the completion of construction works, it is advisable to design the foundation in such a manner that it can be modified at a later date. Such a subsequent modification can be accomplished by additional masses of concrete connected to the original by controllable prestressing, by driving piles, or by compacting the subsoil in other ways.

In addition we give below some guiding principles concerning the design of turbine foundations:

The mechanical design should leave adequate free space for the supporting structures.

Voids or grooves causing difficulties in the structural design of columns and beams should be avoided.

Openings should always be surrounded by reinforcement.

The framework should be arranged perpendicular to the turbine axis, and be braced together by beams running parallel to the latter.

The horizontal beams of the frames should be arranged directly and concetric-ally on the axes of the columns so that the axes coincide.

Large spans and eccentricities should be avoided.

The base plate of the turbine should be as stiff as possible in the horizontal direction.

Small masses should be avoided for cantilever slabs.

Instead of increasing their thickness, ribbed slabs, sometimes stiffened with edge ribs, should be used.

CHAPTER V

BUILDING MATERIALS
FOR MACHINE FOUNDATIONS

Building materials for machine foundations can be divided into two main groups:
(i) structural materials, used chiefly to carry and transmit loads,
(ii) materials damping vibration and sound.
In addition we shall deal with materials used to protect foundations against weather, moisture and chemical action.

1. The behaviour of materials under alternating loads

In practice all structural analyses are based on the validity of Hooke's law although it is known that this assumption does not exactly correspond to the actual changes taking place in the material. It is thus assumed that structures under static loads generally suffer elastic deformation only. However, plastic deformation, caused by dynamic fluctuating loads has far greater significance for us than deformations due to static loads.

The behaviour of a test specimen under alternating forces, i.e. under successive cycles of loading and unloading, is represented graphically in Fig. 66 where deformations and loads are plotted on the horizontal and vertical axes, respectively. The *OABD* area corresponds to the work done by external forces during the loading cycle while the *CCED* area represents the work developed on release. The difference between these two forms of work (the work performed by loading and that released by unloading), equals the energy absorbed by the test specimen during the process. When the stress varies between equal values in tension and compression the stress–strain diagram of the beam is called the hysteresis curve. The shaded area in the figure indicates the energy absorbed in one cycle. Part of the energy is converted into heat, yet changes in the internal structure of the material also occur. The gradual increase of non-elastic deformation leads to "fatigue failure" of the material. Before fracture, a rise in temperature of the specimen can be observed.

No structure carrying dynamic loads can be designed economically without the knowledge of the limit stress which the material is capable of withstanding even under an infinite number of loading cycles. That stress characterizes the fatigue or endurance limit of the material.

Fatigue. If a test material capable of resisting both tensile and compressive strengths is subjected to repeated loads smaller than the static ultimate load, failure will occur after a certain number of applications. The number of cycles prior to failure changes with the magnitude of the periodical force. The greater the load causing fracture (the nearer it is to the static ultimate load), the smaller the number of repetitions. On the other hand, the greater the number of loading cycles the smaller the dynamic force causing fracture. By reducing the load to a certain limit, a value will be reached at which the test specimen can be subjected to an infinite number of cycles without the danger of fracture.

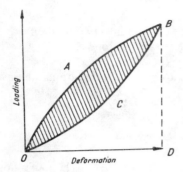

Fig. 66. Load-deformation diagram under load (A) and at release of load (C)

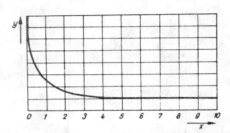

Fig. 67. Relation between the number of loading cycles and ultimate strength

x—number of load repetitions up to failure, y—stress

By plotting the number of loading cycles to failure against the corresponding stresses (Fig. 67), a rapidly falling curve is obtained. Stresses decrease with increasing number of loading cycles and eventually the curve approaches asymptotically the endurance limit of the material. It will be perceived therefrom that a relatively small number of repetitions results in a considerable reduction in the ultimate strength of the material. A further increase in load repetitions is, as regards practical use, of less significance. The fatigue limit of a material is practically identical with the highest stress to which it may be subjected an infinite number of times without failure.

The fatigue limit is expressed in the Goodman–Johnson formula as a function of stress fluctuations. This can be regarded as a first approximation of general value because there are still many materials whose dynamic properties have not yet been investigated. If R is the ultimate strength under static load and σ_{min} and σ_{max} are the lowest and highest stresses which may occur, respectively, then the fatigue limit can be expressed as

$$\sigma_z = \frac{0.5R}{1 - 0.5\dfrac{\sigma_{min}}{\sigma_{max}}} \tag{166}$$

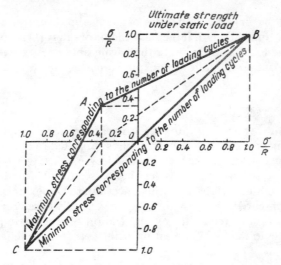

Fig. 68. According to the fatigue diagram, loads within the area $ABOCA$ are harmless

If the stress corresponding to static load is

$$\sigma_{sz} = \frac{\sigma_{max} + \sigma_{min}}{2} \qquad (167)$$

and the stress caused by dynamic load is

$$\sigma_d = \frac{\sigma_{max} - \sigma_{min}}{2} \qquad (168)$$

that is, it corresponds to the stress fluctuation, then the highest and lowest stresses developed in the material are respectively

$$\sigma_{max} = \sigma_{sz} + \sigma_d \qquad (169)$$

and

$$\sigma_{min} = \sigma_{sz} - \sigma_d \qquad (170)$$

The limit resistance of the material with the stress corresponding to the fatigue limit σ_{max}, By substituting the above values in Eq. (166) we obtain the following result:

$$\sigma_z = \sigma_{max} = R - 2\sigma_d \qquad (171)$$

The ultimate strength of the material, i.e. the maximum stress when under static load, is expressed from Eq. (171) by

$$R = \sigma_{st} + 3\sigma_d \qquad (172)$$

Representing graphically the above equation (Fig. 68), we may establish that any stress variation which remains within the $ABOCA$ lines has no detrimental results.

It follows that the magnification factor of the maximum unit stress corresponding to the endurance limit equals 3. If the same factor of safety (k) is applied to dynamic loads as to static loads and denoting the permissible stress corresponding to the latter by σ_p, we obtain the following expression:

$$\sigma_p = \frac{R}{k} > \sigma_{st} + 3\sigma_d \tag{173}$$

In general, for investigations into fatigue in cases of, for example, wind loads (see Vol. III) which may lead to failure of structures subjected to dynamic disturbances, the design life of structure n_d can be obtained by $n_d = n_0(1 + \beta V_f)$, where n_0 is the expected life of the structure, β is a safety index (see Ang-Cornell [33]) and V_f is a coefficient of a random variable denoting uncertainty. Design life and computed life are then to be compared. The design codes are generally based on a constant range criterion. About fatigue reliability by application of stochastic processes see the relevant references in Yao [1352], treating problems of fatigue reliability and design.

2. The elastic properties of materials

In order to predict the behaviour of materials under dynamic load, besides the fatigue limit, their elastic and damping properties must be known. Since the elastic properties of a material under dynamic loads differ from those under static loads, we cannot content ourselves with establishing the modulus of elasticity (E) for static loads alone.

The elastic properties exhibited by the material under repeated loads must be determined exactly, and it has to be proved whether or not those properties can be considered equal under conditions of both static and dynamic loads.

According to the theory of vibrations, the damping of free or harmonic vibrations and, in the case of resonance, the magnitude of the amplitudes of a system subjected to forced vibration, depend upon the internal resistance of the material. This internal resistance, which is in fact, energy absorption or internal friction, is essentially characterized, under conditions of stress caused by dynamic loads, by the non-elastic deformation of the material.*

For measuring the dynamic modulus of elasticity (E_d) there are different methods which all assume that Hooke's law is valid also in the dynamic state.

For materials having low internal damping (from 0.1 to 10 cps) the "free vibration method" is well adopted. In this way specimens are tested for bending in long prismatic rods and for torsion by strings of circular cross section.

By applying a sinusoidally varying force the maximum amplitudes in the case of resonance could be investigated by the "resonance method". Here transverse vibrations are induced and the measured values are evaluated on the specimens. The frequency–response curves of the material are plotted with excitements at a

* For details see E. S. Sorokin's paper in Korenev [621]

constant amplitude but with increasing frequency. The dynamic modulus of elasticity can be calculated from the measurements of the ω_r resonance frequencies and determined graphically, $\Delta\omega$ (half power width, the distance between frequencies above and below ω_r at which the vibration amplitude is $v = v_{max}/\sqrt{2}$, where v_{max} is the resonant amplitude). As shown in Fig 69a [154] with materials having low internal damping, the resonant curve has a shape of $\Delta\omega$ narrow segments, although

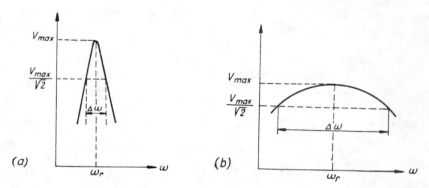

Fig. 69. Resonance method for measuring E_d resonance curves in case of (a) low and (b) high internal damping

ω_T can be accurately determined, measurement errors may occur. For materials with high internal damping the resonant curve takes a flattened shape according to Fig. 69b, and the measurement of ω_z is uncertain and so are the values of $v_{max}/\sqrt{2}$, values which determine $\Delta\omega$. The method is most convenient to use in the case of materials having medium damping. The disadvantage of the method is that the values of the modulus of elasticity are supplied only at the resonant frequency of the specimen.

The dynamic modulus of elasticity could also be investigated by the "wave propagation method" as well, where using piezoelectric or other improved pickups short high frequency pulses are transmitted through the specimen and from the measured propagation time (t) over a distance, the velocity and from this E_d can be computed.

3. Building materials for structures used mainly to resist and transmit loads

A) BRICK

Brickwork foundations have the disadvantage that bricks laid in mortar can be used effectively to resist compressive stresses only, the tensile and shear strength of the bricks being very small. Dynamic loads inevitably involve alternating stresses and brickwork cannot be used to resist such forces effectively because stress variation may separate the elements of the structure. Machines of small dimensions, where the calculation of static forces is sufficient, can be supported on brickwork laid in cement mortar. In some cases reinforcement may be used to enable brickworks to resist tension as well. Foundations must be built only of properly burnt bricks resistant to frost. The modulus of elasticity of brickwork varies, according to experiments, between wide limits and therefore it is necessary to consider the possible development of resonance. The modulus of elasticity of brickwork depends, to a great extent, upon the compressive stresses caused by static loads and increases together with these. There is great divergence in values as is shown by the fact that, according to experimental results, the modulus of elasticity varies from 10,000 to 100,000 kg/cm^2. The value of the modulus is, according to general experience, influenced only to a very small extent by the composition of the mortar used.

B) STONE

Generally the same observations apply to masonry as to brickwork. Great attention must be paid to the complete filling of joints with mortar (this requirement is valid for brickwork too). The stones must be properly bonded. In the absence of experimental results, requirements for concrete structures may be provisionally applied to stonework as well.

C) PLAIN CONCRETE

Plain concrete is used for block foundations of machines. It may be used in combination with reinforced concrete, as a substructure of the latter, the stresses here being appreciably smaller.

For the determination of endurance limits it has been shown by corresponding experiments that the expression $\sigma = \sigma_{st} + 3\sigma_d$, previously explained, can be accepted also for mass concrete structures. The modulus of elasticity determined under dynamic loading is, according to experiments, identical with the modulus corresponding to static load, with, however, a possible deviation of 30 per cent.

D) REINFORCED CONCRETE

The best material for machine foundations is reinforced concrete. It can resist both compressive and tensile stresses. Its durability can be ensured for an infinitely long time both under wet and dry conditions. With proper additives reinforced concrete can be protected against acids, oil, etc.

The behaviour of reinforced-concrete structures under dynamic loads has been studied extensively.

According to this, the magnification factor of 3 can be diminished. In the case of a supposed $\mu = 3$ value a theoretically unlimited number of cycles is supposed (Fig. 70). For a smaller number of cycles a lower μ value can be taken from the permanent

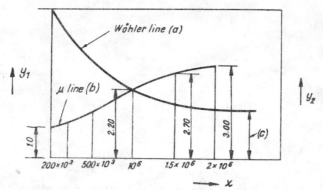

Fig. 70. Permanent stress (Wöhler) line and coefficient of fatique (μ line) depending upon the number of cycles

y_1—static stress, y_2—allowable stress equal to 1/3 static stress, x—number of cycles; (a) Wöhler line, (b) μ line, (c) alternating stress = 1/3 static stress

stress (Wöhler) line [1008]. Thus, the number of lower of lower cycles around $\mu=2$ can be taken into consideration. Thus for concrete including prestressed concrete the value of $R = \sigma_{st} + 2\sigma_d$ should be accepted. The value of 2 is maximum and varies between 1.5 and 2 as shown in [151].

In the case of smaller exciting forces, e.g. water-waves, the value is even smaller, i.e. not more that $\mu = 1.1$ as shown in the example on pp. 972–974 of Ref. [1008].

It should be mentioned here that the GDR code TGL 25 731 prescribes that instead of supposing higher loads by multiplying by the factor μ (which is given in this code as having a maximum value of $\mu = 3$), that lower stresses be taken according to TGL 11 422 for reinforced concrete. This is effected by introducing a factor κ depending upon the relation min $l/$max $\sigma = \rho$.

As for the fatigue problems regarding reinforced concrete see also Hanson [422a] and also ACI publication sp 41 [308a].

For different kinds of concrete the stresses for bending axial compressions for axial strain and for the modulus of elasticity are given after TGL 21 003 in Table 19. Relations of the modulus of elasticity of steel to concrete n_e are given in Table 20. The decreasing factors κ corresponding to the different ρ values are given in

TABLE 19

Concrete stresses and modulus of elasticity

Types of stress		Classification of concrete			
		B III	B IV	B V	B VI
Bending compression	σ_b (kg/cm^2)	115	155	220	275
Axial compression	σ_{bc} (kg/cm^2)	90	125	175	220
Axial strain	σ_{bs} (kg/cm^2)	7.5	9.0	12.5	15.0
Modulus of elasticity	E_b (t/cm^2)	265	305	350	400

TABLE 20

*Relations of the modulus of elasticity of steel
to concrete n_E according to different concrete types*

	Classification of concrete			
	B III	B IV	B V	B IV
n_E	16	14	12	10

TABLE 21

Decreasing factors κ_b

$\rho_b^2 \left(\dfrac{\min\sigma}{\max\sigma} \right)$	$\leqq 0.1$	0.2	0.3	0.4	0.5	> 0.6
κ_b	0.75	0.80	0.85	0.90	0.95	1.00

TABLE 22

a) Values for computations of steel

Computation values	Sort of steel		
	St A–0	St A–1	St–ill
$\dfrac{\sigma_{strain}}{\sigma_{compr}}$ kg/cm^2	1950	2100	3400
Modulus of elasticity $[E]_s$ t/cm^2	2100	2100	2100

b) Decreasing factors κ_a for steel

Steel	In the case $\rho_a = \kappa_a \min\sigma/\max\sigma$						
St A–0	–1.0	–0.2	0	0.2	0.4	0.7	$\geqq 0.8$
St A–1	0.45	0.70	0.80	0.85	1.0	1.00	1.0
St A–III	0.31	0.47	0.53	0.57	0.67	0.83	1.0

Table 21. Computation values for steel are given in Table 22a; decreasing factors for different sorts of steel in Table 22b.

Different values are quoted in the literature for Young's modulus of elasticity for reinforced concrete. Thus Barkan suggests a value of 300,000 kg/cm^2 for E; this contrasts with Makarishev's view, he suggests that 230,000 kg/cm^2 and 260,000 kg/cm^2 should be assumed for concrete qualities B 140 and B 170, respectively.

The German DIN 4024 specifies 300,000 kg/cm² for B 225 concrete. Elastic moduli increased by 10 per cent should be used for higher concrete qualities. In subsequent numerical examples all calculations were based on a modulus of elasticity of $E = 300,000$ kg/cm² (see also footnote on p. 000).

The TGL of the GDR No. 112–0500 specifies the following values: for B 225, $E = 265,000$ kg/cm²; for B 300, 305,000 kg/cm²; for B 450, 350,000 kg/cm²; for B 600, 400,000 kg/cm².

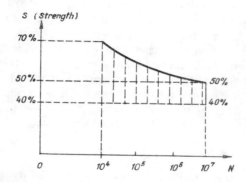

Fig. 71. Safe *S–N* (Wöhler curve for prestressing stands for a lower stress limit of 40 per cent strength, after Abeles [4].

S–N means stress range 'S' for number of repetitions 'N' before failure, where Wöhler curve relates to the corresponding loading range

The latest experiments show good agreement with theoretical results provided the calculation is based on an elastic modulus determined simultaneously by experiment.

Experiments have further shown the rigidity of reinforced concrete structures to decrease with increasing load. The extent of this reduction varies according to the increase in the load and is inversely proportional to the age of the concrete and to the number of loading cycles. After a certain number of loadings the value of E becomes constant; for this conditions it obeys Hooke's law. The experiments have also shown that with stresses exceeding the permissible value, dynamic rigidity is smaller than that corresponding to the static value. If loads do not exceed the permissible stress limits, dynamic and static rigidities can be taken as practically identical.

As for prestressed concrete for different kinds of loadings in order to ascertain their cumulative effect, extensive fatigue tests have been performed by Abeles [4]; the result has been ascertained that prestressed concrete has greater fatigue resistance with well bonded steel than that of the steel itself. For prestressing stands for lower stress limits of 40 per cent strength the Wöhler curves (strength (S) versus number of repetitions (N) before failure), are given in Fig. 71. It was shown in an example that for a definite upper limit of loading, the occurrence of visible cracks can be avoided.

About fatigue problems of prestressed concrete composite beams see Chung and Chung [181a].

E) METALS

The metal used most frequently for machine foundations is mild steel. This steel should be protected against the effect of smoke, gases, acid or alkaline atmosphere, calcium sulphate and magnesium chloride, with a rust-preventing layer, and on steel in contact with the soil a bitumen coating must be applied to prevent corrosion.

There is extensive literature on the fatigue of metals, and on their elastic moduli, studies being necessary chiefly for mechanical engineering. Stresses arising in metal structures are almost equal for static and dynamic loads. However, it should be noted that with welded structures, local stress concentrations may occur at the joints leading to a reduction in the resistance of the material to dynamic loads. The permissible stress can, according to experiments, be calculated by the following expression:

$$\sigma_p = \sigma_{st} + 2\sigma_d \tag{174}$$

In calculations the elastic moduli E_d (corresponding to dynamic loads) and E_{st} (corresponding to static ones) may be taken as equal since experiments indicate the deviation between the two values to be not more than 5 per cent.

According to TGL 25 731 [1243] for steel the prescriptions of TGL 13 500 [1242] point 2.3 on p. 5 can be taken into consideration.

F) TIMBER

For permanent machine foundations timber can be used only in positions where it would not be liable to decay, i.e. where it is either constantly dry or permanently submerged (e.g. wooden piles). The timber used should always be treated with preservative.

Tensile and compressive strengths of timber are about the same, thus wood is equally resistant to alternating stresses. The strength of timber reduces with increasing moisture content.

Experiments were made by Korchinski to ascertain the strength of timber under dynamic loads for Scotch fir, oak, European fir, spruce and Siberian deciduous trees. The aim of these experiments was the determination of their resistance to tensile and compressive as well as to bending and torsional efforst. The conclusions showed that the dynamic strength was 24 to 33 per cent of the static strength of the timber. Experiments relating to the permissible stress have indicated that the relationship $\sigma_p = \sigma_{st} + 3\sigma_d$ is valid also for timber, however, care must be taken to reduce the permissible stress when there are large shear stresses, and where high local stresses are to be expected.

The experimental investigation of static and dynamic rigidities have revealed that the elastic modulus can be taken as approximately constant up to a certain frequency, e.g. for a 4 m long wooden beam up to 20 cps.

Table I in Vol. II p. 26 contains data for stresses and elastic properties of wood parallel with the fibres and perpendicular to it (see also results of Sakai, [1061, 1062]).

4. Vibration- and sound-absorbing materials

Machines producing vibrations should be separated from their substructure or foundation by a vibration-damping layer, which provides at the same time an elastic support for the machine.* Such damping layers absorb vibrations by virtue of their resilient properties. Vibration-absorbing pads are inserted between the machine and its supporting structure or foundation, but they can also be placed between the machine foundation and the ground. The latter alternative is chosen when the aim is to reduce the effect of vibrations on structures in the neighbourhood of the foundation. Materials capable of elastic deformation are suitable for this purpose. Steel springs should be mentioned as the most perfect dampers together with timbers, the elastic properties of which are well known. Commonly used vibration absorbers such as cork, rubber and felt, as well as special plastic dampers will be considered subsequently.

A) CORK

The favourable properties of cork which play a part in its suitability for damping vibrations are its low density, impermeability to gases and liquids at certain moisture contents (owing to its completely closed inner air cells), low thermal conductivity, and finally, its high compressibility amounting to 25 per cent, which ensures springing. It is mainly these qualities that give cork its suitability for absorbing vibration and also noise.

Finely ground cork, when mixed with moisture-proofing additives, can be pressed into sheets. Owing to its damping qualities, the pressed-cork sheet obtained in this way is an excellent vibration-absorbing material suitable for the foundation of high-speed machines, up to loads of 15 kg/cm². Its ultimate strength is 50 kg/cm². For high-speed machines several sheets are employed, placed on each other to give a total thickness up to 12 cm. The layers are enclosed in a frame of flat steel to avoid expansion. If cork were free to expand, it would suffer permanent deformations within a very short period of time and would lose its efficiency. The lateral expansion of cork should be prevented in order to improve its vertical elastic properties. The

---

* It should be taken into consideration in this respect whether the foundation and the machine form a single unit, or whether the base frame of the machine is alone capable of withstanding the strains caused by the vibrations. Rigid connections are necessary in Case 1; the damping effect of an isolating layer can be introduced in Case 2.

elasticity of cork becomes exhausted in 10 to 20 years. The elastic modulus is between 80 and 250 kg/cm^2. According to experimental data a pressed-cork sheet of 10 mm can be loaded up to 1 kg/cm^2, and its elastic modulus is 40 kg/cm^2. The absorption factor varies between 0.10 and 0.13. The elastic modulus of natural cork at a permissible stress of 2 kg/cm^2 is 75 to 200 kg/cm^2, its absorption factor is 0.08. For permissible shear values 60 to 80 kg/cm^2 could be adopted. Deformation values are in the case of 2 kg/cm^2 (for 4 to 6 cm thickness): from 0.5 to 8 cm. The above data are naturally of informative character only. In the presence of oil and water, many materials—including cork—used for the isolation of foundations are apt to suffer from deterioration or consolidation under vibrating loads. Such disadvantages have been overcome, for example, by using "Coresil" foundation plates which, according to Hammond [415], are permanently resilient without any deterioration. Natural cork, specially selected, is contained in plate form in a steel frame and bonded together with adhesive. The plates are up to 7.6 cm thick and are impregnated with a preservative.

B) RUBBER

Vulcanization, under the action of heat and additives, induces chemical changes in natural rubber and yields a material with greatly improved elastic properties. Soft rubber obtained in this way is an excellent resilient damping pad; it can be directly vulcanized to metals. Since the resistance of rubber to mineral oil, benzene and petrol is limited, it must be protected against these. Buna rubber, produced synthetically, has similar properties; however, in addition to the qualitites of vulcanized natural rubber, the synthetic material has some other properties of its own, e.g. it offers a better resistance to oils than natural rubber.

When using rubber for damping machine vibrations care must be taken to ensure that, for its elastic properties, it should not rely on volume changes but on its ability for deformation (without any appreciable change in volume). Thus in contrast to cork, characterized by considerable changes in volume, with rubber it is important that the vibration-absorbing material should not be confined on all sides. Between bodies confining the inlaid rubber there must be no connecting metal parts which might prevent the rubber from absorbing vibrations and deforming sideways. To ensure lateral expansion the rubber layer is composed of smaller pieces with interspaces in between. Another possible way is to use the supporting rubber blocks only at certain points. The adhesive power of rubber vulcanized to metal can be as high as 70 kg/cm^2. Utilizing this property, so called rubber springs can be made, where rubber is vulcanized to the metal; this may result in an increase of the energy-absorbing capacity by 30 per cent. Rubber springs have the advantage of being able to take compression as well as shear and torsion; at the same time they are very suitable for damping vibrations. If the rubber spring is too long, multiple metal inserts should be employed to avoid the danger of buckling. Vibration-damping rubber springs will be dealt with in detail in Vol. II Chapter V, pp. 223 ff.

Under the action of the atmosphere rubber suffers a reduction in its elastic properties; "creeping" takes place which considerably impairs its ability to damp vibration. In such cases the distance between machine and support will also change. Where the load is permanent the permissible stress of rubber should be limited to less than 12 kg/cm². Rubber cannot endure prolonged exposure fo temperatures below 25° C or above 60° C. The elastic modulus (E) of rubber is 10 to 90 kg/cm². The permissible stress for a 16 mm thick ribbed synthetic-rubber sheet is, according to data published by Korchinski, 0.5 kg/cm², its elastic modulus, 65 kg/cm², and its absorption coefficient 0.65. Published data for vibration dampers composed of synthetic rubber and cork layers give a permissible stress of 2 kg/cm² an elastic modulus of 70 kg/cm² and an absorption coefficient of 0.20.

For rubber springs, according to Makhult [802], the allowable stresses for compression are between 4 and 6.5 kg/cm² and in case of shock 30 kg/cm². Values for shear are between 1.5 and 2.5 kg/cm² and in the case of shock, a max. of 7 to 10 kg/cm².

C) FELT

Animal wool after having been washed is compressed by felt-fullers in the presence of steam in a special way to yield a homogeneous mass. In prolonged use, especially under the action of repeated wetting and drying, the material becomes hardened and loses its elastic properties. Therefore felt is more suitable for damping the propagation of sounds, and it can be used for machine foundations only after special treatment. Its compressive strength is 80 kg/cm²; the elastic modulus is 800 kg/cm². There are descriptions of bitumen-impregnated jute, hemp and flax sheets under the trade hame 'Antivibrit' having a permissible stress of 10 kg/cm², elastic modulus of 45 kg/cm², and an absorption coefficient of 0.14.

About permissible stresses and elastic modulus for hard felt see Chapter I, in Vol. II on page 25.

D) POLYVINYL CHLORIDE (PVC) AND OTHER SYNTHETIC MATERIALS

One of the plastic substitutes for rubber is PVC. This thermoplastic material is produced as a white powder from acetylene by appropriate treatment with hydrogen chloride.

At elevated temperatures mechanical pressure can convert the material into a homogeneous molten mass. It is solid at temperatures below 70 to 75 °C and above this point a slow and gredual softening of the material takes place up to 200 to 220 °C. At this temperature it is liquid on the surface yet any higher temperatures cause decomposition, characterized by carbonization and the formation of hydrochloric acid. In the temperature range from 70 to 220 °C, PVC can be moulded by mechanical force.

The material is a good electrical insulator, resistant to the action of chemicals, acids, alkalis and oils.

If PVC is compounded with high-boiling plasticizers, used depending upon the ratio of plasticizer, the material obtained has at normal temperatures or even below freezing point the same properties as soft rubber. If the solid solution produced with the aid of the plasticizers is frost-resisting, the PVC mixture will also retain its plastic properties at low temperatures, and this resilient material is a good substitute for rubber. An additional advantage is that some of the mechanical properties of a plasticized PVC are improved inasmuch as its elasticity is increased, though the tensile strength is reduced. Plasticizers slightly impair resistance to chemical action, and the resistance of the plastic to concentrated acids is reduced or entirely lost. Petrol causes the loss of the elastic properties of PVC which becomes hardened.

Vibration-damping rubber springs can also be made of plasticized PVC. Oil-proof rubber which has been employed for this purpose is not readily available, and cushion springs made of synthetic rubber have shown very short life. On the other hand, springs made of PVC have proved successful.

As for the other synthetic materials it should be mentioned finally that data for these materials are given by the appropriate factories. Information concerning such materials are given in Harris-Crede's Handbook [435], Koloušek et al. [610], in the USSR recommandations [1172], by Buzdugan [152], and by Lipiński [697].

E) TIMBER AS A VIBRATION-ABSORBING MATERIAL

Its inherent structure makes timber elastic tc a certain degree; it is therefore used mainly for hammer foundations, being placed between the anvil and the foundation block. For large hammer foundations multiple layers of hardwood beams (oak or beech) are used; pine of various sorts is employed only when no other timber is available. With smaller hammer foundations hardwood blocks are confined by metal bands to prevent their lateral expansion. Timber as an elastic support should, on the basis of practical experience, be used only for bearing weights not exceeding 2 tons. Care should be taken to prevent the moisture content from rising to above 15 to 20 per cent. The allowable compressive and tensile strength of wood parallel to the grain is about 100 kg/cm^2, depending upon the quality of the timber. Across the grain only 20 to 30 per cent of these values should be assumed. The elastic modulus, for purposes of calculation is generally taken as 100,000 kg/cm^2 and usually varies between 90,000 and 120,000 kg/cm^2.

F) METAL STRUCTURES

The most effective elastic supports are helical springs made of steel, which are best suited for reducing amplitudes, and for absorbing a small part of the energy of vibration. The propagation of the latter can be almost completely prevented by their use. A further advantage is that the properties of the material employed are known exactly, and thus springs can be designed far more accurately than supports made of other materials. The use of steel springs will be considered in detail in the following chapters; let it suffice here to note that elastic supports of machine foundations may

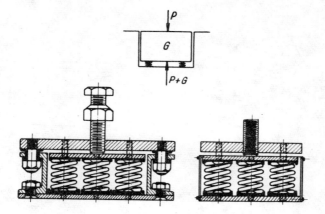

Fig. 72. Device with spiral coils in casing

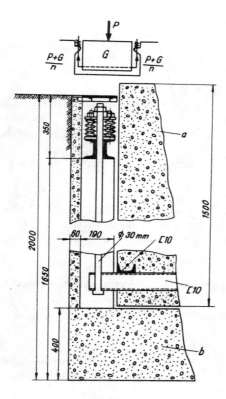

Fig. 73. Foundation suspended on springs (n—number of springs)
a—suspended part of foundation, b—lower part of foundation

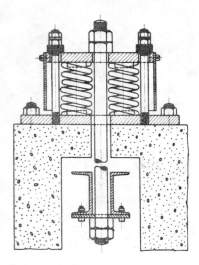

Fig. 74. Spring casing for suspended
foundation

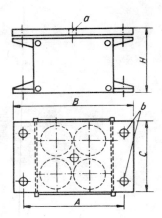

Fig. 75. Characteristic data of
spring casing

a—support bolt (d_1, l_1), b—anchor bolt (d_2, l_2)

be of two types. Springs supporting a machine foundation directly are shown in
Fig. 72, while Figs. 73 and 74 show designs where the foundation is suspended on
springs. The springs must be adequately protected, yet readily accessible.

Springs are employed as a rule if, e.g., the lack of space prevents the application of
foundations of proper mass and size.

As can be seen in Fig. 72, springs are seldom used singly in practice but are usually
installed in groups.

Data of shock absorbers for various allowable loads are given in Table 23. The
notations used in the Table are explained in Fig. 75. The higher the speed of a
machine the smaller the springing is needed. About spring problems, more details
are given in Chapters II, p. 88 and I, p. 72 in Vols II and III, respectively.

5. Materials for protecting machine foundations

The concrete of foundations must be protected against any potential harmful
chemical action (acids, alkalis, salts, etc.).

The methods employed for sealing machine foundations are essentially the same
as those commonly used for other concrete structures. The most important sealing
materials are natural asphalt or pitch, as well as the products which are commonly
described as bitumens.

These materials are satisfactorily resistant both to temperature variations and to
moisture and, depending upon their composition, can be applied hot as well as cold.

TABLE 23

Characteristic dimensions of shock absorbers

Permissible	Weight of shock absorber	Number of springs	d_1/l_1	d_2/l_2	A	B	C	H
kg	kg		mm	mm	mm	mm	mm	mm
100 150 200	4.5	1	12.5/90	12.5/50	105	150	62	100
200 300 500	8	2	20/100	12.5/50	110	155	125	100
450 600 1,000	12.5	4	20/100	15/50	155	210	125	100
600 900 1,500	18	6	20/110	15/50	155	210	175	100
1,000 1,750 2,500	22	9	20/110	20/50	225	270	175	100
3,000 4,000 5,000 6,000	35	9	25/125	20/50	240	280	175	100

Cut-back bitumen mixed from refinery by-products and natural asphalt is also a suitable waterproofing material, used mostly as coating.

Timber should be impregnated with preservatives against decay and the harmful influences of weather. Suitable materials are the solutions of the salts of alkaline substances, of zinc, mercury, copper, iron and aluminium, as well as materials containing oil. Impregnation or preventive coatings can give only moderate protection if the atmosphere is very moist.

CHAPTER VI

PRINCIPLES OF COMPUTATION
FOR MACHINE FOUNDATIONS

In this chapter we shalll deal with data to complete the basic theory of vibration technique for practical use in machine foundation computation. First of all the modes of vibration will be shown then the two main cases of vibration isolation —the active and passive—will be discussed in general. Analysis of elastically supported foundations will be treated then the handling of vertical vibrations both with and without damping effect. Rotating vibrations and those occurring in instances of horizontal displacements will also be discussed, and those resulting from the simultaneous occurrence of vertical and horizontal displacements. Next, the frequency dependent case will be shown and finally the passive case with the base excited foundations.

1. Modes of vibration

The actual machine–foundation system has six degrees of freedom: three translational and three rotational. As reference, a coordinate system going through the common centre of gravity of the machine and foundation is selected. All the disturbing forces and moments, and the displacements at any point of the foundation are related to these axes. Figure 76 shows the centroidal axis and the corresponding modes of vibration of the system.

It is assumed in the analysis that the system has two vertical planes of symmetry and that the horizontal axes lie in those planes. Thus, these axes are principal axes of the body, that is, the products of inertia are zero. Therefore, the directions of the reference coordinates should be chosen accordingly and the eccentricities should be kept to a minimum.

2. Active and passive vibration isolation

The discussion of the principles of computation for machine foundations should begin with the examination of the methods of vibration isolation. These vibrations could not wholly be eliminated only the reduction of vibrations can be considered.

Vibration isolation problems may generally be divided into two types (Fig. 77):

i. Active elimination of vibrations (Fig. 77a). Here the machine induces the vibrations and the foundation is put on the soil itself or on springs or vibration isolating layers, the induced vibrations are damped by soil, springs or the isolating

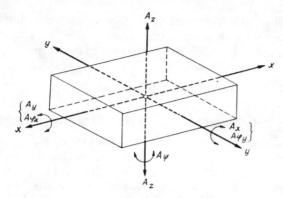

Fig. 76. Modes of vibration

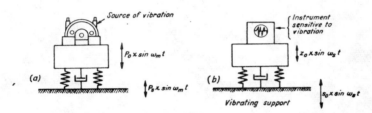

Fig. 77. Active (a) and passive (b) vibration isolation

layer. This is an active case where the machine is transmitting vibrations and our aim is to eliminate these vibrations.

ii. Passive vibration isolation is the case where, for example, sensitive instruments are isolated against the vibrations (Fig. 77b). The disturbance may be generated at the point of erection of the instrument but it may be due to an adjacent source, often to traffic. In laboratories, industrial plants or workshops equipped with sensitive instruments the vibration absorbers can be mounted on the individual instruments, for instance under the legs, which may in some cases made of small springs. The instrument to be protected is thus practically made to float on its legs.

3. Analysis of elastically supported foundations

Vibrations of foundations can in general be reduced to those of an elastically supported solid body. Subsequent considerations will be based on the assumption of a linear relationship between the reaction of the soil which naturally affects vibrations and the displacement of the foundation. The determination of this relationship, in the form of coefficents for uniform and non-uniform elastic compression as well as for uniform and non-uniform displacement, has already been dealt with. The method with lumped parameter systems as a way to handle the interaction of soil and foundation will be treated in detail in Chapter XII.

A) THE VERTICAL VIBRATION OF FOUNDATIONS

(a) Vertical vibrations of foundations without regard to the damping effect of the soil

Let us first examine the vibrations of a foundation which are caused by a vertical force $P(t)$ alternating at a given time interval. Assuming that the centre of gravity of the foundation, that of the machine and that of the ground plane coincide with the line of action of force $P(t)$, only vertical vibrations will occur (Fig. 78).

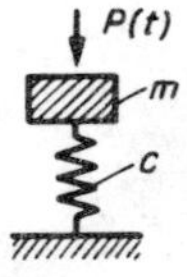

Fig. 78. Vibration of mass m, caused by a vertical periodically charging force $P(t)$

Let z be the vertical displacement of the foundation and its sign positive in the downward direction, then the reaction of the soil, considered as a spring, is

$$R = Q + cz \qquad (175)$$

where Q is the total weight of foundation and machine,
    c the coefficient of stiffness of the soil:

$$c = C_z F \qquad t/m \qquad (176)$$

where C_z is the coefficient of uniform compression in t/m^3,
    F the area of the lower plane of the foundation, m^2.

To establish the differential equation for vertical vibrations the following equation of motion is used as a basic, in which the inertial force has also been added with a negative sign to the external force acting on the body:

$$-m\ddot{z} + Q + P(t) - R = 0 \qquad (177)$$

where

$$m = \frac{Q}{g}$$

Substituting $Q + cz$ from Eq. (175) for R, we get

$$m\ddot{z} + cz = P(t) \tag{178}$$

that is, inertial force + spring force = extermal force, and dividing by m we obtain:

$$\ddot{z} + \lambda_z^2 z = p(t) \tag{179}$$

where

$$\lambda_z^2 = \frac{c}{m} = \frac{C_z F}{m} \tag{180}$$

and

$$p(t) = \frac{P(t)}{m} \tag{181}$$

is the acceleration acting on the mass. For $p(t) = 0$

$$\ddot{z} + \lambda_z^2 z = 0 \tag{182}$$

This equation corresponds to the case when motion occurs only as a result of the inertia of the foundation and the elastic reaction of the soil. Foundation vibrations of this type are called free or natural vibrations.

The solution of the differential equation is:

$$z = A \sin \lambda_z t + B \cos \lambda_z t \tag{183}$$

Vertical natural vibrations of the foundation are independent of the conditions of generation of the vibrations, they depend only on the mass of the foundation and the elastic stiffness of the soil.

The period of vibrations is $T_z = 2\pi/\lambda_z$ and the cpm and cps are, respectively

$$N = \frac{60}{2\pi} \lambda_z \quad \text{and} \quad n = \frac{\lambda z}{2\pi} \tag{184}$$

Coefficients A and B in Eq. (183) yield the amplitudes of the natural vibrations of the foundation. They depend on the initial conditions of motion, i.e. on its velocity or on the extent of displacement of the foundation.

For natural vibrations generated by a single impact

$$i = 0, \qquad z = 0; \qquad v = v_0$$

On differentiating Eq. (183) with respect to time, the velocity is obtained as:

$$\dot{z} = A\lambda_z \cos \lambda_z t - B\lambda_z \sin \lambda_z t \tag{185}$$

For $t = 0$ the initial velocity $z = v_0$, and

$$A = \frac{v_0}{\lambda_z}; \qquad B = 0$$

The displacement is

$$z = \frac{v_0}{\lambda_z} \sin \lambda_z t \qquad (186)$$

Inasmuch as the generating force alternates according to sin ωt, or cos ωt, the equation of the vertical forced vibrations of the foundations will be

$$\ddot{z} - \lambda_z z = p \sin \omega t \qquad (187)$$

where ω is the frequency of the generating force.

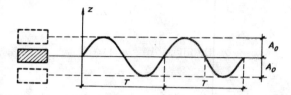

Fig. 79. Vibrating mass floating freely on the springing

Here, natural vibrations will be damped by the soil as soon as forced vibrations of the foundation begin and only forced vibrations will remain. The equation for the latter is

$$z = A_z \sin \omega t \qquad (188)$$

Substituting this in differential equation (187), we obtain the amplitude

$$A_z = \frac{P}{m(\lambda_z^2 - \omega^2)} \qquad (189)$$

If we then suppose that $\lambda_z^2 \gg \omega^2$ the case of a relatively stiff spring; or $\lambda_z^2 \ll \omega^2$, a relatively soft spring, it will be clear that in the latter case, where λ_z can be neglected, the vibrating mass should in a way float freely on the springing (Fig. 79) the corresponding amplitude being

$$A = -\frac{P}{m\omega^2} = A_0 \qquad (190)$$

As according to (25) and (49), ω_0 being here λ_z neglecting ω_0 as $\lambda_z^2 \gg \omega^2$:

$$A = \frac{P}{c} = \frac{P}{m\lambda_z^2} \qquad (191)$$

and the relation

$$\frac{A}{A_0} = \frac{\dfrac{P}{c} \cdot v \cdot m \cdot \omega^2}{-P} = \left(\frac{\lambda_z}{\omega}\right)^2 \cdot v \qquad (192)$$

represents the relation of the undamped amplitude of the system to the amplitude of the freely floating system. The corresponding diagram (Fig. 80) showing the amplitude relation versus the frequency relation $\dfrac{\omega}{\lambda_z}$ is the response curve.

The frequency of forced vibrations does not depend on the mass of the foundation and its elastic properties but only on the frequency of the generating force. After transformation the equation becomes

$$A_z = v A_{st} \tag{193}$$

where $A_{st} = P/m\lambda_z^2$ is the displacement of the foundation due to the effect of force P. If this force is regarded

$$P/m\lambda_z^2$$

as a static one, the relationship between the effects of static and dynamic forces can be expressed by the factor v, called the dynamic factor (see also Eq. 51) and is

$$v = \frac{1}{1-\xi^2} \tag{194}$$

where $\xi = \omega/\lambda_z$.

Thus the dynamic factor depends only on ξ, that is, on the ratio ω/λ_z or N_m/N_e, consequently on the ratio of the machine to natural frequency.

The circular frequency of the generating force and the speed of the machine N_m, as well as the frequency λ_z of the natural vibration and the natural frequency per minute of the foundation are related as

$$\omega = \frac{2\pi}{60} N_m \qquad \text{and} \qquad \lambda_z = \frac{2\pi}{60} N e_e$$

If N_m is small compared to N_e, the dynamic factor v approaches unity, consequently the dynamic action differs but slightly from the static one.

The value of ξ increases together with N_m, and thus the denominator of Eq. (194) decreases, and the dynamic factor v is increased.

For $N_m/N_e = 1$, resonance occurs, the denominator becomes zero, and the value of v is theoretically infinitely large. If N_m continues to increase and thus $\xi > 1$, then the dynamic factor decreases continuously approaching zero. The practical conclusion is that natural frequency can be controlled so as to be lower or higher than the frequency of the generating force, and thus the amplitudes can be limited to the permissible value. It can be seen in Fig. 80 that the values near to 1, near to the resonance case between 0.8 and 1.3 are to be avoided. Left of these values in the overtuned cases—though the values are low—, we will see that the dynamic forces are high enough. We see that right of the value 1 the curves are the low tuned cases and the best relations are between 2 and 3 or 5 and 6. In the first case we have stiff springing and in the second case soft springing with foundation masses of relatively high values. Shallow foundations of large area fulfil the requirements of these low tuned cases.

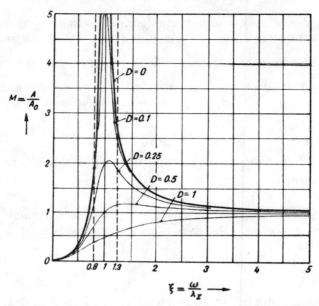

Fig. 80. Resonance curves for $M = A/A_0$ magnification factor depending upon $\xi = \omega/\lambda_z$

If the frequency of the generating force, e.g. traffic, is given, then to isolate say instruments against vibrations, a construction must be chosen with a natural frequency lower than the frequency of vibrations caused by road traffic.

If, for example, for reciprocating machines the natural frequency of the foundation is chosen in a way that $\xi < 1$, i.e. the natural frequency is higher than the speed, then ξ increases with the mass of the foundation provided that the bearing surface of the latter remains unchanged. Because of the relationship expressed by Eq. (194) the value of v will be increased too, which would involve more violent vibrations and large amplitudes. Crank-shaft machines must therefore be designed with shallow foundations of large area.

(b) Vertical vibrations of foundations with regard to the damping effect of the soil

An infinitely large value of the dynamic factor v during resonance would occur only if the soil were an elastic body. Let us assume that the reaction of the soil depends not only on the displacement of the foundation but also on the velocity of motion. Let us assume, as a first approximation, that the damping reaction is directly proportional to the velocity of vibration.

We have seen that according to (52) the differential equation for the forced vibrations is

$$m\ddot{z} + kz + cz = P_0 \sin \omega t \tag{195}$$

where $P = P_0 \sin \omega t$ is the exciting force.

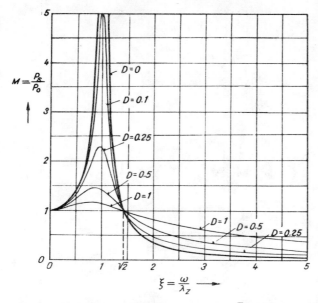

Fig. 81. Resonance curves for force transmission values for $M > \sqrt{2}$, the factor is 1 and above it the curve decreases approaching zero. $M = P_s/P_0$ depending upon $\xi = \omega/\lambda_z$

Let us consider the force transmitted to the support P_s and the vibrational force developed by the machine. We know from the chapter of damped forced vibration that the amplitude of vibration is

$$A = \frac{P_0}{c} \cdot \frac{1}{\left(1 - \frac{\omega^2}{\lambda_z^2}\right)^2 + \left(2D \cdot \frac{\omega^2}{\lambda_z^2}\right)^2} \tag{196}$$

and the force transmitted to the support

$$P_s = A \cdot c \cdot \sqrt{1 + \left(2D\,\frac{\omega}{\lambda_z}\right)^2} \tag{197}$$

The ratio of the transmitted force to the exciting force is called transmissibility.

$$T = \frac{P_s}{P_0} = \frac{\sqrt{1 + \left(2D\,\frac{\omega}{\lambda_z}\right)^2}}{\sqrt{\left[1 - \left(\frac{\omega}{\lambda_z}\right)^2\right]^2 + 4D^2\left(\frac{\omega}{\lambda_z}\right)^2}} \tag{198}$$

Figure 81 shows the relationship between the transmissibility—in this case the force transmission into the support—and the frequency ratio.

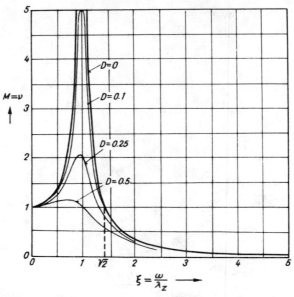

Fig. 82. Resonance curves for the magnification factors $M = v$.

The phase shift between the disturbing force and the displacement caused thereby is

$$\tan \varphi = \frac{k\omega}{\lambda_z^2 - \omega^2} \tag{199}$$

Finally let us examine the relations in the case of forced sinusoidal vibrations regarding the magnification factor. We have seen from Eq. 49, that

$$A = \frac{P_0}{c} \cdot \frac{1}{1 - \left(\frac{\omega}{\lambda_z}\right)^2} \tag{200}$$

Putting the v values against the $\frac{\omega}{\lambda_z}$ values we obtain Fig. 82; the curve showing the relationship of the magnification factor to the frequency relation values. The response curve for $D = 0$ shows a peak value for $\frac{\omega}{\lambda_z} = 1$, and a value near zero at $\frac{\omega}{\lambda_z} = 5$.

We have seen the v value in the case of damping according to (60):

$$v = \frac{1}{\sqrt{\left[1 - \left(\frac{\omega}{\lambda_z}\right)^2\right]^2 + 4D^2 \left(\frac{\omega}{\lambda_z}\right)^2}} \tag{201}$$

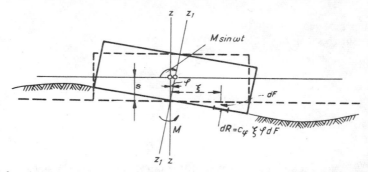

Fig. 83. The foundation experiences rotational vibration owing to an external moment $M \sin \omega t$, acting periodically

the corresponding curves in the figure are all below the undamped case. In the case of resonance $v = \dfrac{1}{2D}$, and the phase shift also depends on D and $\dfrac{\omega}{\lambda_z}$

$$\tan \varphi = \frac{2D \left(\dfrac{\omega}{\lambda_z} \right)}{1 - \left(\dfrac{\omega}{\lambda_z} \right)} \tag{202}$$

The response curves of Figs 80, 81, and 82 are illustrated in the z direction but principally they are valid not only for the vertical forced vibrations, but also useful for the rotational, horizontal and combined vibrations taking into account the corresponding forces, moments, etc. These cases are treated in the following.

B) ROTATIONAL VIBRATION OF FOUNDATIONS

Let us investigate the vibration of a foundation subject to a moment $M \sin \omega t$ acting in one of the principal planes. It is assumed further that the centre of the mass of the foundation and the centre of the bearing area lie in this principal plane. The following considerations apply only to cases where the resistance of the soil to lateral displacement of the foundation is infinitely large compared with the resistance against rotation, i.e. where only rotational vibrations can occur.

The differential equation of motion for a foundation rotating through angle φ under the effect of the external moment $M \sin \omega t$ (Fig. 83) is

$$-\Theta_s \ddot{\varphi} + \Sigma M_i = 0 \tag{203}$$

where Θ_s is the moment of inertia of the mass of the foundation and the machine related to the axis of rotation (for foundations resting on the ground surface to the axis of inertia of the base);

ΣM_i represents the sum of all external moments reduced to the axis of rotation.

The values ΣM_i can be obtained
(i) from the weight of the foundation

$$M = Qs\varphi \tag{204}$$

where s is the distance of the centre of inertia of a mass of weight;
  Q that from the axis of rotation;

(ii) from the reaction of the soil

$$M_r = -C_\varphi I_\varphi \tag{205}$$

where C_φ is the coefficient of non-uniform compression of the soil;
  I the moment of inertia of the base area about the axis of rotation.

Accordingly Eq. (203) may be rewritten as fc ws:

$$-\Theta_s\ddot{\varphi} + Qs\varphi - C_\varphi I\varphi + M\sin\omega t = 0 \tag{206}$$

For $M = 0$, the equation of natural rotational vibration is obtained, the solution of which is

$$\varphi = C\sin(\lambda_\varphi t + \varphi_0) \tag{207}$$

where the square of λ_φ, the frequency of the natural rotational vibration, is

$$\lambda_\varphi^2 = \frac{C_\varphi I - Qs}{\Theta_s} \tag{208}$$

The solution of Eq. (206) is the same as with vertical forced vibration, but the values of M, Θ_s and λ_φ must be substituted instead of P_z, m and λ_z.
The amplitude of vibration is

$$A_\varphi = \frac{M}{\Theta_s(\lambda_\varphi^2 - \omega^2)} \tag{209}$$

Product Qs in Eq. (208) is small compared with $C_\varphi I$. If we neglect this product, Eq. (208) becomes

$$\lambda_\varphi^2 = \frac{C_\varphi I}{\Theta_s} \tag{210}$$

If the area is a parallelogram with sides a and b, side a is perpendicular to the axis of rotation, then

$$I = \frac{ba^3}{12}$$

and

$$\lambda_\varphi^2 = \frac{C_\varphi}{\Theta_s}\frac{ba^3}{12} \tag{211}$$

From the above expressions of natural vibration it follows that the dimensions of the area have a considerable effect on natural frequency. The base dimensions of the foundation perpendicular to the axis of rotation have an especially great effect on the values λ_φ and A_φ.

The amplitude of the vertical component of the vibration of the foundation is

$$A = \frac{a}{2} A_\varphi \tag{212}$$

Rotational vibrations occur in high machine foundations which are subject to disturbing moments, or where an unbalanced force acts in the horizontal direction as in the case of saw frames (Fig. 84) for which Eq. (209) is valid.

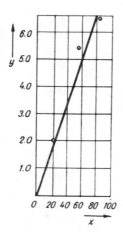

Fig. 84. Amplitudes of a machine foundation subject to rotational vibration, as a function of its height

x—amplitude, in 10^{-2} mm   y—height of foundation, in m

C) VIBRATIONS OF THE FOUNDATION AT HORIZONTAL DISPLACEMENT

Under the action of horizontal forces, foundations suffer horizontal displacements resulting in horizontal vibration, provided the soil has an appreciably higher resistance to compression than to sliding. The equations for natural and forced vibration of a foundation exposed to a horizontal disturbing force $P_x \sin \omega t$ will be the same as the corresponding equations describing vertical vibration, only C_x must be substituted for C_z. The differential equation of horizontal vibratory motion is

$$\ddot{x} + \lambda_x^2 = P_x \sin \omega t \tag{213}$$

where x is the horizontal displacement of the inertia centre of the foundation, and

$$\lambda_x^2 = \frac{C_x F}{m} \tag{214}$$

is the square of its horizontal natural frequency, C_x denoting the coefficient of uniform displacement.

The amplitude of the forced vibration is

$$A = \frac{P_x}{m(\lambda_x^2 - \omega^2)}$$

Besides the horizontal vibration, there is a possibility of the simultaneous appearance of rotational vibration around the vertical axis, produced by a disturbing moment acting in the horizontal plane. Here the differential equation of the vibratory motion is:

$$\Theta_z \ddot{\psi} + C_\varphi I_z \varphi = M_z \sin \omega t \tag{215}$$

where φ is the rotational angle of the foundation;

C_φ the non-uniform coefficient of displacement.

The solution of the equation yields

$$\varphi = \frac{M_z}{\Theta_z(\lambda_\varphi^2 - \omega^2)} \tag{216}$$

where

$$\lambda_\varphi^2 = \frac{C_\varphi I_z}{\Theta_z} \tag{217}$$

represents the square of the horizontal natural vibration of the foundation.

D) VIBRATIONS ACCOMPANYING SIMULTANEOUS VERTICAL AND HORIZONTAL, LINEAR AND ROTATIONAL DISPLACEMENTS OF FOUNDATIONS

(a) Differential equations of vibratory motion

Let us now examine the case of a foundation acted upon simultaneously by vertical and horizontal disturbing forces and by a moment. It is postulated that the centre of inertia of the foundation and of the machine coincide with the centre of gravity of the base plane. The foundation, under the action of the disturbing loads, suffers a longitudinal and rotational displacement.

The motion of the centre of gravity of the foundation can be described, in the system of co-ordinates shown in Fig. 85, in terms of the projections x and z axes of the linear displacements, and by the rotational displacement around axis y. The differential equations of vibration are thus

$$-m\ddot{x} + \Sigma X_i = 0 \tag{218}$$

$$-m\ddot{z} + \Sigma Z_i = 0 \tag{219}$$

$$-\Theta\ddot{\varphi} + \Sigma M_i = 0 \tag{220}$$

where m is the mass of the foundation,

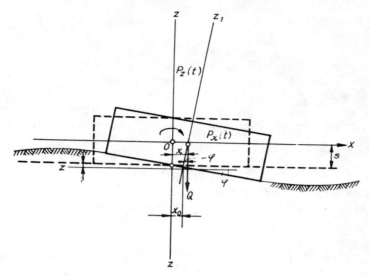

Fig. 85. Disturbing loads and displacements causing simultaneous vertical and horizontal displacement and rotation

X_i and Z_i represent projections in the x and z directions respectively of the external forces acting on the foundation.

External forces acting upon the foundation are:

1. Q, the combined weight of foundation and machine, with projections on the x and z axes

$$X_1 = 0$$
$$Z_1 = -Q$$

2. Soil reaction due to the weight of the foundation and the machine with the projections

$$X_2 = 0$$
$$Z_2 = C_z F z_{st} \tag{221}$$

where C_z is the uniform compression coefficient,

F the area of base,

z_{st} the settlement produced by the weight of the foundation and the machine.

3. For a displacement z of the foundation at the time of investigation, the soil reaction is

$$z_3 = C_z F z$$

4. The horizontal soil reaction due to a horizontal force is

$$X_4 = -C_x F x_0 \tag{222}$$

where C_x is the uniform displacement coefficient of the soil,
   x_0 the horizontal displacement of the centre of gravity of the base plane $x_0 = x - s\varphi$, and
   x is the horizontal displacement of the common centre of inertia of the foundation and the machine due to the horizontal force.

Substituting this into Eq. (221) we obtain:

$$X_4 = -C_x F (x - s_\varphi) \tag{223}$$

The moments acting upon the foundation are:
   1. The moment about the axis y produced by the soil reaction Z_2 is

$$M_1 = Qs\varphi \tag{224}$$

   2. The moment about the axis y due to force X_4 is

$$M_2 = C_x F s (x - s\varphi) \tag{225}$$

   3. The rotational displacement of the base plane by angle φ gives rise to a soil reaction, the moment of which about axis y is obtained in the following way:
The reaction dR acting upon an elementary area dF of the base plane is

$$dR = C_\varphi \xi_\varphi dF \tag{226}$$

where C_ϕ is the non-uniform compressibility coefficient of the soil and the distance of the elementary dF from the centre of gravity of the base plane.

The moment about the axis x due to the elementary reaction dR is:

$$dM_3 = -C_\varphi \xi_\varphi^2 dF \tag{227}$$

Integrating the above expression, we obtain for torque M_3

$$M_3 = -C_\varphi I_\varphi \tag{228}$$

where I is the moment of inertia of the base plane related to the vertical axis going through the centre of gravity of the base plane and perpendicular to the plane of vibration.

The list of forces and moments should be completed by the projections of the disturbing forces (P_{xt} and P_{zt}) and by the disturbing moment M_t.

Taking all these into consideration the differential equations (218), (219) and (220) assume the form

$$-m\ddot{z} + C_z F z = P_z(t) \tag{229}$$

$$m\ddot{x} + C_x F x - C_x F s\varphi = P_x(t) \tag{230}$$

$$-\Theta\ddot{\varphi} - C_x F s x + (C_\varphi I - Qs + C_x F s^2)\varphi = M(t) \tag{231}$$

The examination of these differential equations leads to the following conclusions:

Equations (230) and (231) are interrelated since both contain x and φ. On the other hand, Eq. (229) bears no relationship to either. Thus under the action of a disturbing force having no vertical component, the foundation will perform no vertical vibrations but will rotate about the axis y, and move horizontally in the direction of axis x. Conversely, if the state of rest of the foundation is upset by a vertical displacement of its centre of gravity or by a vertical disturbing force, the foundation will perform vertical vibrations only.

The solutions of Eqs. (230) and (231) reveal vertical vibrations to be independent of those produced as a result of lateral movement and rotational displacement. Vertical vibrations described by Eq. (229) have been dealt with previously, and the conclusions arrived at there retain their full validity.

(b) Natural vibrations of foundations

Natural vibrations of foundations are those performed under the influence of elastic soil resistance and inertia force alone after having been subjected to the single (non-periodic) action of a force changing their position or velocity. The equations describing natural vibrations are:

$$m\ddot{x} + C_x F x - C_x F s\varphi = 0$$

$$\Theta\ddot{\varphi} - C_x F s x + (C_\varphi I - Q s + C_x F s^2)\, \varphi = 0 \tag{232}$$

After the partial solution of the equations, and having determined the assumed constant amplitudes A and B, the following equation can be derived:

$$\lambda^4 - \frac{\lambda_\varphi^2 + \lambda_x^2}{\gamma} + \frac{\lambda_\varphi^2 \cdot \lambda_x^2}{\gamma} = 0 \tag{233}$$

where λ_ϕ and λ_x are the limit frequencies when either only rotational or only horizontal forced vibrations occur. The squared values are given as

$$\lambda_\varphi^2 = \frac{C_\varphi I - Q_s}{\Theta_s} \; ; \qquad \lambda_x^2 = \frac{C_x F}{m}$$

The value γ in the equation is:

$$\gamma = \frac{\Theta}{\Theta_s}$$

Here Θ denotes the moment of inertia for the common centre of gravity of the foundation and the machine, and Θ_s is the moment of inertia of foundation and machine related to the axis perpendicular to the plane of vibrations, and passing through the centre of gravity of the base plane. The two are related as:

$$\Theta_s = \Theta + ms^2 \tag{234}$$

Roots λ_1 and λ_2 of Eq. (231) yield the principal natural frequencies of the foundation. The smaller of the two is always lower than λ_φ and λ_x whereas the larger one is always higher than λ_φ and λ_x, as follows from the solution of the equation of second order.

The determination of the ratio between amplitudes A and B results in the equation

$$p = \frac{A}{B} = \frac{\lambda_x^2 s}{\lambda_x^2 - \lambda^2} \tag{235}$$

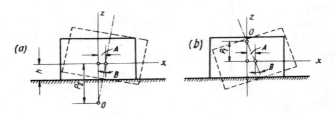

Fig. 86. The foundation vibrates with natural frequencies λ_1 and λ_2 around the upper and lower centres of rotation, respectively

If the foundation vibrates at the lower principal frequency λ_2, then $\lambda_x^2 - \lambda_z^2 > 0$, consequently $p > 0$, and amplitudes A and B will be of the same sign. In this instance the centre of gravity of the foundation will not be in a state of equilibrium. The motion takes place on a circular path with radius p_2 about an imaginary centre which is the centre of gravity (Fig. 86). The value of p_2 can be computed from Eq. (235), if the natural frequency λ_2 is substituted for λ.

If the foundation vibrates at the higher natural frequency λ_1, then $\lambda_x^2 - \lambda_1^2 < 0$, and the foundation will vibrate about a centre lying at the distance p_1 above the centre of gravity. The value of p_1 can be obtained from Eq. (235) in a manner similar to that of p_2.

The relationship between p_1 and p_2 is:

$$p_1 p_2 = i^2 \tag{236}$$

where $i^2 = \Theta/m$, i being the radius of gyration of the mass of the foundation and the machine. It should be remembered, when selecting the dimensions for the foundation, that the limit frequencies λ_φ and λ_x are governed solely by the coefficients C_φ and C_x. The actual values of these being often unknown, it is expedient to assume the coefficients between certain limits.

Correspondingly, we can calculate the value

$$\beta_{1,2} = \frac{\lambda_{1,2}^2}{\lambda_\varphi^2} = \frac{1}{2\gamma} [1 + \mu \pm \sqrt{(1+\mu)^2 + 4\gamma\mu}] \tag{237}$$

where μ represent the ratio of the squares of the limit frequencies.

With given dimensions of the foundation, $\beta_{1,2}$ depends exclusively on the coefficients of compression and displacement of the soil, which is assumed to be elastic. If the limit values of these coefficients are given, all possible values can be calculated. Changes in $\beta_{1,2}$ with μ are shown in the diagrams of Figs 87 and 88. The curves are drawn for the various values of γ ($\gamma = 0.2$ to 0.9). The value of 0.2 for γ applies to high foundations.

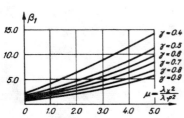

Fig. 87. Changes in coefficient β_1 with $\lambda_x^2/\lambda_\varphi^2$

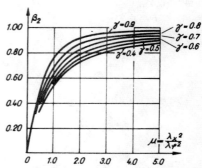

Fig. 88. Changes in coefficient β_2 with $\lambda_x^2/\lambda_\varphi^2$

Corresponding to the limit values of C_x and C_φ are

$$\lambda_{1,2}^2 = \lambda_\varphi^2 \beta_{1,2} \tag{238}$$

(c) Forced vibrations of foundations

Let us examine in detail some frequently occurring cases of loading.

(i) It is assumed that the common centre of gravity of the foundation and the machine is acted upon by a horizontal disturbing force, varying according to the law $P_x \sin \omega t$. Then the foundation undergoes a rotational displacement through angle φ, and is displaced horizontally by x.

The differential equations of the motion are:

$$m\ddot{x} + C_x F_x - C_x F s\varphi = P_x \sin \omega t$$

$$\Theta \ddot{\varphi} - C_x F s x + (C_\varphi I - Qs + C_x F s^2)\,\varphi = 0 \tag{239}$$

The solution of these equations yields for the amplitudes A_x and A_ϕ of the forced vibration the following values:

$$A_x = \frac{C_\varphi I - Qs + C_x F s^2 - \Theta\omega}{\Delta(\omega^2)} P_x \tag{240}$$

$$A_\varphi = \frac{C_x F s}{\Delta(\omega^2)} P_x \tag{241}$$

where

$$\Delta(\omega^2) = m\Theta(\lambda_1^2 = \omega^2)(\lambda_2^2 - \omega^2)$$

Here the auxiliary value $\Delta(\omega^2)$ must not be mistaken for the logarithmic decrement Δ, occurring in Chapter II, and later in the text.

(ii) If the foundation is acted upon by a disturbing moment varying according to $M \sin \omega t$, which originates from a couple or from a force of any direction acting outside the centre of gravity, then the differential equations of the vibratory motion will be:

$$m\ddot{x} + C_x F x - C_x F s\varphi = 0$$

$$\Theta\ddot{\varphi} - C_x F s x + (C_\varphi I - Qs + C_x F s^2)\varphi = M \sin\omega t \tag{242}$$

The amplitudes are:

$$A_x = \frac{C_x F s}{\Delta(\omega^2)} M \tag{243}$$

$$A_{\dot{\varphi}} = \frac{C_x F - m\omega^2}{\Delta(\omega^2)} M \tag{244}$$

Since the vibrating system in question has two natural frequencies, there are two possibilities for resonance. The characteristic form of the resonance curve is shown in Fig. 89. This curve was obtained by Barkan in an experiment on a large foundation having a base area of 4 m^2.

The forced vibrations of a foundation occur around an imaginary centre the distance of which from the centre of inertia is given by the expression $p = A_x/A_\varphi$. Its value, if the disturbing moment alone is acting, will be:

$$p = \frac{\lambda_x^2}{\lambda_x^2 - \omega^2} s \tag{245}$$

On closer examination, this expression suggests the following conclusions concerning the relative magnitudes of λ and ω:

1. For $\omega \ll \lambda_x$, p differs only slightly from s, that is, the centre of vibration is close to the lower plane of the foundation. The value of p increases as λ_x/ω decreases.

2. For $\omega = \lambda_x$, p will be infinitely large, and the foundation will perform horizontal vibrations only.

3. For $\omega \gg \lambda_x$, p approaches zero asymptotically, and the foundation will perform only rotational vibrations about the centre of inertia. The above relationships are represented in Fig. 90.

Figure 91 shows the positions of the vertical principal axis of an experimental foundation subject to various disturbing frequencies. The points marked by small circles are the amplitudes of the foundation obtained experimentally which correspond almost exactly to the calculated values.

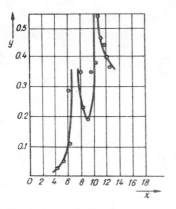

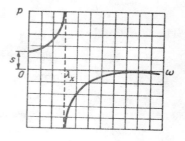

Fig. 89. System with two degrees of freedom. The two points of resonance correspond to the two natural frequencies

x—natural frequency per sec, y—vibrational amplitude, in mm

Fig. 90. Vibration of distance (p) between centre of vibration and centre of inertia as a function of frequency (ω)

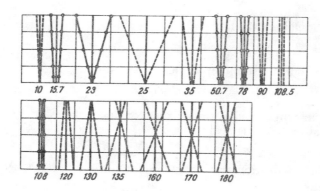

Fig. 91. Motion of vertical axis of experimental foundation at different disturbing frequencies

(d) Influence of the eccentric position of the masses of the foundation and the machine on the natural frequency

The simplest case will be considered: when the inertial centre of the mass of the machine and the centre of gravity of the base plane lie in one of the principal planes of the foundation but not on the same vertical.

Here again three factors govern the motions of the foundations, namely the displacements x and z of the centre of gravity of the foundation in the direction of the coordinate axis, and the rotational displacement φ of the foundation.

The forces acting on the foundation are:
1. The vertical projection of the combined weights of machine and foundation

$$Z_2 = Q$$

2. The horizontal soil reaction

$$X_1 = -C_x F (x - s_\varphi) \qquad (246)$$

where $(x - s_\varphi^1) = x_0$ is the horizontal displacement of the centre of gravity of the base plane.

3. The vertical reaction of the soil is

$$Z_1 = -C_z F(z - \varepsilon_\varphi^1) \qquad (247)$$

where $(z - \varepsilon_\varphi^1) = z_0$ is the displacement of the centre gravity of the base plane projected on the vertical,
ε the eccentricity.

The moments due to external forces are:
(i) the moment of soil reaction due to the vertical load

$$M_1 = Q s \varphi \qquad (248)$$

(ii) the moment of the horizontal soil reaction about the axis y

$$M_2 = C_x F (x - s\varphi) s \qquad (249)$$

(iii) the moment resulting from the vertical soil reaction

$$M_3 = C_z F (z_2 - \varepsilon^2 \varphi) \qquad (250)$$

(iv) the moment caused by the soil reaction due to the rotational displacement of the foundation by angle φ

$$M_4 = -C_\varphi I_\varphi \qquad (251)$$

The differential equations describing the natural vibrations of the foundation will be accordingly

$$m\ddot{x} + C_x Fx - C_x Fs\varphi = 0 \qquad (252)$$

$$m\ddot{z} + C_z Fz - C_z F\varepsilon\varphi = 0 \qquad (253)$$

$$\Theta\ddot{\varphi} - C_x Fsx + (C_\varphi I - Qs + C_z F\varepsilon^2 + C_x Fs^2)\,\varphi - C_z F\varepsilon z = 0 \qquad (254)$$

After introducing the assumed coefficients A and B the solution of the differential equation yields the following expression of the natural frequency:

$$\varepsilon^2 \lambda^2 = \frac{i\,(\lambda_z^2 - \lambda^2)(\lambda_1^2 - \lambda^2)(\lambda_z^2 - \lambda^2)}{\lambda_x^2 - \lambda^2} \qquad (255)$$

where $i = \Theta/m$
$\lambda_1 \lambda_2$ represent the natural frequencies for $\varepsilon = 0$.

A diagram drawn on the basis of the above equation is shown in Fig. 92. The curves consisting of branches A and B are plotted from the right-hand side of the equation and intersect the abscissa at points $\bar{\lambda}_z^2\bar{\lambda}_1^2$ and $\bar{\lambda}_z^2$. The left-hand side of the equation is represented by the straight line C. Points of intersection with the curves yield the roots λ_1, λ_2 and λ_3 of the equation. If the eccentricity is small, these differ but slightly from the values of λ_2^2, λ_1^2 and λ_z^2. Thus for such foundations the expressions derived for $\varepsilon = 0$ apply.

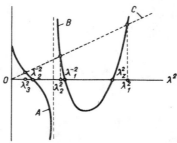

Fig. 92. If the machine mass is placed eccentrically on the foundation, the intersection points of straight line C with curves A and B give the natural frequencies of the system

4. Forced vibrations excited by rotating masses

The cases treated so far were all excited by constant forces. As we have seen in Chapter II, p. 67, the main difference in treating these cases is that the value of P_0 constant force should be replaced by $P_0 = m_e \cdot e \cdot \omega^2$.

The corresponding differential equation will be

$$m\ddot{z} + k\dot{z} + cz = m_0 e\omega^2 \sin \omega t \tag{256}$$

m_0, k and c are constant values, the vibration is linear and consequently

$$z = z_0 \cdot \sin(\omega t - \varphi) \tag{257}$$

and the amplitude

$$z_0 = \frac{m_e \cdot e}{m + m_e} A_2 \tag{258}$$

The value of A_2 for $\left(\dfrac{\lambda_z}{\omega}\right)$ will be

$$A_2 = \frac{\dfrac{\lambda_z}{\omega}}{\left(1 + \dfrac{\lambda_z^2}{\omega^2}\right)^2 + \left(2D\dfrac{\lambda_z}{\omega}\right)^2} \tag{259}$$

as m_e is much smaller than m it is possible to neglect m_e, thus (258) could be written as

$$z = \frac{m_0 e}{m} A_2 \tag{260}$$

As in the relation of (192) the value of A was equal to $A_0 \cdot \dfrac{\lambda_z^2}{\omega^2}$ multiplied by the magnification factor v, it is clear that

$$A_2 = A \cdot \frac{\lambda_z^2}{\omega^2} \tag{261}$$

Consequently, for the values of A_2 the same diagram holds true as shown in Fig. 80.

5. Passive vibration isolation

Let us assume that the floor or soil that acts as a support has a periodic motion defined by the motion of the support

$$s = s_0 \sin \omega_s t \tag{262}$$

and the displacement of the mass of the system is

$$z = z_0 \cdot \sin(\omega_s t - \varphi) \tag{263}$$

The force acting on the system is

$$P_0 = s_0 \cdot c \cdot \sqrt{1 + \left(2D\frac{\lambda_z}{\omega}\right)^2} \tag{264}$$

and putting the above expression into Eq. 196 we obtain the motion of the system due to the periodic motion of the support:

$$A = Z_0 = \frac{P_0}{c} \frac{1}{\sqrt{\left(1 - \frac{\lambda_z^2}{\omega^2}\right)^2 + \left(2D\frac{\lambda_z}{\omega}\right)^2}} = \frac{s_0 \sqrt{1 + \left(2D\frac{\lambda_z}{\omega}\right)^2}}{\sqrt{\left(1 - \frac{\lambda_z^2}{\omega^2}\right)^2 + \left(2D\frac{\lambda_z}{\omega}\right)^2}} \tag{265}$$

The effect of the vibration is best characterized by the ratio of the two amplitudes of vibration:

$$\frac{Z_0}{S_0} = \frac{\sqrt{1 + \left(2D\frac{\lambda_z}{\omega}\right)^2}}{\sqrt{\left(1 - \frac{\lambda_z^2}{\omega^2}\right)^2 + 2D\frac{\lambda_z^2}{\omega}}} \tag{266}$$

the same relation as the one that characterizes the force transmission into the support. The curve of transmissibility shown in Fig. 81 may be used also in the passive isolation case.

The corresponding phase relationship is

$$\tan \varphi = \frac{2D\left(\frac{\lambda_z}{\omega}\right)^2}{1 - \left(\frac{\lambda_z}{\omega}\right)^2 + \left(2D\frac{\lambda_z}{\omega}\right)^2} \tag{267}$$

INSTRUMENTATION AND EQUIPMENT FOR GENERATING DYNAMIC FORCES AND FOR VIBRATION MEASUREMENTS

In order to be able to compare the dynamic behaviour of the soil and foundation complex instrumentation is necessary in order to excite vibrations and to measure them. On this basis we will treat equipment for generating dynamic forces, and instruments for measuring and recording vibrations.

Equipment used for investigations can be classified into two groups: 1. vibrators or generators; 2. instruments for measuring and recording vibrations.

1. Equipment generating dynamic forces

If these devices are used in soil investigations artifically produced periodic and continuous vibrations are introduced into the soil.

The vibrator is installed at ground level, its foundation and the participating soil form a uniform vibrating system. In order to understand the conception of the soil mass vibrating together with the vibrating equipment let us assume that a plate resting on the ground surface is acted upon by periodic impulses of equal magnitude. The soil below the plate will be compressed, compacted, and compaction will be highest at the centre of the bearing surface. After a certain number of impulses the soil attains a degree of compactness which cannot be increased merely by increasing the number of impulses. Further compaction can subsequently be achieved only by greater impulses. Generating equipment is also useful for resonance testing of full-scale structures, e.g. for testing the dynamic behaviour of buildings, dams, etc.

A) HERTWIG'S VIBRATING MACHINE

DEGEBO has developed an instrument which is very suitable for large-scale soil investigations. It has a bearing area of 1 m^2 with a maximum weight of 2.8 tons. The weight can be altered by interchangeable plates mounted on the machine. The equipment consists of two adjustable eccentric masses which rotate in opposite directions. When correctly adjusted the machine (Fig. 93) transmits only vertical forces to the soil.

The vibrating masses which move in opposite directions are mounted in such a way that individual components of the resulting centrifugal forces are of opposite

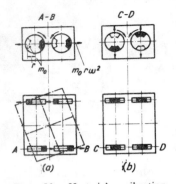

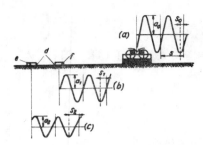

Fig. 93. Hertwig's vibration machine

a—position of the machine at π/2; b—position of the machine at π

Fig. 94. The vibrating masses of Hertwig's instrument describe sine waves

a—vibration of the machine and soil, b—soil vibration at measuring point 1, c—soil vibration at measuring point 2, d—arrangement of seismograph, e—measuring point 1, f—measuring point 2

direction but equal magnitude and are taken up by the casing of the machine. During a revolution the vertical centrifugal forces reach a maximum value and drop again to zero according to a sine function (Fig. 94).

The frequency, the mass of the equipment and the magnitude of the centrifugal forces can be adjusted to different values. With the aid of this machine, the following data depending on speed can be determined: (i) the amplitude, (ii) the phase displacement between the mass produced the vibrations and the soil vibrating with the machine, (iii) the power absorbed by the machine, (iv) the settlement of the machine. These values are plotted as a function of frequency in Fig. 95.

The mass of the machine can be considered as vibrating with part of the soil mass. The eccentrically mounted weight, which is the vibrating mass, attains the peak amplitude when the speed concides with the natural frequency of the soil, i.e. when resonance occurs. The natural frequency of the soil can thus be determined. The vibrating masses are driven either by a petrol engine or an electric motor. Electric motors driven by accumulators are very often used to ensure the uniform speed which is required for the accuracy of this method. The entire equipment is mounted on special trucks, on which all the auxiliary equipment (lifting tackle, etc.) can be accommodated and transported to the site. Relying on the same principle less heavy types, suitable for motorcycle transport, have been developed.

DEGEBO has also developed a model which has a diameter of about 40 cm and so can be lowered into a bore hole.

B) GEODYNE EQUIPMENT

For investigating the dynamic properties of soil, a typical piece of equipment, the so-called Geodyne instrument (Fig. 96), can also be applied. Two eccentrically arranged masses are mounted in such a way as to be adjustable in relation to one

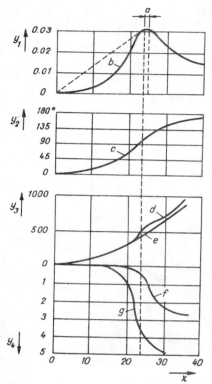

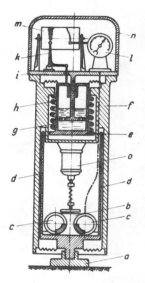

Fig. 95. Amplitude curve (top), phase curve (centre), the output curve and settlement curve (bottom) as functions of speed (in cps)

x—generating frequency cps, y_1—amplitude, in cm, y_2—angle of phase shift, y_3—power output, in W, y_4—settlement, in mm, a—resonant range, b—amplitude curve, c—phase curve, d—power curve, e—idling curve, f—settlement curve on compacted soil, g—settlement curve on incompacted soil

Fig. 96. The Geodyne instrument.

a—base plate (exchangeable), b—supporting trestle, c—disc with eccentric mass, d—light mass, e–g—damping cylinder, f—heavy mass, h—inserted spring, i—base plate of recording device, k—writing pen, l—recording device, m—chart cylinder, n—casing, o—electric motor

another. As a consequence, the magnitude of the vibrations produced can be controlled.

This instrument prepares a graphic plot of the vibrations. The force producing the vibrations is transmitted through a plate of 200 cm² area to the soil. The interchangeable plate may be circular; it may have the shape of an isosceles triangle, a rectangle or a polygon. The settlement of the equipment into the subsoil depends —apart from other factors—on the shape of the plate as well. With this equipment 1000–4500 vibrations may be produced and recorded in a minute.

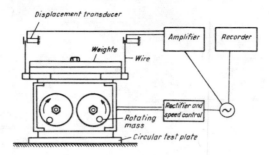

Fig. 97. Small field vibrator after Moore [842]

Fig. 98. Large vibration exciter after Keightley [556]

C) SMALL FIELD VIBRATIOR

For small-size footings a vibrator driven by a 1/4 HP motor mounted on a steel plate connected to a test plate (4) and constructed as a rotating mass (1) oscillator was applied by Moore [842] (Fig. 97) with speeds to 3000 rpm. Two transducers (2 and 3) are fitted for converting the mechanical motion into electrical signals. The transducers, connected by means of a soft iron core moving freely within a copper wire soil, are connected to the vibrator by a 0.1 cm diameter wire. The amplified signals (5) are fed into a mirror-type galvanometer serving as recorder (6).

D) EXCITERS FOR BUILDING INVESTIGATIONS

Such exciters used also for clarifying the behaviour of dams have been developed in the USA for resonance testing of full-scale structures by Hudson [486] and by Keightley [586], by the application of counter rotating eccentric weights up to speeds of 10 cps (Fig. 98). The small building exciter for use on the top of a building

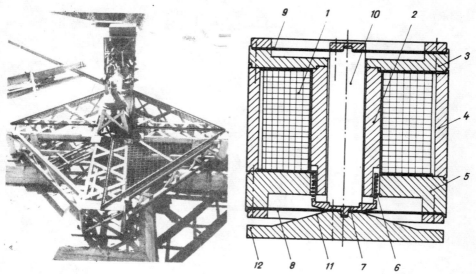

Fig. 99. Building vibrator exciter after Prince [974]

Fig. 100. Electrodynamic exciter after Scheiter [1090]

or on different floor levels has been adopted in Mexico by Prince [974] (illustrated in Fig. 99). Here the shaking machine can supply up to 20 tons of centrifugal force at 5 cps.

E) ELECTRODYNAMIC EXCITERS

For model investigations small electrodynamic vibrators are used as described by Scheiter [1090]. As illustrated in Fig. 100, in (1) through (2, 3, 4 and 5) a constant magnetic field (6) is induced. Inside (6) is an axially arranged body (7) with a central arrangement fixed (10) to two membranes (8 and 9). Using alternating current, a dynamic effect from plate (11–12) will be produced on the bottom of the exciter.

A small electromagnetic vibrator of about 10 kg force capacity has been developed for high frequency vibrations, from 30 to 1000 cps by the WES (see Ref. [1024]).

F) TWO DEGREES OF FREEDOM VIBRATORS

Referring to publications of Ballard [60] and Maxwell and Fry [815] a two degree of freedom vibrator has been developed by Weissmann [1309]. While for the determination of the in situ shear modulus of soils the one degree of freedom systems with variable eccentric rotting weights are used in the low frequency range, for the higher frequencies a second electromagnetic vibrator is needed. With considerable reduction of the weight of the vibrator, the two degree of freedom system generator delivers forces for a frequency range of 4 to 100 Hz eliminating thus the application of a second vibrator for higher frequencies.

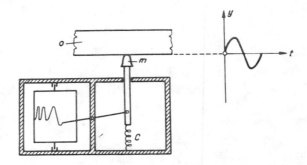

Fig. 101. Schematic arrangement of relative vibration-measuring instrument

2. Instruments for measuring vibrations

In order to interpret correctly the experimental results, the designers of machine foundations must be familiar with the instruments for measuring and recording vibrations and with the methods and techniques used to measure them. Only thus will they be able to make the right choice of instruments because controls for successful investigations can be carried out only on the basis of an adequate knowledge of the principles and limits of accuracy of the measuring methods to be used.

The parameters necessary for describing vibrations are determined by using the following instruments: the force that produces the vibrating motion is measured by a dynamometer; the path, the velocity and acceleration of the vibrations are determined by a vibrometer; the strains resulting in the elastic element of the vibrating structure are observed with strain gauges.

The vibrometer is brought into contact with the vibrating body during measurement. Instruments working without direct contact are very seldom used. Vibrometers working in direct contact can give either relative or absolute values.

The operating principle of relative vibrometers is shown in Fig. 101. The instrument is attached to an immobile body which serves as a fixed point. The contact feeler of the instrument, of mass m, is pressed by means of a spring of constant c against the vibrating body O. The amplitude of the vibration is recorded by a pen connected to the feeler arm. A path vs. time plot is thus prepared by the instrument. Contact vibrometers cannot be used under all circumstances, e.g. in moving vehicles where there is no fixed point available.

Absolute vibrometers do not require a fixed point since the casing of the instrument is attached directly to the vibrating body. The operating principle of

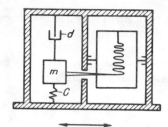

Fig. 102. Schematic arrangement
of absolute vibration-measuring
instrument

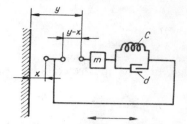

Fig. 103. Principle of the absolute
vibration-measuring instrument

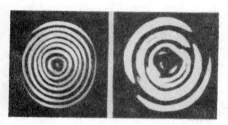

Fig. 104. Mercury vibration indicator.
Vibrations cause concentric rings to appear on
the surface

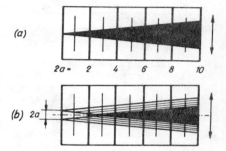

Fig. 105. Determination of the amplitudes by
means of a "wedge"

these instruments is shown in Figs. 102 and 103. The recording arm is attached to an elastically suspended body which is damped. While the casing moves together with the vibrating body, the mass inside remains immobile as a consequence of its inertia and thus the recording of the vibration is made possible. If the movement of the casing is x and the absolute displacement of the mass is y: the measured displacement will be $y-x$.

With purely mechanical instruments operating on the above principle the displacements of the mass relative to the casing can be measured by optical means as long as the frequency of the soil examined is considerably higher than the natural frequency of the suspended mass. However, the instruments generally used rely on electro-mechanical operation principles. Although the vibrations are again perceived mechanically they produce variations in an electric current in proportion to the displacement, to the velocity, or to the acceleration, and these are recorded electrodynamically (e.g. by a cathode ray oscilloscope).

A simple method for measuring vibrations is to use a flat glass pen containing liquid mercury (Fig. 104). Vibrations produce concentric waves on the surface thereof and from them conclusions can be drawn as to the properties of the vibrations.

An even simpler means consists of a small cone built up of very fine and dry sand on a glass plate. Under the effect of the vibrations this cone collapses and the rate of slump is in proportion to the magnitude of the vibrations.

Amplitudes can be measured in a very simple visual way with the help of the "wedge" or "key" illustrated in Fig. 105a. The wedge-shaped figure attached firmly

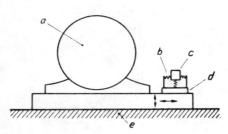

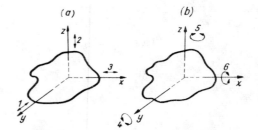

Fig. 106. Instrument measuring mechanical vibration. The fixed part vibrates with the machine foundation, while the movable part, the "vibrating mass", remains motionless owing to its inertia

a—machine, b—springs, c—vibrating, mass remaining motionless owing to its inertia, d—immovable mass co-vibrating with the mass being examined, e—soil

Fig. 107. The six relative motions of a mass

to the vibrating body will vibrate together with the latter in the plane of the paper. In consequence of the motion a vibrating picture shown in Fig. 105b is formed. The human eye is incapable of discerning the impressions of the picture if the frequency exceeds 20 cps. The value to be observed is indicated in the figure: it is the height of the resulting white triangle, which is proportional to the amplitude.

A) MECHANICAL VIBROMETERS

For the mechanical measurement of vibrations the casing of the instrument is attached to the vibrating mass preferably consisting of the soil, the foundation and the machine. The "swinging mass" coupled by preferably soft springs to the "fixed" part of the instrument, owing to its inertia, does not follow the vibrations of the fixed part (Fig. 106).

The mass, supported by springs on its bedding can according to the six degrees of freedom be displaced in three mutually perpendicular directions and can be rotated around three mutually perpendicular axes passing through its centre of gravity (Fig. 107). These component movements suffice to describe every possible displacement. All motions, no matter how complicated, can be represented by the vectorial sum of the above projections. The same holds true of velocity, acceleration, etc., characterizing motion.

Rotational motions are, in practice, generally of secondary importance and linear displacements, i.e. translational motions, are mostly encountered. These can be resolved into a horizontal and a vertical component.

Vibrometers designed according to the mechanical principle of operation operate in the following manner. The mass, supported by springs, is controlled in a way that

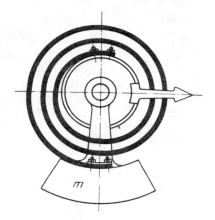

Fig. 108. The principle of Geiger's vibrograph

it can be displaced only in a predeterminated direction x. In this case the movements in direction x characterize only the displacement of the swinging mass relative to the foundation. This displacement is magnified and transmitted to a pen below which a strip of paper is unwound from a drum by clockwork at a known velocity. Thus the vibrations are recorded graphically by the pen, i.e. an oscillogram is prepared. Direction x should always be selected to coincide with the direction of the vibrations being examined. Thus for instance, when recording vertical vibrations, the suspended mass should be confined to vertical displacements only.

Figure 108 shows a schematic arrangement of the measuring mechanism of the Geiger vibrograph. For measuring lower frequencies, an additional mass must be attached. The suspended mass is supported on bearings and for smaller displacements its rotation can be neglected since its centre of gravity is far enough from the centre of rotation. For vertical measurement gravity is balanced by a helical spring.

Other types of mechanical vibrometers are capable of recording not only the component in a single, but the components in three directions at the same time. These instruments have three recording pens, each of which registers the relative displacement of one of the three different directions x, y and z. Inasmuch as the diagrams corresponding to the different relative motions are recorded under each other on the same strip of paper, the phases of the displacements can be directly observed and measured.

Feeler vibrographs have found widespread application. Many firms manufacture such instruments but they all work on the same principle. Examples of this type are

Fig. 109. "Tastograph" manufactured by the Metallwerke Meerane (Sachsen)

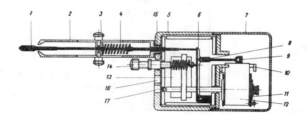

Fig. 110. Schematic arrangement of the tastograph

1—feeler, 2—tube, 3—fastening screw, 4—preloading spring, 5—casing, 6—transmitting lever, 7—protecting cap, 8—transmitting arm, 9—recording lever, 10—writing table, 11—unwinding drum, 12—recording paper, 13—driving gear, 14—screw for adjusting pen, 15—enlargement, 2 and 4 times, 16—enlargement 5 to 16 times, 17—enlargement 10 and 20 times

the instruments of the VEB Geräte- und Regler-Werke (formerly Askania), Teltow, Berlin, or the vibrographs of the Metallwerke Meerance, Sachsen, FRG (Fig. 109), to be discussed below in more detail. The schematic arrangement of this instrument is shown in Fig. 110.

The feeler rod (1) moving in tube (2) is pressed by the preloading springs (4) against the transmission arm (6). Pre-tension can be adjusted by screw (3). Arm (6) is loaded by setting a spring by means of screw (14). The registering arm (9) is coupled to the above transmission arm by the transmission rod (8). The needle of the registering arm (9) touches the writing surface (10), on which a strip of paper (12) unwinds from drum (11) driven by the clockwork mechanism (13). The transmission ratio of the diagram can be altered by removing tube 6 (2) together with feeler rod (1) and inserting it into one of the holes (16) or (17). Consequently the feeler rod (1) acts on transmission arm (6) closer to the pivot of the latter and the displacements of the needle on registering arm (9) will become larger. The entire equipment is accommodated in casing (5). The number of vibrations transmitted to the strip of paper by the registering needle is measured by the instrument.

The diagram of damped vibrations of 6000 cpm generated by an electro-magnet of 4 to 6 volts, is automatically transmitted each second, or at each revolution of the drum to the strip of paper.

The natural frequency of feeler vibrographs, as used in practice, is between 3 and 5 cps, consequently these instruments are reliable only for measuring vibrations of frequencies above 8 cps. Amplitudes can be measured in the range between 0.01 and 20 mm.

B) ELECTRO-MECHANICAL PICK-UP HEADS

Essentially there are two ways for the electro-mechanical measurement of vibrations: 1. Motion can be transformed into electric energy; 2. The electric energy, its output or any of its other characteristics, can be controlled by the motion.

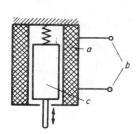

Fig. 111. Induction receiver with standing spool

a—fixed coil, b—contacts for measuring circuit, c = permanent magnet

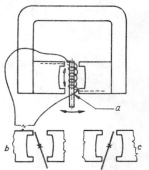

Fig. 112. Induction receiver with movable coil. The mechanical motion changes the magnetic field

a—the movable coil, b—position 1, c—position 2

1. The first group of pick-up heads comprises induction pick-up heads in which the relative desplacements cause changes in a magnetic field acting on a coil. With the solution according to Fig. 111 the strength of the magnetic field is influenced by a permanent magnetic arm moving to and fro. The arrangement shown in Fig. 112 features a moving coil the motion to and fro of which modifies the magnetic field. The Factory for Geophysical Instruments (Geofizikai Mérőműszerek Gyára), Hungary, has developed and manufactured a practical type of geophone (Fig. 113), the relatively heavy casing of which is fastened preferably with quick-setting gypsum plaster to the body to be examined.

A permanent magnet (17) is rigidly built into the casing of the geophone and in its magnetic field an induction coil (14) is permitted to move. The coil is embedded in a plastic disc which is fixed to a thin taut wire by means of a small arm. Because of its inertia the disc does not follow the movement of the casing and is returned to its position of rest by the torsional elasticity of the supporting wires (11 and 15). Electric current is induced at each similar movement. Larger geophones which, because of their greater weight, remain in permanent contact with the element to be investigated rely on the same principle.

Electro-mechanical pick-up heads belonging to the second group can be defined according to whether they control d.c. or a.c. amplifiers.

In practice, metal wire resistors are mostly used in the form of the strain gauge. The strain gauge—also called "tensometer" or "extensometer"—consists of a thin measuring wire embedded in paper or in a synthetic material (Fig. 114). If the strain

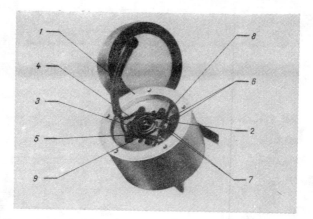

Fig. 113. A small geophone of simple construction (manufactured at the Hungarian Works for Geophysical Instruments)

1—casing, 2—torsional fibre, 3—connecting screw (between ring magnet and casing), 4—restraining pin to prevent excessive amplitudes of coil, 5—swinging coil, 6—fastening of torsional fibre, 7—fastening of swinging part to torsional fibre, 8—permanent magnet, 9—arm of coil

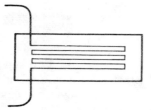

Fig. 114. Strain gauge, embedded in paper or plastic and provided with connections to measuring circuit

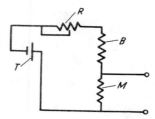

Fig. 115. Circuit of strain gauge

R—resistance, B—the strain gauge, M—external resistance, T—battery

gauge is cemented to a member whose elongation is directly proportional to displacement, the length and thus the resistance of the embedded wires will also vary proportionately to displacement.

The wiring diagram of a strain gauge is shown in Fig. 115. The resistance R must be regulated to maintain a constant potential regardless of any change in the voltage of the battery. The change in potential corresponding to the external resistance is used for measuring, and the external resistance is chosen so as to yield maximum voltage fluctuation on it, which is transmitted to the amplifier of the measuring oscillograph. This requirement will be met if the external resistance is equal to the sum of the resistances of the strain gauge and the internal resistance of the battery.

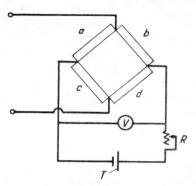

Fig. 116. Bridge circuit of strain gauge a–d—gauges, *V*—voltmeter, *R*—resistance, *T*—battery,

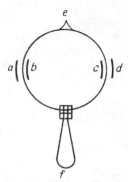

Fig. 117. Schematic arrangement of a manual pick-up unit with bridge circuit

a–d—strain gauges, e—small mass, f—large mass

Fig. 118. Manual pick-up unit with bridge circuit in use

The bridge circuit, shown in Fig. 116, is far more useful inasmuch as the resistances of the strain gauges (*a*) and (*d*) facing each other change in a sense opposite to those of the gauges (*b*) and (*c*). As the percentage change in the resistance of strain gauges is nearly the same, gauges with resistances as high as possible should be used, otherwise several strain gauges should be connected in series. With higher resistence, higher voltage can be applied and it should be noted that the sensitivity shows a linear increase with voltage.

In practice two types of pick-up heads with bridge circuits are employed: (i) those pressed manually against the vibrating body; (ii) those to be placed on it.

The elongation due to the bending of a spring can be measured by both systems.

   (i) The essential features of a hand-operated pick-up head are shown in Fig. 117. The measuring point is very gently pressed against the body to be examined (Fig. 118). The mass of the handle must not vibrate. Vibrations of the handle perceived by hand indicate that the spring is too strong and that the frequency of the body being examined is close to the natural frequency of the system consisting of the mass of the handle and the annular spring. For low frequencies a pick-up head provided either with a softer spring or with a more massive handle should be used. The frequency range is limited by the natural frequency of the system consisting of the mass of the measuring point and the annular spring. With vibrations of higher frequencies the spring is unable to press the point against the body which is vibrating with a greater

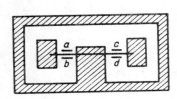

Fig. 119. Schematic arrangement
of pick-up unit to be mounted on a
vibrating body
a–d—strain gauges

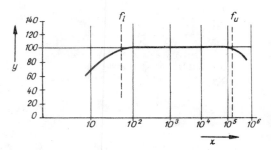

Fig. 120. Frequency limits of amplifier
x—frequency, in cps, y—velocity

acceleration, and the fact is shown by shocks or by a rattling noise. We must then use either a pick-up head with a stronger spring, or—if possible—the mass of the measuring point must be reduced.

(ii) The schematic arrangement of a pick-up head that can be placed on the vibrating body is shown in Fig. 119. The operation of this instrument is more complicated than that of the had-operated one. It has, however, the great advantage that there is no upper limit frequency to worry about as long as the instrument can be fastened reliably so that during vibration it does not strike the body under examination.

Of pick-up heads relying on resistance, those using a bridge circuit are especially suitable for highly accurate work since they have no frequency distortion and the amplitude is entirely linear with displacement. A further great advantage of these pick-up heads is that they can be used throughout a broad frequency band and their output can be amplified to an almost unlimited extent. On the other hand, a limitation of these instruments is that they have a very low output and the strain gauges are subject to rather considerable wear and have to be replaced almost every year.

2. Carrier frequency pick-ups form the second group of pick-up heads governed by controlled motion. The resulting modulated alternating current has to be rectified and filtered. The great advantage of this system is that variations of resistance due to temperature variations can very casily be eliminated. The transmissible frequency band can be regulated by altering the mechanical frequency

of the pick-up head and in principle the output voltage can be amplified infinitely. In general, the handling and operation of these instruments are very complicated.

Pick-up heads with variable self-inductance or capacity operate on a similar principle. A great drawback of the first is that the iron core which responds to the vibrations being measured is too bulky. The most up-to-date method is based on frequency modulation (FM), where the modulated wave varies in such a way that the frequency increases or decreases, but the voltage undergoes no variation. An advantageous feature of these instruments is that the mass of the capacitative pick-up head is small and the frequency range is wide.

The alternating voltage transmitted from the pick-up head in proportion to the vibrations being measured must be amplified. There are two types of amplifiers in use: direct-current amplifiers and alternating-current amplifiers. The numerical rate of amplification is the ratio between the voltage required by the recording instruments and the voltage given by the pick-up head. Amplification (V per cent), however, is in general not the same for all frequencies (Fig. 120). Vibrations with frequencies below the lower limit frequency f_1 cannot be amplified by the amplifier at the required rate, whilst vibrations of frequencies above the upper limit f_u pass through the inner resistance of the amplifier valves and in this way, as in a by-pass, are lost without any amplification. The limit frequency of amplifiers is generally specified in common electronic practice at the point where amplification is 0.707 times the value of the straight branch of the curve in Fig. 120.

The manufacture, handling and maintenance of the above instruments with strain gauges are rather complex. Factory-made pick-up heads have proved more satisfactory since they give a much higher output voltage and their characteristics are guaranteed by the manufacturer. Such are for instance, the two types of Philips pick-up heads, which are discussed below [1070].

The Philips Electrodynamic Pick-Up Head shown in Fig. 121 is a vibrometer by which relative displacements can be observed.

The feeler F projects from the metal casing and is controlled by the diaphragm springs B. Coil C moves together with the feeler rod in the magnetic field D. This motion induces electrical current in the coil in proportion to the velocity. The connection to the amplifier is at point E. The weight of the moving mass is only 10 gr. The sensitivity of the instrument is considerable: 302 mV/cm/sec ± 1.2 per cent within the frequency range between 1 and 1000 cps. Its great sensitivity renders it especially suitable for measuring vibrations of thin walls, etc. and such having very high frequencies.

The Philips Electromechanical Pick-Up Head shown in Fig. 122 is an absolute vibrometer. Its swinging mass consists of two coils concentrically suspended within two magnetic fields by means of two diaphragm springs. The lower coil in the Figure is the measuring coil in which voltage proportionate to velocity is induced. The upper coil is an empty copper cylinder in which a three-phase alternative current is generated for damping the system. The natural frequency of the instrument is 12 ± 2 cps, the weight of the participating mass being 50 gr. The instrument can be very advantageously used for measuring vibrations of the soil and machines and for balancing the latter. By a rigid connection between the instrument and the body to be tested, the resulting contact resonance can be as high as 2500 to 3000 cps.

A wide variety of factory-made pick-up heads are available among the piezoelectric ones. If piezoelectric elements, e.g. barium titanate, are subjected to mechanical pressure in certain directions relative to the main crystal faces, on the

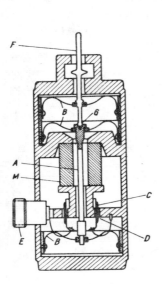

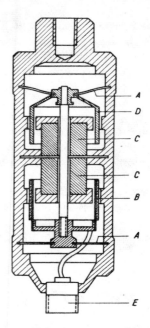

Fig. 121. Pick-up unit by the Philips Works (a 'relative' vibration measuring instrument)

A—pin, *B*—spring membrance, *C*—coil, *D*—magnetic field, *E*—end of coil, *F*—feeler, *G*—end of feeler, *M*—magnet

Fig. 122. Pick-up unit by the Philips Works (an "absolute" vibration measuring instrument)

A—spring suspension, *B*—measuring coil, *C*—magnets, *D*—damping coil, *E*—connection to measuring coil

two opposite sides electric charges of opposite signs are produced (the electric charges are proportional to the distortional forces). The recording of measurements, such as by taking a photograph of the trace on a cathode-ray oscillograph, provides a suitable method for measuring the vibrations. Such highly sensitive instruments are made, for example, by the GEC (see Hammond Ref. [416] p. 338) or, for example, by the Danish firm Brüel and Kjaer) see, e.g. Brüel [131], and Broch [128] with a frequency range of 5–30,000 cps, and pick-up heads of very small sizes —heights not more than 20–30 mm—with hexagonal bases of 14 mm across the flats (Fig. 123) measuring the acceleration.

In these conventionally used compression type accelerometers, the piezoelectric elements are in direct contact with the base whereas in the Delta Shear type of the same factory (as shown in Fig. 124), they are not in direct contact with the base, thereby reducing the possibility of measuring errors due to mounting surfaces that do not flex. Around a triangular centre post, three slices of piezoelectric elements are within a preloaded ring and are surrounded by the seismic mass. In this arrangement, better amplitude linearity over a much wider dynamic range and better long-term stability are ensured. Delta Shear accelerometers are fabricated in "Uni-Gain", "Multi-Purpose" and "Triaxial" types. The last-named (as suggested by the name) enables triaxial measurements.

Another portable vibration meter (among others) for the measurement of vibrations (all parameters, displacements, velocity and acceleration) has been developed by Dawe Instruments Ltd.* It is normally not essential which quantities

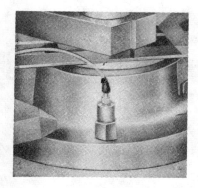

Fig. 123. Compression type piezoelectric accelerometer of small dimensions (B & K)

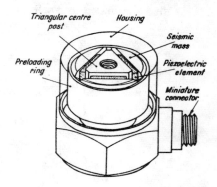

Fig. 124. Shear type accelerometer (Delta Shear of B. & K.) with piezoelectric elements prestressed in compression

of the three well known connected relationships of s, v, and a ($v = ds/dt$, $a = dv/dt = d^2s/d^2t$) are actually measured because the remaining quantities can be found by electronic differentiation or integration.

C) OSCILLOSCOPES

Amplified voltage can be transmitted to an oscilloscope. In these instruments a beam of light or a beam of rays is deflected in proportion to the voltage or any other electrical variable. Two kinds of oscilloscope are in general use: 1. the moving-coil type; 2. cathode-ray type.

1. The Moving-coil Oscilloscope. The principle underlying the operation of such instruments is that a coil suspended in a homogeneous magnetic field is rotated against the torsional resistance of the suspending element, the angle of rotation being directly proportional to the current in the coil.

To the coil a small mirror is fixed which reflects a beam of light onto a screen. The voltage, which is proportional to the vibrations to be examined, induces a current in the coil the intensity of which depends on the resistance of the coil and is proportional to voltage. The light spot that appears on the screen represents displacements in proportion to the amplitudes of the vibrations under examination. Owing to its inertia the human eye is incapable of following the displacements and only a straight line is visible. For this reason the vibrations are recorded on a photographic film moving at constant speed in a plane perpendicular vertically to the plane of the rays.

* See *Insulation*, May, 1960

A drawback of the moving-coil oscilloscope is its high self-inductance owing to which the deflections depend, besides current intensity, on frequency as well.

Conditions can be improved by using a loop oscilloscope (Fig. 125). The coil here is reduced to two flexible wires, i.e. consists of a single turn (loop) only. The torsional element is thus eliminated and self-inductance is minimized.

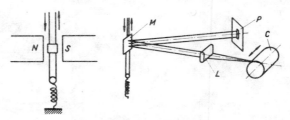

Fig. 125. Loop oscilloscope

N and S poles, M—mirror, P—plate with slot, L—lens, C—cylinder

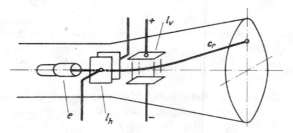

Fig. 126. Cathode-ray oscilloscope (CRO)–electron ray projector

l_h—pair of plates deflecting horizontally, l_v—pair of plates deflecting vertically, C_r—cathode ray

Between two poles of a magnetic coil a looped wire is mounted, this is wound around a disc which has a small mirror fixed to the loop. The entire vibrating system is submerged in transparent damping oil. Through a slot in the plate P shown in the figure a beam of light is directed on the mirror M and is then reflected—collected by a lens L to a point—onto a drum C rotating at a constant speed and wrapped with light-sensitive paper. If current flows through the looped conductor in the direction indicated by arrows, it causes the left wire of the loop to move forward and the other backward; the mirror is rotated by this movement. Consequently, the point of light on the recording drum is displaced, proportionately to current intensity, in the direction indicated by the arrow. It is very important, however, that the natural frequency of the loop should be much higher than the frequency of the alternating current.

Even so, this method also has serious limitations since it requires a low voltage and a relatively high current intensity because of its small resistance. For this reason it can be connected to the amplifier only with difficulty. Its natural frequency depends on the mechanical rigidity of the loop.

2. The Cathode-ray Oscilloscope. With the aid of this up-to-date instrument, which has proved very satisfactory in practice, entirely distortion-free vibration diagrams can be obtained since cathode rays do not posses inertia. The diagrammatic arrangement of the cathode-ray oscilloscope is shown in Fig. 126.

A focused small-diameter beam of cathode rays is produced in the vacuum tube. At the wider end of the flaring tube the beam strikes a fluorescent screen causing a "trace" or luminous spot that can be seen in the middle of the screen if the system is in a state of rest. The vibrations to be studied are transformed by any of the described methods into alternating voltage which is transmitted to two parallel pairs of deflecting plates l_h and l_v mounted below and above the path of the rays inside the cathode-ray tube. When, for example, the upper plate receives a positive charge, it attracts the electron rays having a negative charge in the first half-period. In the next half-period the positive charge of the plate is transformed into a negative one, the polarity being reversed and the beam is deflected in the opposite direction, i.e. downwards. Consequently the luminous point is vertically displaced upwards and downwards. In the case of high-frequency vibrations only a vertical line is visible. If now another set of two parallel plates is mounted in the cathod-ray tube, at right angles to the former, they will deflect the

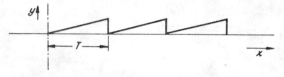

Fig. 127. Sawtooth waves
x—time, y—voltage

cathode rays in the horizontal direction. A picture of the vibrations cannot be obtained by combining the two component deflections unless sawtooth waves are introduced into the plates which deflect the beam into the horizontal direction.

The voltage diagram of this vibration is shown in Fig. 127. Over the rising branch the cathode ray sweeps the screen from left to right and if the periodical vibration to be measured and causing vertical deflection exerts its influence at the same time, the trace of the vibration appears on the screen. Over the falling branch of the sawtooth diagram the voltage suddenly drops, and the beam of rays sweeps back to the left side of the screen. A new period begins, and the trace of the vibrations appears thus as a stationary wave. This can be photographed and so recorded. The instrument described above is shown in Fig. 128. Period T of the sawtooth vibration, produced by a special generator, must be equal or be a multiple of the period of the vibrations to be studied otherwise no stationary wave suitable for photography can be obtained. Up-to-date oscilloscopes are therefore equipped with a "synchronizer". As the trace of the vibrations is hidden by the camera mounted on the oscilloscope, it appears in the viewing mirror fitted at the side as shown in Fig. 128.

The two-channel oscilloscope has been developed for the simultaneous recording of two vibrations (Fig. 129). By means of this instrument the direct determination and recording of phase differences of different vibrations is achieved.

For the simultaneous determination of several vibrations oscilloscopes with more than two channels have been developed and manufactured.

In order to obtain reliable results when measuring vibration with the instruments discussed under (*A*) and (*B*) the following requirements and characteristics must be observed:

1. For the pick-up heads:

(i) For selecting the proper pick-up head, the characteristics of frequency and amplitude must be known, or at least estimated. If they are estimated, an adequate allowance must be made for possible errors.

(ii) The order of magnitude of the amplitudes and of the necessary amplification must be known. If, for example, when examining disturbing vibrations, known to

 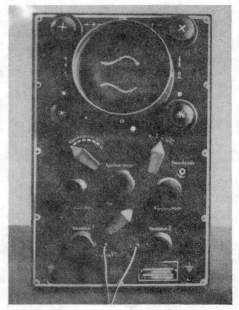

Fig. 128. Oscilloscope. The "sawtooth" frequency equals half the illustrated frequency. In the side mirror the correct function can be observed during recording

Fig. 129. Two-beam oscilloscope. The common frequency and the separate vertical deviations of both vibrations enable the phase shifts to be measured

have no disturbing effects, below frequencies of 10 cps and amplitudes of 1 μm we must employ pick-up heads that transform vibrations linearly, above a frequency of perhaps 2.5 cps, and yield, at an amplitude of 1 μm, a voltage high enough to enter the amplifier.

(iii) For phase measurements we must know the phase displacement of the pick-up head. This can be determined by comparison with pick-up heads of other systems.

2. For the amplifier:

(i) The band width should cover the frequencies in question (for instance from 0.1 up to 1000 cps) and should be linear within 2.5 per cent. Knowing the characteristics we may calculate with adequate safety even if this requirement is not fulfilled.

(ii) The amplification of the amplifier should not only be adequate but also variable in accordance with the signal obtained. Furthermore, it should be unaffected by variations in the line voltage and by the ageing of the valves.

3. For recording:

(i) The sensitivity of the system must be checked by controlling its amplifying and recording devices at the same time. A complete check of the entire instrument is called calibration. The result of the calibration is a ratio, giving results with a minimum accuracy of ± 55 per cent between the lower and upper limit frequencies and showing how many times the amplitude, as recorded, is greater than that of the mechanical vibration to be investigated.

This ratio is called the magnification of the system.

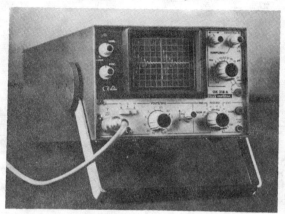

Fig 130. Portable oscilloscope: 0–15 Mhz of ITT metrix (Instrumentation Division of Société des Produits Industriels ITT, Annecy, France)

(ii) If the recording is not carried out with cathode tubes, it should be remembered that the recording device itself has its own frequency characteristics and, from the point of view of the system, the lower limit is determined by the maximum lower limit of the transmission frequency of the elements employed and the upper limit is determined by the minimum upper limit of the transmission frequency of the elements. This means that the individual elements of the system must, as far as possible, be matched.

Finally it should be mentioned that to replace more elaborate equipment, simple automatic and portable oscilloscopes have been developed such as the IIT Metrix instrument of Fig. 130, with d.c. input from 0 to 15 MHz. To ensure portability the oscilloscope can be operated from an external 24 V d.c. supply or from a battery.

D) VIBRATION MEASUREMENT ARRANGEMENTS

The basic elements in the vibration analysis system is are given in Fig. 131. The system consists of a vibration pick-up (1), a preamplifier (2), an analyser (3) and a recorder (4).

A vibration pick-up can be mounted, besides the mentioned method of pressing it against the vibrating body, by the different methods shown in Fig. 132.

The mounting with steel stud is the best stiff solution (a). When electrical isolation is necessary an isolated stud with mica washer should be adopted (b), a thin layer of wax is applied to stick the accelerometer to the vibrating surface (c) and in (d) a permanent magnet gives electrical isolation.

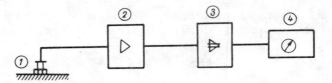

Fig. 131. Basic elements in the vibrations analysis system.

Vibration pick up (1), preamplifier (2), analyser (3), recorder (4).

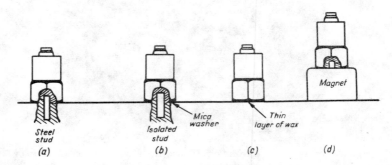

Fig. 132. Different methods of vibration pick-up mountings of B. & K.

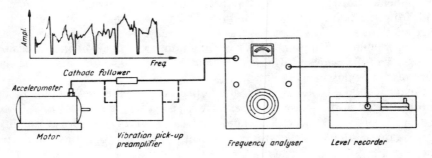

Fig. 133. Automatic frequency analysis of vibration on a motor

Measurement arrangements for the determination of an automatic frequency analysis of vibration on an electric motor is given in Fig. 133.

Here a piezoelectric accelerometer is measuring the vibrations of a motor connected through a cathode follower which is an impedance transformer used for measuring the charge voltage of the measuring head through a vibration pick-up preamplifier to a frequency analyser able to determine the frequency composition of the vibrations. This is connected to the level reader to detect signals graphically on white paper for ink writing or on transparent paper for stylus writing.

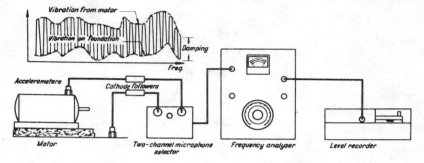

Fig. 134. Frequency analysis and measurement of vibration damping

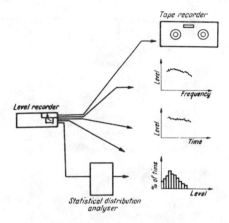

Fig. 135. Alternative connections from the level recorder

For the measurement of damping as well an instrumentation is shown in Fig. 134.

Here two cathode followers are applied for two accelerometers, one on the motor and the other one on the soil or floor, connected to a two channel selector which ensures single connection to the frequency analyser. Here too the level recorder detects the signals graphically.

The level recorder could be alternatively connected (Fig. 135) to a tape recorder to reproduce the original signal and to provide thereby more detailed information than using paper-recording systems. According to the connection, level vs. frequency or level vs. time or level vs. percentage of time can be reproduced.

The here applied statistical distribution analyser [151] works with a set of several contacts by a slider mounted on the writing arm of the level recorder and allows statistical level analysis which shows the level distribution over a period of time.

It should be mentioned further that, according to Fig. 136, the level recorder can easily be connected to a digital encoder to transform the data recorded on the level recorder into code signals. Further through tape punches—used where a high punch speed is required, a great amount of data can be read out in a

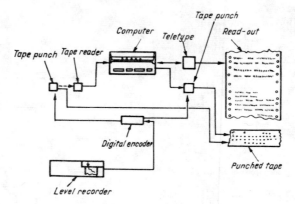

Fig. 136. Level recorder connected to computer and teletypewriter

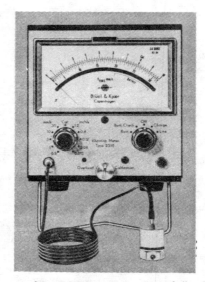

Fig. 137. Instrument of B. & K. for measurement of vibration of machines according to different standards.

short time using a tape reader for fast read – in programs and data to the computer with many extension units to a teletype-writer installed in a way by which it can be used to prepare programs while the digital computer is working on other problems.

A specialized instrument of Brüel & Kjaer to measure the vibration sensitivity of a machine according to different standards is illustrated in Fig. 137. The recommendations are treated in more detail in Chapter XV and in Vol. IV. The chart showing the severity grades and machine group classifications recommended by

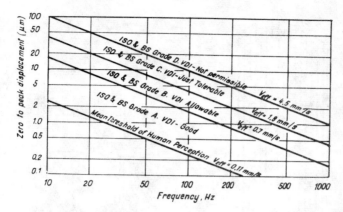

Fig. 138. Chart showing the vibration severity grades and group classifications according to ISO drafts 2372 and 2373, VDI 2056 and BS 4675.

Velocity and displacement limits are to be multiplied by the following factors for the different machine groups: $K = \times 1$; $M = \times 1.6$; $C = \times 2.5$; $T = \times 4$.

ISO, VDI and BS are given in Fig. 138. (For more details, see Figs. 227–230.) The chosen parameters are in RMS values of the velocity in the frequency range of 10 Hz to 1 kHz.

In general under normal operating conditions continuously running machinery produces nearly constant vibration levels. Machine troubles are almost always characterized by an increase in vibration levels. Rapid increases up to high vibration levels generally indicate that failure is imminent and steps should be taken to prevent possible danger. A single bearing failure in a key machine can result in important losses in production.

A heavy duty vibration pick-up together with a monitoring instrument and warning system has been developed by Brüel & Kjaer [1293/a] to avoid progressive deterioration characterized by a sudden increase in vibration level. An accelerometer detects the vibration from the machine and sends out an electrical signal proportional to the acceleration and hence to the force applied. The monitor unit receives this signal, integrates it to obtain a signal proportional to the velocity and feeds it to a meter display and to three indicators. If the vibration velocity falls below the preset condition, the "Minimum Level" is indicated by a lamp. When the level has increased to a predetermined amount above normal value, the "Alarm" lamps lights. The final stage "Trip Level" indicates that the vibration has exceeded an even higher preset value and possibly that failure is very near. An "Automatic Shut—Down Sequence" can be started by closure of the "Trip Relay" or a decision can be made for the continuous running or shutting dawn of the machinery.

For instrumentation used in USSR practice see Maksinov—Sheinin [805].

Finally, for recording strong motions caused by earthquakes, blasting and similar potentially destructive vibrations which are liable to cause damage to sensitive seismometers and other vibration transducers, off-scale instrumentation has been developed by "Teledyne—Geotech" by the application of portable, self-contained torsion accelerographs with built-in calibrator and digital time recorder.

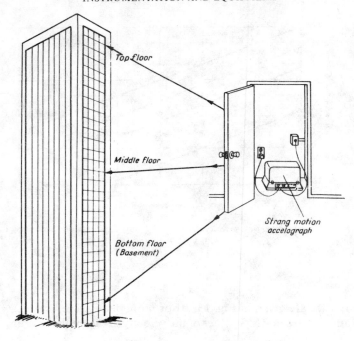

Fig. 139. Application of strong motion accelographs "Teledyne-Geotech" inside a 30-storey building at three built in registered points

Full scale deflections of $1/4g$, $1/2g$ and $1g$ standards are available from the instrument which contains three torsion-type accelerometers. Ground motions both fundamental and higher modes of vibrations can be recorded in nuclear reactors, dams, tall buildings, etc. As an example recordings can be made inside a 30-storey building at three built-in registered points: one at the top (RFT-250S) for externally triggered and two for seismically triggered (RFT-25OM) film recordings (as shown in Fig. 139 [570]). The accelerographs should be bolted and cemented in an enclosed and locked area.

The Teledyne—Geotech strong motion accelerographs are included in the Building Code of the City of Los Angeles and are used in many parts of the USA. The requirement is that in all high rise building they be located in the basement, midway, and on the top of the building, using 70 mm film format for the recording. More details are given by Halverson in [482].

PART TWO

INTERACTION BETWEEN SOIL AND FOUNDATION

CHAPTER VIII

DYNAMIC EFFECTS ON THE SOIL AND THEIR EXAMINATION

Extensive research in last decade into the dynamic properties of soil has promoted the development of computation methods for machine foundations which permit the behaviour of soil to be taken into account.

1. Dynamic soil investigations in general

As indicated by practical experience, the behaviour, resistance and bearing capacity of soil are greatly influenced by vibration and tremors. Soil vibrations may be due to various natural and to artificial causes, viz. earthquakes, explosions, increased traffic, consolidation and pile-driving operations, and the vibrations of machines. Vibrations can equally well be caused by special vibrating equipment. By means of similar generators, the effects of periodic forces rather than those of individual shock waves can be investigated.

Essentially, dynamic soil investigations consist in inducing controlled sinusoidal vibrations into the soil.

From the behaviour of the soil subjected to vibrations, conclusions can be drawn concerning its elastic properties inasmuch as these govern the velocity of propagation of periodical vibrations. High propagation velocities have been observed in heavy soils, low ones in light, loose soils.

When carrying out dynamic soil investigations, mechanical loads of periodically alternating intensity are applied to the ground surface. These loads cause considerable deformations at the place of application, i.e. of the vibrating equipment. On the other hand, the velocity of propagation yields information concerning the behaviour of soil situated at a distance from the source. While the data observed at a distance from the vibrating equipment are of interest for soil exploration, the measurements taken at the source are of great importance from the point of view of machine foundations.

Observed values at the point of generation should include the frequency, the amplitude, and the settlement of the soil and these should be related to the frequency, to the magnitude of the disturbing force, and to the time of the operation of the vibrator.

The dynamic soil test method can successfully be employed above all in granular soils. In cohesive, clayey soils the effects of vibrations do not show themselves immediately since the process of consolidation is slow in them. During the test the effects vary within seconds or even fractions of a second and for this reason the vibrations generally do not cause any settlement.

Dynamic soil investigations yield characteristic values which enable us to compare soils of different kinds and to complement the information obtained by more conventional methods of soil mechanics.

By equipment generating dynamic forces (treated in Chapter VII), artifically produced periodic and continuous vibrations are introduced into the soil.

The outlines of the soil mass to be investigated by dynamical methods are shown in Fig. 140.

Outside the assumed bulb-shaped curve the magnitude of the amplitudes and the energies produced gradually decrease and at the edge they are of equal value. As a consequence of compacting, the elastic modulus, the amplitudes and the velocity of propagation of the waves increase, the rate of damping diminishes. As we leave the point at which the impulsive force is applied, the modulus of elasticity, the amplitude and the wave velocity decrease whereas the rate of damping increases.

The size and other problems related to the participating soil mass will be discussed together with the results from work on dynamic soil investigations. We will see in Chapter XII that on introducing the lumped parameter system this mass should generally be neglected. Therefore, the participating soil mass will in the following be known as the quasi-participating or quasi-co-vibrating soil mass.

Within the quasi-participating soil mass, internal changes occur in the soil material such as: rearrangement of particles, escape of pore water, changes in the modulus of elasticity, etc. The size of the quasi-participating soil mass may increase as well, if the active force increases and the speed of the machine is very near to the natural frequency of the soil, i.e. when resonance occurs. The quasi-participating soil mass is larger in cohesive soils than in non-cohesive ones.

The determination in practice of the size and outline of a quasi-participating soil mass is very difficult. Many investigators have tackled this problem but because of the differences between soils they have not yet succeeded in finding an unambiguous solution. The supposed co-vibrating soil mass has an indeterminate outline. Attempts were made to determine it by starting with the equation:

$$\frac{m_0 r \omega^2}{a} \cos \varphi = K - m\omega^2 \tag{268}$$

where m_0 = the mass mounted eccentrically within the vibrator

      r = the eccentricity of the mass m_0

      ω = the circular frequency of the vibrator

      a = the amplitude at the circular frequency ω

      φ = the phase delay of the vibrations of the total equipment relative to the eccentric mass at a circular frequency ω

      $K = C_z F$, the spring constant

      $m = m_g + m_s$, the mass of the vibrator and of the quasi-participating soil mass.

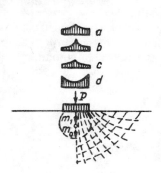

Fig. 140. The quasi-participating soil mass as supposed
conventionally, shown in order of demonstration, for a flat
foundation

a—curve characterizing density, b—
amplitude curve, c—change in the modulus of elasticity, d—curve of damping,
m—mass of foundation, m_0—
quasi-participating soil mass

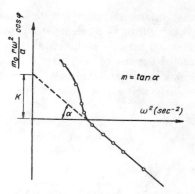

Fig. 141. Determination of the weight
of the quasi-participating soil mass in
the first stage of the suppositions.

If the amplitudes corresponding to different frequencies are observed and

$$\frac{m_0 r \omega^2}{a} \cos \varphi \tag{269}$$

is plotted against ω^2 (Fig. 141), then the distance at which the extension of the straight line through the points obtained intersects the ordinate axis is proportional to the constant K. The value of m is the slope (tangent) of the straight line, while the quasi-co-vibrating soil mass is:

$$m_s = m - m_g \tag{270}$$

where m_g represents the mass of the vibrating equipment.

The natural frequency of the soil depends on the coefficient of uniform compressibility C_z characterizing the dynamic properties of the soil. This coefficient is also referred to as the dynamic bedding coefficient.

As is well known, the natural frequency can equally be expressed in the form

$$n_e = \frac{1}{2\pi} \sqrt{\frac{c}{m}}$$

Thus

$$C_z = \frac{c}{F} = \frac{4\pi^2}{F} n_e^2 \frac{G}{g} = \frac{4\pi^2}{g} n_e^2 \sigma \tag{271}$$

Some values obtained for the coefficient of uniform compressibility, i.e. the dynamic bedding coefficient, are to be found in Table 24.

When dynamic stress is applied to the soil, the penetration coefficient is less affected by the size of the bearing surface than when the stress is static. The reason for this is that dynamic loads—even if only a very small area is loaded—induce rather large soil masses to co-vibrate.

TABLE 24

Dynamic bedding coefficients for different base areas

Surface area	Soil stress	Natural frequency	Dinamic bedding coefficient C_z
[m²]	[kg/cm²]		[kg/cm³]
0.50	0.54	18.7	13.2
0.75	0.36	19.8	9.8
1.00	0.27	21.0	8.3

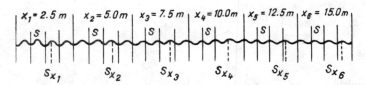

Fig. 142. Seismogram of a dynamical soil investigation with six measuring points

It should be noted that the assumption of an elastic subsoil is not in full agreement with actual conditions and for this reason mathematical treatment, which is correct for fully elastic materials, can only be applied to soil—a partially elastic material—with the greatest care.

The elastic displacement due to horizontal dynamic stresses can be expressed by the constant C_x characterizing the shear resistance of the soil. This was one of the suppositions in the early stage of development.

2. Methods for measuring soil vibration

For testing vibrations generated artificially, the measuring instruments should be arranged radially, at about equal distances from the vibrating equipment. In order to obtain reliable results the measurement should be taken within a distance of 15–20 metres and at a maximum of 200 metres. The individual measuring points should not be more than half a wave apart, and not closer than 1 metre. As soon as the vibrating equipment reaches a predetermined frequency n, the vibrations should be recorded with the aid of previously erected vibrographs. In practice, frequencies ranging from 12 to 14 cps have proved to be the most satisfactory for investigation purposes. The seismogram of a dynamic soil investigation is shown in Fig. 142 with measurements taken at six different points. In Fig. 143a diagram of a seismogram is shown with three points of measurements situated at different distances apart.

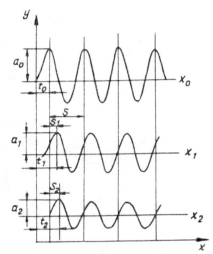

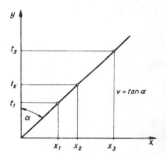

Fig. 143. Seismogram of a survey with three measuring points $(x_0. x_1. x_2)$

The phase shifts S_1, S_2 between individual waves. x—time t, in sec; y—amplitude a, in mm

Fig. 144. The phase shift for given vibrations

x—distance, in m; y—time t, in sec; α—constant at a given frequency "n"

The results obtained are graphically illustrated in most instances. The different sine wave vibrations show a phase displacement in comparison with each other. The degree of this phase displacement is illustrated in Fig. 143b where the distances (t_0, t_1, t_2) of the maximum displacements from the vertical axis show phase displacements of s_1 and s_2. If the measuring points were too far apart, some of the vibrations would have been overstepped. It is for this reason that the individual measuring points must not be more than half a wave apart. Since the intervals on the x axis, denoting time, always correspond to a full revolution of the machine shaft, the distance between two time marks will be $1/n$ sec if n is the frequency expressed as cycles per second. Thus the instants of maximum displacement are for every individual measuring point

$$t_x = \frac{s_x}{s} \frac{1}{n} \qquad (272)$$

By plotting time against the corresponding distances x (Fig. 144) we obtain the interval (v) of the phase displacement corresponding to a certain vibration. If the amplitudes are plotted against distance, a curve is obtained that diminishes with distance from the source following the function e^{ax} (Fig. 145).

In carrying out dynamic soil investigations a vibration-generating machine needs to be operated first at a low speed, then accelerated gradually. The observed values include, in addition to soil vibrations, the amplitudes, the phase displacements between the vibrating equipment and the machine vibrating with the soil mass, the output, and the settlement of the machine due to vibrations. The velocity of the propagation of the waves should also be measured.

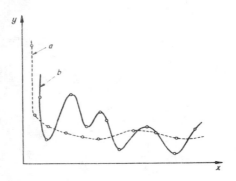

Fig. 145. Amplitude plotted vs distance

x—distance, in m; y—amplitude a, in mm; a—for homogeneous soil, b—for stratified soil

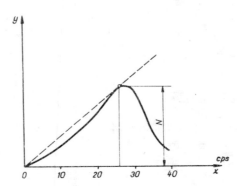

Fig. 146. Resonance curve

x—frequency n in cps; y—amplitude A in mm

When the machine foundation vibrates, the particles of soil are set into vertical vibration and when the amplitude reaches its maximum at certain frequency, the condition known as resonance takes place (Fig. 146).

It is a well known fact that the output, the amplitude and the phase displacement depend on the frequency, whereas the natural frequency of the soil, the common frequency of the machine and the soil, and the damping coefficient can be determined independently of one another. According to theoretical investigations the natural frequency can be computed by the following formula:

$$n_e = \frac{1}{2\pi} \sqrt{\frac{c}{m + m_0}} \tag{273}$$

As can be seen from this formula, the natural frequency depends on the mass of the vibrating equipment, on the supposed soil mass vibrating with the machine (m_0), and on an elasticity constant c.

The magnitude of the quasi-participating soil mass, the determination of which is very difficult in practice, can be eliminated by introducing a value for soil stress. If we know the dynamic bedding coefficient C_d, the natural frequency n_e can be determined from it.

The natural frequency varies for different soils. Dense soils have higher natural frequencies whereas loose soils have lower ones.

Vibrations of the soil are damped by internal friction. This is the work necessary to overcome the resistance between the soil particles tending to pack together or, in other words, the work necessary to destroy the cohesion between the soil particles, the shearing resistance of the soil. The work done results in permanent deformation. If we succeed in determining the damping coefficient and compare it to the measured settlement of the vibrating equipment, conclusions can be drawn concerning the behaviour of the soil under vibrating loads.

TABLE 25

Relations between approximate values of velocity of propagation
of waves and permissible soil stress

Type of soil	v	σ_p
	m/sec	· kg/cm^2
Three m peat on sand	80	0.0
Silty sand	110	1.0
Wet sand	140	2.0
Dry sand	160	2.0
Silty sand on marl	170	2.5
Coarse gravel	180	2.5
Alluvial marl	190	3.0
Homogeneous sand	220	4.0
Gravel under 4.0 m sand	330	4.5
Dense coarse gravel	420	4.5

The velocity of propagation of the waves yields useful information regarding the relative bearing capacity of the soil. The greater the velocity of propagation of the waves, the greater the bearing capacity of the soil. This corresponds, however, only approximately to actual conditions (Table 25) and for this reason the wave velocity should be considered characteristic for the elastic modulus of the soil, only on the assumption that the soil is an elastic isotropic material, and not for the permissible soil stress.

For the velocity of propagation of waves we have the following formulae:

$$v = K\sqrt{\frac{G}{\gamma}} \qquad \text{m/sec} \tag{274}$$

and

$$G = \frac{v}{2(v+1)}E \tag{275}$$

where K = a constant depending on the wave
  G = the coefficient of shear resistance of thes soil
  E = the modulus of elasticity of the soil
  γ = the density of the soil
  v = the Poisson's number (see **Chapter IX**).

The velocity of propagation of the waves in homogeneous soil can be illustrated graphically by a sloping straight line, as shown in Fig. 146. The greater the bearing capacity of the soil, the higher the wave velocity and the flatter the slope. Figure 147 shows the same diagram but for a stratified subsoil. The change in the quality of the soil produces a break in the velocity line. From this observation conclusions can be

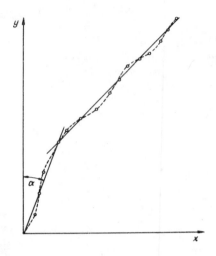

Fig. 147. The propagation velocity of the wave in homogeneous soil can be represented by a straight line

x—distance, in mm; y—time t, in sec

drawn concerning the effects of soil stratification which, in turn, supply data for further soil investigations.

For the relation between the amplitudes of waves originating from the same source Barkan's investigations have yielded the following expression:

$$\frac{A}{A_1} = \sqrt{\frac{r_1}{r}}\, e^{-k(r-r_1)} \tag{276}$$

where A_1 represents the amplitudes at distance r_1 from the source,
$\quad\quad A$ the same for r.

The coefficient k is the absorption coefficient which is characteristic for the absorption capacity of the soil. In perfectly elastic soil this coefficient would be zero. Thus the departure of the physical properties of the soil from those of a perfectly elastic body is characterized by this coefficient.

Coefficient k can be regarded as a coefficient of both geometrical and internal material damping (see pp. 276–277) being useful in isolation problems of four lations (see Vol. IV. pp. 62–67).

Experimentally, coefficient k can be determined in the following way: Of three bore-holes drilled into the ground one is sunk a little below the surface and is loaded with explosives, the others are drilled to depths corresponding to the points about which information is desired. Very sensitive geophones are lowered to the bottom of the latter. The amplitudes of the waves caused by the explosion are recorded by the geophones and, since the distances between the firing point and the geophones are known, the absorption coefficient k can be computed by Eq. (276).

For machine foundations we must determine whether the natural frequency of the system consisting of the soil, the foundation and the machine coincides with the frequency of the machine or with a multiple of it, because then resonance would occur and measures must be taken for detuning. The natural frequency of the soil can be determined empirically from the settlement of the vibrating equipment and from the measured amplitudes. If the natural frequency thus determined lies close to the frequency or speed of the machine, the two values must be detuned. This can be done by enlarging the foundation, by altering the speed or by using a deeper foundation.

3. The examination of existing foundations

For investigating completed foundations the instruments should preferably be mounted at the corners of the foundation to be studied. It is usually necessary to investigate not only the vertical, but also two mutually perpendicular horizontal vibrations.

Vibrations occurring at the start, during normal operation and upon cutting-off of the machine, should be determined during the investigation. If several machines are involved, the investigation should be extended, besides simultaneous normal operation, to all combinations that may possibly ensue under operating conditions.

If several instruments are used simultaneously, the observed vibrations should be related to a common time scale. When measuring uniform vibrations the origin of the time must be chosen to correspond to the position of the vibration generating equipment. For a vertical reciprocating engine, for example, it must be between the upper and lower dead centre positions of the piston.

When measuring the vibration of piles or walls fixed in the ground, free natural vibrations can be produced by a single impulsive force. Explosives or the rupture of a tightened rope may induce the necessary force. Naturally, such forces can also be transmitted periodically, e.g. by means of eccentrically arranged weights. A few kilograms, attached to the spokes of a bicycle wheel, are sufficient to produce the desired vibration. Vibrating equipment of this kind is attached to the structure to be examined, the wheel is set in motion and vibrations increasing to beyond the natural frequency are generated.

As is well known, the relation of the natural frequency to the generated frequency is indicative of the extent to which the structure is suitable to resist periodic forces. If necessary, the natural frequency of the structure should be altered. If the structure can be considered stiff, the dynamic forces may cause displacement or tilting. If, on the other hand, the structure is flexible, torsional deformation or even pure shear may occur. The measurements will provide information regarding the elastic behaviour on the part of the structure subject to vibrations. From the forces occurring at vibrations due to simple bending, the magnitude of the deflection, and subsequently the natural frequency can be determined. The comparison of measured and computed values yields information regarding the magnitude of the elastic modulus. The behaviour of building materials under dynamic forces has been investigated in this way (for the results, see Chapter V).

TABLE 26

Type of structure	Natural frequency n_0, cps
High bridge pier	1.0
Two-storied building	5.0
Compressor foundation	5.5
Pile foundation	4 — 20
Brick work 38 cm thick	12.0
Practical limits of natural frequencies	1 — 50

In general, natural frequencies of various machine foundations have an order of magnitude of a few cycles per second. There are, however, machine foundations whose frequencies exceed 25 cps, a value corresponding to a speed of 1500 rpm. Concrete and brick structures generally have rather low frequencies, which means that they are deeply tuned.

In Table 26 informative values are given for the natural frequencies of machine foundations and other structures.

Vibration measurements on existing structures are made only if called for by any alarming condition of the structure, with the purpose of detecting the causes of the harmful vibrations and to suggest structural modifications to eliminate them. Recently, measurements have been made in some instances while foundations were vibrating within the limits of normal operational safety.

Below some examples of vibration measurements are given.

EXAMPLE 1

Machine foundation of relatively small dimensions. The machine and its foundation may be considered a single concentrated mass vibrating on the soil. The amplitude (A) corresponding to the maximum displacement occurs when $N_m = N_e$, that is, when the generating speed (N_m) and the natural frequency of the mass are equal and thus resonance is likely to occur. The corresponding results are shown after Hertwig in Fig. 95.

EXAMPLE 3   COMPRESSOR FOUNDATION   215

EXAMPLE 2

Machine with large foundation. Let the natural frequency of the foundation as an elastically supported mass be N_e.

In such instances we must determine whether the natural frequency of the foundation (N_e) is in correspondence with that of the soil (N_s). Results of a practical example are shown after Bendel in Fig. 148. The amplitudes are plotted here against frequency. For $N_m > N_e$, the speed of the machine is higher than the natural frequency of the foundation, $N_e > N_s$ denotes that the natural frequency of the foundation is higher than that of the soil.

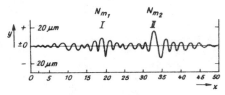

Fig. 148. Occurrence of the second resonance. The vibration waves are illustrated schematically in the correct form

x—frequency, y—amplitudes

When starting the machine resonance may occur at N_{m1} rpm, if vibrations corresponding to the natural frequency of the soil are transmitted to the foundation by the machine. On acceleration, a secondary resonance may occur when $N_{m2} = N_e$, that is the rpm value of the machine reaches the natural frequency of the foundation.

It follows that a natural frequency higher than the rpm of the machine should be selected for the foundation. To avoid resonance between foundation and soil, it is advisable in the case $N_{m1} = N_s$, that is, when the rpm value of the machine attains the natural frequency of the soil, to increase the speed of the machine as quickly as possible so as to remain for as little time as possible within the limits of the resonance of the soil.

EXAMPLE 3

Compressor foundation. The foundation in question performed movements which prevented further operation. In order to carry out the necessary investigations mechanical vibration-measuring instruments were mounted at the four upper corners of the upper slab of the foundation. The instruments used enabled the vibration to be amplified 14–27 times. The upper and the lower slabs of the foundation are connected by means of four columns and a wall (Fig. 149). Measurements were taken when the machine was started, later at normal operational speed and, finally, when the machine was stopped. One vertical and two horizontal components mutually perpendicular (namely in the direction of the shaft and perpendicular to it), were observed. Thus the vibrations were measured

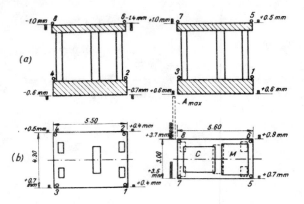

Fig. 149. Points for vibration measurement on a compressor foundation indicating the measured amplitudes

a—amplitudes in the vertical plane, b—amplitudes in the plane of the base, A_{max}—maximum amplitude, C—compressor, M—motor

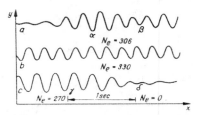

Fig. 150. Results of measurements on a compressor foundation

x—time, y—amplitude

altogether in three directions. A contact was created on the shaft of the machine that made recording of the vibration possible by means of a measuring film.

This is illustrated in Fig. 150 where measured vibrations* are plotted in a coordinate system, the horizontal and vertical axes of which denote time and amplitude, respectively. Normal operating speed of the machine was $N = 330$ rpm. The following conclusions can be arrived at from the figure:

(i) At starting, the maximum amplitude was found at 306 rpm, that is, at 5.1 cps (shown in Fig. 150 by a). Afterwards the amplitude dropped to a minimum value, (denoted by β), later it increased again.

(ii) At 330 rpm (indicated in Fig. 150 by b) it reached what could be regarded as a constant value corresponding to 5.5 cps.

(iii) While stopping the machine the amplitude reached a maximum value (denoted by γ) corresponding to 270 rpm (equal to 4.5 cps) and finally at the point denoted by δ the vibrations ceased. As the natural frequency of the foundation was

* After Förtsch and Muchs [330] and Schultze and Muchs [1109].

EXAMPLE 3 COMPRESSOR FOUNDATION 217

as high as 330 rpm, the operational rpm was in correspondence with it, and this condition resulted in resonance.

In order to determine the nature of the vibrations of the foundation, the measured values of the amplitude—as displacements—were plotted in mm (as shown in Fig. 149). The horizontal displacements in the direction of the shaft could be considered negligible. It was found that the lower and upper slabs rotated about an axis parallel to that of the machine, in the line of intersection formed by a vertical plane passing through the machine shaft and by the bottom slab. At normal operational speed the displacements amounted to 1 mm whereas at starting and stopping they reached a value as high as 2 mm. To these vibrations occurring about a horizontal axis, a vibration about a vertical axis was added, this axis was found to be in the vicinity of the wall built into the foundation. Consequently the motion of the upper slab with respect to its lower counterpart could be regarded as of a shearing character. The vibrations, on the other hand, could be considered torsional because simultaneously with the almost equal horizontal motions of the four corners of the bottom slab, vibrations of far greater extent and differing from one another were observed in the corresponding four points of the upper slab. On the side towards the driving engine these displacements amounted to about 1 mm at normal operational speed whereas at the compressors they amounted to about 3.5. mm. At starting and stopping these motions reached values as high as 7 and 9.3 mm, respectively.

Simultaneously with the measurement of the vibrations in the foundation, the velocity of wave propagation and the damping due to the soil were also determined. According to the result obtained the soil showed but little absorption capacity, which meant that the vibrations could reach adjacent structures too.

The settlement of the foundation took place after a few hours of operation, and cracks occurred at its edges. Settlement at a uniform rate would have caused no harm, but—as was to be expected from the measurements—the rate of settlement was greater at the edges than at the centre of the foundation. Consequently the foundation had to be considered as a body supported only at its centre, and it could therefore be set in vibration by relatively small forces. This resulted in an arched bearing surface; the bearing surface of the foundation became shorter and consequently the original natural frequency tended to decrease. The natural frequency was in this instance higher that the rpm but in consequence of the continuous decrease it approached the latter to a dangerous extent so that further settlement might be expected resulting eventually in the tilting of the entire structure.

The investigation revealed the following shortcomings:

(i) Unbalanced mass forces were transmitted by the machine itself.

(ii) The natural frequency of the foundation was equal to the speed of the machine.

(iii) According to torsion measurements, the bottom slab was very sensitive to vibrations.

(iv) The foundation was over a stratum of sand that could very easily be compacted by vibration. This stratum could not resist the stresses due to vibration and permitted tilting vibrations to increase continually.

The detection of the faults made the reconstruction of the machine foundation possible. The repair works were extended not only to the structural parts of the mechanical equipment, but to the entire foundation.

It must be mentioned here that sandy soils which have no cohesion and can easily be eroded are liable to settlement caused by vibration—the process is accelerated by the flow of groundwater over a period of several years. Settlements may, however, occur where no movement of ground water is observed but the subsoil of fine sand is irregularly stratified. The harmful settlements observed at the Klingenberg power station (Klingenberger Kraftwerke, Berlin) were due to such causes. The settlement observed at this power station exceeded 10 cm at several points. Reconstruction could be carried out only by lifting the foundations with hydraulic jacks and by subsequently inserting in situ piles into the soil.

Drawing on these experiences, a system of pile foundations combined with open caissons was used in similar soil in Hungary at the Bánhida power station. The solution employed has proved very satisfactory.*

EXAMPLE 4

Examination of harmful vibration in a motor-generator assembly. Vibration of the rotor bearings of a motor-generator assembly in Hungary resulted in the shutdown of the machine. The arrangement of the equipment is shown diagrammatically in Fig. 151 and the points where phase measurements were made are indicated.

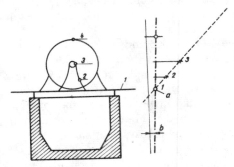

Fig. 151. Measuring points and the results of measurements made on a defective motor generator

a—centre of rotation on the bearing supports (in relation to the machine), b—minimum displacement of foundation. (The foundation does not swing), the parallel displacement is permissible [~ 10 μ]

(i) Phase measurements were made at points denoted by 1, 2, 3 and 4. Variations of magnitude occurred in the following order: 3, 2, 1 and 4. This was to be expected as the rotor set the bearing into vibration and, in turn, by means of the supports, also the foundation. As a result the stator, too, was set into vibration.

* See preface by W. Gehler to the author's paper published in *Beton und Eisen*, Vol. 15. Berlin, 1931.

EXAMPLE 5   VIBRATIONS RESULTING FROM MOULDING MACHINES   219

(ii) The maximum values of the amplitudes were measured at the points indicated in the figure. The results obtained were as follows:

The amplitude at the foundation	8 μm
The amplitude at the footing	16 μm
The amplitude at the bottom of the bearing bracket	25 μm
The amplitude at the middle of the bearing bracket	130 μm
The amplitude at the bearing	200 μm
The amplitude at the highest point of the stator	9 μm

The amplitudes plotted along the diagrammatic outline of the equipment and then connected showed that the foundation had been correctly designed and installed since the momentary centre of gyration of the machine was at the upper edge of the foundation, i.e. the machine moved more or less independently of the foundation.

The motion of the stator, which is connected rigidly to the foundation and is coupled but magnetically to the rotor, was negligibly small, like that of the foundation.

(iii) The amplitudes were measured at different frequencies of the machine. It was found that at a normal operational speed of 1500 rpm (which corresponds to 25 cps) there was no danger of resonance.

It could thus be established that the foundation was adequately designed but the machine was not properly balanced. After balancing no further trouble was encountered.

EXAMPLE 5

Vibrations resulting from moulding machines. In a Hungarian foundry, the moulding machines built in the workshop produced, during operation, soil vibrations of such an extent that completed moulds stored in the vicinity were destroyed.

If acceleration is plotted against distances (to a logarithmic scale), a straight line is obtained as shown in Fig. 152. The individual moulds were studied at different accelerations whereupon it was found that all the completed moulds resisted an acceleration of about 100 cm/sec^2 in the course of an eight-hour operation. This acceleration was observed within a circle of 18 m radius. Since four machines were operated simultaneously, it was necessary to determine, on the basis of calculations of probability, how many times the accelerations caused by machines 2, 3 and 4 were liable to coincide during an eight-hour operation. It was found that three of the machines were likely to cause harmful vibration every day, whereas the fourth machine would not cause any.

These investigations showed the desirability of increasing the distance in question to 24 m. This, however, was found impossible as a free area around the machines was necessary for other purposes. Finally the foundations of the machines were entirely isolated from the adjacent area, were supported by springs and provided with readily accessible separation joints which could be cleaned easily.

EXAMPLE 6

Vibration of a floor: two cases. Two cases are treated in Fig. 153 showing the analysis of the vibration of a floor, first when a rotating motor (1) installed in a factory was set up on solid supports and then when it was suspended on vibration absorbers. The measurements were taken with an accelerometer (2) of Brüel and Kjaer (see Fig. 155). At 50 and 150 cps, powerful vibrations can be seen; however, the application of

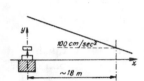

Fig. 152. Variations in acceleration with distance

x—distance, *y*—acceleration on logarithmic scale

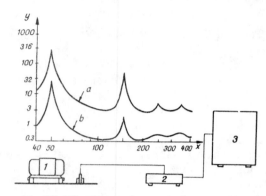

Fig. 153. Vibration measurement of an a.c. motor

a—with solid supports, b—with resilient supports 1—a.c. motor. The instruments of
Brüel and Kjaer: 2—accelerometer of piezoelectrical type, 3—preamplifier, 4—level
recorder for automatic analysis of a frequency spectrum. Units of acceleration on axis
y—1 cm sec^{-2}; on x—vibrations in cps

resilient supports reduces the effect of the vibrations considerably. The simple measuring arrangement is connected as well with a preamplifier (3) and a frequency analyser (4) of the same factory.

EXAMPLE 7

Vibration of foundation of a turbo-generator and building. A method devised by the author and applied under his direction was used to examine the vibrations of the foundation of a Hungarian turbo-generator and the building enclosing it [742]. Measurements were taken during the starting up of the turbo-generator and thus values could be obtained not only at the normal operational speed, but also at intermediate stages. The duration of the acceleration was expected to be about 40–50 minutes and during this time several measurements had to be made in many different parts of the building and at several different speeds. This short time did not allow the use of conventional instruments. This suggested the use of the multi-channel looped oscilloscope previously used only for geophysical measurements.

A 26-channel measuring apparatus with looped galvanometer (manufactured by the Hungarian Factory for Geophysical Measuring Instruments) was used for this purpose. The equipment was mounted and transported on a special truck, as shown

EXAMPLE 7   TURBO-GENERATOR AND BUILDING VIBRATIONS   221

Fig. 154. Group of instruments mounted on a lorry. Table for the anode or dry batteries; fuse panel and stabilizator for anode voltage

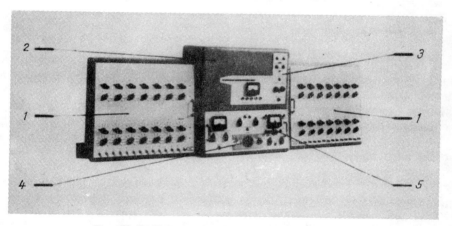

Fig. 155. Oscilloscope amplifier and central switch board

1—amplifier casing, 2—oscilloscope, 3—mixing and tuning unit, 4—telephone (loudspeaker and microphone) 5—controlling oscillator with an ohmic impulse meter

in Figs. 154 and 155. The measurements were made with the aid of geophones attached at the different measuring points which relayed information to an ordinary photographic film. By this arrangement the synchronization of the individual surveys was automatic. Figure 156 shows a diagrammatic section of one of the power station buildings with the measuring points 1–26. Figure 157 illustrates a set of the synchronized vibration curves. Some characteristic details of these curves are shown in Fig. 158.

As can be seen from Fig. 158 rather complicated periodic vibrations were obtained. The frequencies of the components, however, can be divided by the frequency of the slowest vibration. Thus the quicker vibrations complete several periods within one period of the slowest vibration. The duration of the complicated

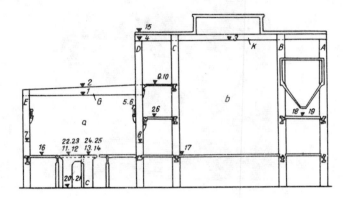

Fig. 156. Measuring points at a power station
(a) machine, (b) boiler house, (c) turbine foundation

periodic vibration is to equal to the duration of the slowest vibration; its resultant, however, is not sinusoidal. The complicated periodic vibrations can be resolved into simple harmonic vibrations which can be divided by a frequency corresponding to the period of the composite vibration (as we have seen in Chapter II, the basic frequency). The resolving of such periodic functions is called harmonic analysis. The resolving into Fourier series can be accomplished by means of instruments designed for the purpose. By the use of harmonic analysis, complicated analytical calculations can be eliminated; on the other hand, resolving can be accomplished even when the function $z = f(t)$ cannot be expressed mathematically. The complicated vibration curves of the present survey are of such a type.

The evaluation of the results was made to be instructive, visually, by the following method. The components due to disturbance are illustrated in Fig. 158, under(*d*). The vibration curve due exclusively to disturbance was obtained at zero speed, i.e. before the machine had been started. Results obtained at four points are shown in Fig. 160. The curve to be examined—in this instance the third one—must be separated from the others (*b*). The separation of the disturbance is accomplished in the following way: The (*c*) curve corresponding to the possible or assumed basic vibration is sketched out by following the outlines of curve (*b*) and the algebraic difference of the ordinates is plottted (*d*). If the separated disturbance curves thus obtained do not differ considerably from the amplitudes of the disturbing vibrations occurring

EXAMPLE 7   TURBO-GENERATOR AND BUILDING VIBRATIONS   223

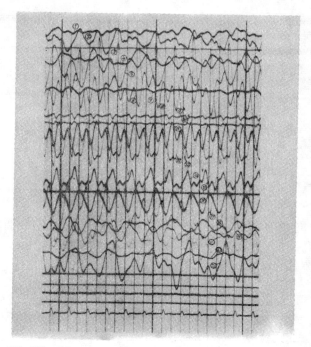

Fig. 157. Vibration curves resulting from synchronized measurement

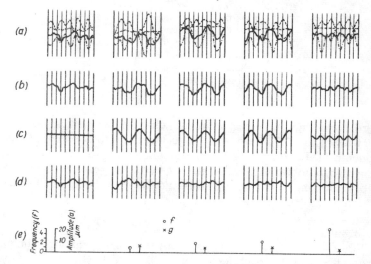

Fig. 158. Application of the method of synchronized measurements during acceleration of a turbo-generator. Characteristic curves

a—curves obtained by means of measurements, b—curve at the point (No. 3) under examination, c—component due to generation, d—component due to disturbance, e—frequencies and amplitudes as determined, f—frequency, g—amplitude

before the machine is started, the curves corresponding to the assumed basic vibration can be considered approximately correct and adequate.

The disturbing components may be due partly to auxiliary equipment (such as the pumps, motors, etc.), and partly to variations in the electric field strength, which is also indicated by the instruments acting as antennae. From the characteristic curves the amplitude curves of the individual elements can be plotted as shown in Fig. 159.

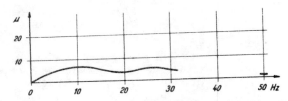

Fig. 159. A method of synchronized measurements. The amplitude curve of the characteristic vibration curve obtained in *Fig. 158.* Ord: 10 μ

TABLE 27

Measured amplitudes on different power house levels

No. of the point	Location of the point	Amplitude at 3000 rpm (μm)
20	On the bedplate	2.8
21	On the bedplate	0.9
22	On the turbine table	3.9
23	On the turbine table	6.0
24	On the turbine table	6.3
25	On the turbine table	5.0
26	On level of the inter-mediate floor	3.3

Synchronized amplitude measurements compared with single measurements on point 20 to 26 (Table 27) showed good agreement. It is to be seen that the maximum amplitude on the bedplate was 2.8 μm. It can be seen from the graphs of Fig. 161 taken on two points that a peak was observed at nearly 700 rpm due to the transistory resonance set up by the elastic motion of the bedding; another peak was about 1280 due to the critical speed of the machine.

In the above example, the following conclusions were drawn from the observational results:

(i) Vibrations due to the operation of the turbo-generator did not extend beyond the limits of the machine house.

(ii) At normal operational speed there was no danger of resonance.

(iii) During acceleration and slowing down some transitional, i.e. temporary, resonances might take place.

EXAMPLE 7   TURBO-GENERATOR AND BUILDING VIBRATIONS   225

The method discussed has proved very satisfactory not only for making simultaneous measurements in different parts of structures subject to dynamic forces, but also for investigating resonance conditions in prefabricated structures or structures using prefabricated elements. Because of their slenderness, these structures are in most instances undertuned and the examination of resonances occurring during acceleration is therefore of great significance. During acceleration, or even at normal operational speed, some elements may be subjected to considerable vibrations owing to resonance. Special examinations of such elements are warranted. It may also happen that the connection between prefabricated elements is not adequate and, in consequence, the element may be subjected to vibrations exceeding the permissible limits.

This method of simultaneous measurements gives information in a relatively short time regarding the resonance conditions of machine foundations and building structures. When excessive vibrations take place in machine foundations the defects can easily be detected by this method, which means that the defects in machines or structures can be eliminated.

The results obtained by the author in the course of his investigations by the above method, will be discussed in relation to the theory of vibrations in turbo-generator foundations, and also in relation to a suggestion for the introduction of a computation method (in Vol. III. Chapter II).

The above-mentioned vibration measurements were performed by MÉLYÉPTERV, the Hungarian Design Office for Civil Engineering, in collaboration with the Design Office for Power Stations and the Geophysical Institute for Oil Exploration.

CHAPTER IX

THE ELASTIC PROPERTIES OF THE SOIL

In the first assumption in dynamic investigations the soil was supposed as being a spring—but it has been stated that theoretical considerations can be accepted only when supported by practical investigations. Relying on experiments some theoretical problems of elastic soil deformations will be discussed here and will be compared with those of practical investigations.

1. Constant characterizing the elastic deformation of the soil

The force acting on the unit surface of a body is called the stress. Stresses acting at a point of the body on the three planes perpendicular to coordinate axes x, y, z (Fig. 160), can be described by nine stress values:

$$X_x, \ Y_x, \ Z_x$$
$$X_y, \ Y_y, \ Z_y$$
$$X_z, \ Y_z, \ Z_z$$

Here X_x, Y_x, Z_x are the stress components which act on a plane perpendicular to the axis.

A) HOOKE'S LAW

If the distances between the elementary parts of a body change as the result of stress, the body suffers deformation. Components of deformation are denoted with reference to the axes u, v, w.

Strains of the individual elementary parts parallel to the axes are expressed for small movements by the following equations:

$$e_{xx} = \frac{\partial u}{\partial x} ; \quad e_{yy} = \frac{\partial v}{\partial y} ; \quad e_{zz} = \frac{\partial w}{\partial z} \tag{277}$$

Angular changes also bring about displacements, the values of which are:

$$e_{xy} = \frac{\partial v}{\partial x} + \frac{\partial u}{\partial y}$$

$$e_{xz} = \frac{\partial w}{\partial x} + \frac{\partial u}{\partial z} \qquad (278)$$

$$e_{yz} = \frac{\partial u}{\partial z} + \frac{\partial w}{\partial y}$$

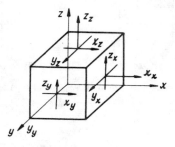

Fig. 160. Force acting on the surface of an elementary body

Deformations, when the body recovers its original form after the load is removed, are called elastic. These increase as the external loading is increased. The relationship between stresses and deformations is expressed analytically by the following equation:

$$X_x = F_{xx}(e_{xx}, e_{yy}, e_{zz}, e_{xy}, e_{xz}, e_{yz})$$
$$\vdots \qquad (279)$$
$$Y_z = F_{yz}(e_{xx}, e_{yy}, e_{zz}, e_{xy}, e_{xz}, e_{yz})$$

Functions F must satisfy the following conditions: if

$$e_{xx} = e_{yy} = \ldots = e_{yz} = 0$$

then

$$F_{xx} = F_{yy} = \ldots = F_{yz} = 0 \qquad (280)$$

Developing the functions F_{xx}, $F_{yy} \ldots$ in Taylor's series, we obtain, provided that deformations are small, the following equations:

$$X_x = C_{11}e_{xx} + C_{12}e_{yy} + C_{13}e_{zz} + C_{14}e_{xy} + C_{15}e_{xz} + C_{16}e_{yz}$$
$$\vdots \qquad (281)$$
$$Y_z = C_{61}e_{xx} + C_{62}e_{yy} + C_{63}e_{zz} + C_{64}e_{xy} + C_{65}e_{xz} + C_{66}e_{yz}$$

The above equations are the analytical expression of Hooke's law which states that each of the stress factors acting on a solid body is the linear function of six deformation components related to the same point.

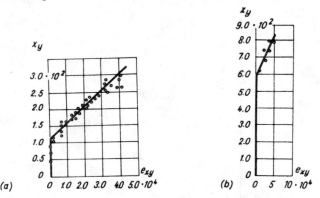

Fig. 161. Relation of soil stress (x_y) and displacement (e_{xy}) within the proportionality limit

a—sand, b—clay. Absc.: cm Ord.: kg/cm²

B) YOUNG'S MODULUS

The ratio of the stress due to compression or tension in one direction and of the strain caused thereby is referred to as the modulus of elasticity or Young's modulus.

The value of this modulus is:

$$E = \frac{\mu(3\lambda + 2\mu)}{\lambda + \mu} \tag{282}$$

where λ and μ are the elasticity constants, the so-called Lamé's constants.

C) POISSON'S RATIO–ELASTIC MODULUS OF SOILS

The ratio of strains in directions perpendicular to each other is expressed by Poisson's ratio. The value thereof is constant for a given material and does not depend on the cross-section. Hooke's law is valid only for homogeneous and isotropic bodies having no initial stress. With soils, however, friction, capillarity, etc. are always present as initial stresses. Therefore soils do not conform to Hooke's law. According to experimental results the relationship between the stress of motion and that of deformation is linear. Deformations occur however, only if the stress reaches a certain value (Fig. 161a for sand, 161b for clay).

The modulus of elasticity can be expressed, taking into account the components of initial stresses X_y^0, Y_z^0, Z_x^0 due to friction, by the following equation:

$$E = aE_0$$

where $E_0 = $ Young's modulus of elasticity.

Experiments carried out with various soil types have shown the coefficient of elastic deformation of the soil to increase proportionally with the normal pressure acting on the soil, when deformation is uniform. The effect of this normal stress on the resistance to deformation is expressed by the coefficient a. Elastic moduli depend therefore on the normal stress (p) and differ but slightly from each other. Thus there is no great deviation from Young's modulus. The ratio of transverse and longitudinal deformation (Poisson's ratio) changes also, i.e. decreases with increasing loads.

The above considerations yield the following conclusions. The settlement of a simple structure under static load consists of two parts: a permanent and an elastic settlement. The elastic settlement is small and can thus be neglected. Therefore, when calculating deformation, instead of the elasticity constants, constants expressing the correlation between the general deformations of the soil and the acting stresses are used. Instead of Young's modulus the general elasticity modulus is used, derived from Young's modulus by multiplying it by the coefficient a.

The value of Poisson's ratio is, according to Terzaghi, 0.3 for sand and from 0.41 to 0.43 for clay. Barkan found Poission's ratio to be independent of moisture content. He obtained for pure clay 0.50; for 30 per cent sandy clay 0.42. In general, Poisson's ratio can be taken as 0.5 for clay, and from 0.30 to 0.35 for sand.

For pure sand Young's modulus can be shown experimentally to be constant and to be affected but slightly by changes in the relative moisture content, in the void ratio and in the particle size.

With cohesive soils the situation is different, inasmuch as E depends to a high degree on the relative moisture content:

$$E = E_0 \left(1 - \frac{q^2}{q_0^2} \right) \tag{283}$$

where E_0 is Young's modulus for the dry material,
   q the relative moisture content,
   q_0 the relative moisture content at which the modulus equals E_0.

The limiting value of the relative moisture q_0 depends on the sand content of clay. The values are:

for pure clay	29 per cent
for clay with 30 to 40 per cent	24 per cent
for clay with 50 to 60 per cent sand	14 to 15 per cent

With clay the value of E is dependent also on the void ratio. For example, as the void ratio changes from 0.32 to 0.93, the value of the elastic modulus decreases from 1,700 to 120 kg/cm^2.

Elastic moduli for various soil types are given in Table 28.

TABLE 28

Young's modulus for various soil types

Type of soil	H kg/cm^2
Plastic, sandy clay with some silt	310
Brown, sandy clay, saturated ....:.....	440
Heavy, dense, sandy clay	2,950
Wet sand, medium size	540
Grey sand with gravel bedding	540
Fine sand, saturated	850
Medium size sand	830
Loess	1,000 to 1,300
Loess-like sandy clay	1,200

2. Elastic deformations of soils

Within the elastic limit, four types of deformation of soil can be distinguished. These are dealt with below under the headings:

    A) uniform compression,
    B) non-uniform compression,
    C) uniform displacement,
    D) non-uniform displacement.

Values of the corresponding proportionality numbers should be examined.

A) UNIFORM COMPRESSION OF SOIL

If during a test the soil is loaded and the total settlement, observed after each additional load, is plotted on a diagram, the settlement curve is obtained. The first branch of the curve is straight; later on, with increasing load, it assumes a curved shape (Fig. 162). The straight section follows the linear relationship

$$p_z = K z_{\text{total}} \tag{284}$$

where p_z is specific pressure on the soil,
      K the proportionality number,
    z_{total} represents total settlement of the bearing surface.

The proportionality limit may serve as a basis for determining permissible stresses. The latter may be taken either as equal to or as smaller than the proportionality limit. Experiments have shown the proportionality limit to be independent of the bearing surface. If the load is applied in increments, and is released after every step, the looped diagram of Fig. 163 is obtained.

By plotting the elastic settlements corresponding to the individual load increments in a coordinate system, the resulting linear relationship between pressure and elastic settlement is

$$p_z = C_z z \qquad (285)$$

where C_z is the coefficient of uniform compression of the soil, that is, the stress causing unit elastic compression in direction z, and z represents the magnitude of the elastic settlement.

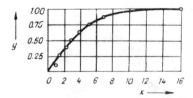

Fig. 162. Relation of soil stress and subsidence

x— subsidence, in mm; y— soil stress in kg/cm²

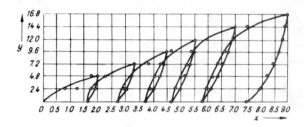

Fig, 163. The graph of subsidences due to repeated loading cycles is a looped curve

x—subsidence, y—loads

The difference between the coefficient of compression C_z and that of proportionality k should now be examined. Whereas the coefficient of proportionality indicates the ratio of pressure to absolute settlement, C_z denoted the relation of pressure p_z to the elastic part of the absolute settlement.

The coefficient of uniform compression C_z would be independent of the shape and size of foundation if the stress distribution under the foundation were uniform. This, however, is not the case. It can be shown that for a circular foundation the value of C_z in equation $p_z = C_z z$ is

$$C_z = 1.13 \frac{E}{1 - \sigma^2} \frac{1}{\sqrt{F}} \qquad (286)$$

As can be seen, C_z depends on the modulus of elasticity of the soil; E, on Poisson's constant σ and on the surface area of the base. The value of the coefficient for a rectangular foundation is, according to Schleicher [1096],

$$C_z = \frac{k_z C}{\sqrt{F}} \tag{287}$$

where

$$C = \frac{E}{1 - \sigma^2} \tag{288}$$

and k_z is a coefficient depending on the ratio between the sides of the foundation

$$k_z = \frac{\pi \sqrt{\alpha}}{\ln \dfrac{\sqrt{1+\alpha^2}+\alpha}{\sqrt{1+\alpha^2}-\alpha} + \alpha \ln \dfrac{\sqrt{1+\alpha^2}+\alpha}{\sqrt{1+\alpha^2}-\alpha} - \dfrac{2}{3} \cdot \dfrac{(1+\alpha^2)^{3/2}-(1+\alpha^3)}{\alpha}} \tag{289}$$

where $\alpha = 2a/2b$, the ratio between the sides of the foundation.

Values of k_z, calculated from the above equation, are shown in Table 29, supplemented by values of k'_z, (the latter being related to absolutely rigid, rectangular foundations).

As will be perceived, the values of k_z and k'_z hardly deviate from each other, indicating that for machine foundations the coefficient of uniform compression is practically unchanged for foundations of different size ratios as long as the elastic limit is not exceeded.

TABLE 29

Values of k_z and k'_z as functions of a

α	k_z	k'_z
1	1.06	1.08
1.5	1.07	—
2	1.09	1.10
3	1.13	1.15
5	1.22	1.24
10	1.41	1.41

Experiments have revealed that the coefficient C_z decreases as the base area increases. The coefficients of compression for two foundations of different base area are related, according to Barkan, by the expression

$$C_{z2} = C_{z1} \sqrt{\frac{F_1}{F_2}} \tag{290}$$

The correctness of this relationship is proved within certain limits by experiments (in full agreement with those of Tschebotarioff). With larger base areas, however, the calculated values decrease more rapidly than the experimental ones. Therefore the larger the base area of the foundation, the greater the mass acting with the foundation, and the more the stress of deeper soil strata affects the settlement of the foundation.

B) NON-UNIFORM COMPRESSION OF THE SOIL

In this case the foundation is not loaded uniformly but by a moment (Fig. 164). The value obtained differs from C_z and according to Barkan, can be calculated for a rectangular bearing by the following equation:

$$C_\varphi = \frac{k_\varphi C}{\sqrt{F}}$$

(291)

where

$$k_\varphi = \frac{2\pi\alpha\sqrt{\alpha}}{2\alpha^2 \ln\dfrac{\sqrt{4\alpha^2+1}+1}{\sqrt{4\alpha^2-1}-1} + \sqrt{4\alpha^2+1}-1}$$

(292)

$$\frac{C_\varphi}{C_z} = \frac{k_\varphi}{k_z}$$

(293)

The values of the ratio C_φ/C_z are compiled after Barkan in Table 30.
On the basis of experiments the following value can be used

$$C_\varphi = 2C_z$$

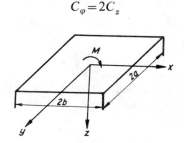

Fig. 164. Moment acting on a foundation

C) UNIFORM DISPLACEMENT OF SOIL

If the lower plane of the foundation is acted upon by a horizontal force, it suffers a displacement corresponding to the force. According to tests the relationship between the stress and the displacement is linear:

$$p_x = C_x u_x$$

(294)

where p_x = the average soil stress due to horizontal force at the bottom of

TABLE 30

Coefficient k_φ and ratio C_φ/C^z for different values of a

α	k_φ	C_φ/C_z	α	k_φ	C_φ/C_z
1.0	1.984	1.87	3	2.955	2.63
1.5	2.254	2.11	5	3.700	3.04
2.0	2.510	2.31	10	4.981	3.53

the foundation

u_x = the elastic part of the bottom displacement due to former stress
C_x = the coefficient of uniform displacement, the average value of which is

$$C_x = \frac{k_x C}{\sqrt{F}} \tag{295}$$

where the coefficient k_x is given as

$$k_x = \frac{\pi}{2\sqrt{\alpha}\left\{\frac{1}{\alpha} \text{ arc sinh } \alpha + \text{arc sinh } \frac{1}{\alpha} - \frac{1}{3}\left[\frac{1}{\alpha^2}(\sqrt{1+\alpha^2}-1) + \sqrt{1+\alpha^2}-\alpha\right] + \right.}$$

$$\left. + \frac{\pi}{+\frac{\sigma}{1-\sigma}\left(\frac{1}{\alpha} \text{ arc sinh } \alpha + \frac{1}{3}\left[\sqrt{1+\alpha^2}-\alpha-\frac{2}{\alpha^2}(\sqrt{1+\alpha^2}-1)\right]\right)\right\}} \tag{296}$$

The ratio between C_x and C_z equals the ratio of k_z to k_x, therefore

$$\frac{C_z}{C_x} = \frac{k_z}{k_x} \tag{297}$$

According to experiments carried out for foundations with different base areas the following equation is approximately valid:

$$C_x = 0.5 C_z \tag{298}$$

D) NON-UNIFORM DISPLACEMENT OF SOIL

If a moment acts on the foundation about a vertical axis, the foundation suffers a rotational displacement, the angle of rotation being proportional to the external moment.

$$M_z = C_\psi I_z \psi \tag{299}$$

where M_z = the moment causing rotation of the foundation through angle ψ;
I_z = the polar moment of inertia of the base surface of the foundation;
C_ψ = the proportionality coefficient.

TABLE 31

Experimental values of coefficients C_x and C_φ

Type of soil	F	C_z	C_ϕ	$\dfrac{C_\phi}{C_x}$
	m²	kg/cm³	kg/cm³	
Grey, plastic, satur-	1.5	1.27	2.72	2.14
ated, sandy day	1.0	1.64	2.33	1.42
	0.5	1.88	2.08	1.01
Grey, saturated, fine	1.0	2.54	3.90	1.54
sand	4.0	2.20	2.85	1.30
	15.0	1.90	2.20	1.16

According to Barkan's experiments the approximate value of C_ψ is, on the average, $1.5C_x$ (Table 31).

Values of C_z, C_x, C_φ, C_ψ should always be determined, if possible, by one of the familiar experimental methods. The values of Table 31 should be used only in the absence of experiments and should be treated only as approximate ones, especially for foundations of base areas greater than 10 m², where values are given according to permissible soil stresses and not according to the soil type (see Chapter XI).

3. Vibration analysis of pile foundations

Pile foundations are used in special cases such as when the load on the soil is greater than the permissible stress, or when the natural frequency of the foundation must be raised, but it is impossible to alter its dimensions, or when vibrational amplitudes or, in general, settlements due to dynamic forces must be reduced.

In addition to the following points further investigations are to be found with a diagram giving the resonant frequency of the vertical vibration in case of loaded rigid stratum by Richart in 1962 [1022]. Studies on rocking vibrations of structures with piles studies have been published by Sh. Yamamoto in 1966, 1967 [1348, 1349] including the horizontal resistance of pile for a rapidly reduced spring system near top of pile [1350, 1351].

A) INVESTIGATION OF PILE FOUNDATIONS

For pile foundations, elastic settlement (as for normal foundations) is directly proportional to load

$$P = C\delta \qquad (300)$$

where C is the elasticity coefficient of the pile (kg/cm) the value of which depends on the characteristics and the driving time of the pile. The period of the vibration is:

$$T = 2\pi \sqrt{\frac{m}{C}} \qquad (301)$$

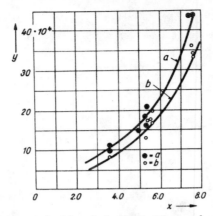

Fig. 165. Coefficient of elasticity of piles (ordinate) as a function of their length

x—length of piles in m, y—coefficient of elasticity of pile
in kg/cm; a—driving, b—pulling

On investigating the vertical vibrations of soil in the neighbourhood of driven piles, Barkan reached the conclusion that the time of vibration gives a basis for calculating the coefficient of elasticity. In Eq. (301) m is the mass of the pile plus that of the loading device. The pile influences the value of the coefficient of elasticity. The period of vibration decreases after a period of rest, whereas it increases with the driven length. The elasticity coefficient of the pile increases with its length, as can be seen in the diagram of Fig. 165.

The elastic settlement of the pile consists of two elements:

$$\delta = \delta_c + \delta_l \tag{302}$$

where δ_c is the elastic shortening of pile,

δ_l the settlement of the pile regarded as a rigid body.

Substituting this in equation (300) we have

$$C = \frac{P}{\delta_c + \delta_l} \tag{303}$$

on the other hand

$$\delta_c = \frac{P}{C_c} \tag{304}$$

and

$$\delta_l = \frac{P}{C_l} \tag{305}$$

where C_c is the coefficient of elastic resistance, depending on the material of the pile,

C_1 is the coefficient of elasticity of the soil, acting against the pile, assumed to be absolutely rigid.

It follows that

$$C = \frac{C_c C_l}{C_c + C_l} \tag{306}$$

$$C_l = cl \tag{307}$$

Accordingly, C_l is proportional to the length of the pile, whereas the coefficient C_c, depending on the material of the pile, is directly proportional to the cross-section of the pile, and inversely proportional to the length of pile:

$$C_c = E_c \frac{f}{l} \tag{308}$$

where E_c represents the elasticity modulus of the pile material.

If values (307), (308) are substituted in the right-hand side of Eq. (306) the value of the coefficient of elastic resistance for the pile is obtained as

$$C = \frac{l}{fE_c + cl^2} fE_c c \tag{309}$$

Differentiating the above expression with respect to l, the maximum value of C is obtained for a pile of the length $l*$:

$$l* = \sqrt{\frac{fE_c}{c}} \tag{310}$$

Length $l*$ may also be described as the critical length of piles. With piles longer than this value, C decreases with the increase of length, and with shorter piles it increases with the ramming depth. Since, however, the data available for both E_c and c are insufficient, the critical length of piles cannot be calculated reliably. The approximate value of the coefficient of elastic resistance is:

$$C_l = csl \tag{311}$$

where s is the perimeter,
        l the length of the pile.

Eastwood in his paper "Model Investigations Concerned with Driving Piles by Vibration" [282] published the results of his investigations on models. His aim was to determine the technical factors influencing pile-driving by vibration. In the experiments he used wooden piles of different lengths (up to 1.83 m) and different cross-sections (2.5, 5.1, 10.2 cm^2).

It was observed that each pile had a certain constant natural frequency independent of the depth to which it was driven. The natural frequency decreases with increased mass of the pile, but not at the rate expected on the basis of the calculated value of N. The natural frequency of piles driven into hydraulic-fit sand was found to be slightly lower than that of the pile driven into a soil containing capilliary water only.

B) INVESTIGATION OF GROUPS OF PILES

When using several piles the base area increases and thus, in contrast to normal foundations, also the value of coefficient K_z (Fig. 166), which becomes for a group of piles

$$K_z = nC_l \tag{312}$$

As revealed by Table 32, based on Barkan's experiments, the elastic resistance coefficient of pile groups depends on the spacing of the piles. The resistance of the

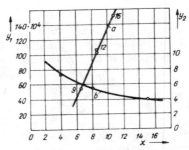

Fig. 166. Variation of coefficient of uniform compression of mat foundation (C_z) and of group of piles (K_z) as a function of the base area

x—area F in m², y_1—K_z for piles in kg/cm³, y_2—C_z for mat foundation in kg/cm³, a—pile foundation, the figures indicate the number of piles, b—mat foundation

individual piles increases together with the distance between the piles and approaches that of isolated piles. A correction factor characterizing the effect of the distance between the piles has been introduced to relate the elastic resistance of a pile group to that of a single pile, provided the coefficient C for the latter is known.

$$C_{l1} = \mu csl \tag{313}$$

TABLE 32

Result of investigations for determining coefficients C and c for piles

Length of pile	Distance apart of piles	Load on foundation	Elastic settlement of foundation	$C = \dfrac{P}{\delta_n}$	$c = \dfrac{C}{sl}$
(m)	(m)	(ton)	(cm)	(kg/cm)	(kg/cm³)
5.4 – 5.6	0.81	30.2	0.049	$6.9 \cdot 10^4$	1.4
	1.22	28.8	0.028	$11.5 \cdot 10^4$	2.3
	1.62	28.8	0.026	$12.4 \cdot 10^4$	2.5
3.6	0.81	28.8	0.063	$5.1 \cdot 10^4$	1.5
	1.22	30.2	0.047	$7.2 \cdot 10^4$	2.2
	1.62	30.2	0.048	$7.0 \cdot 10^4$	2.1

Table 33 gives experimental values of μ for coefficient t, the distance between the piles, and d, their diameter.

C) VERTICAL ECCENTRIC LOAD ON PILE FOUNDATIONS

Let us examine the magnitude of the angle through which a foundation is rotated by an external moment. The corresponding equation is

$$M = C_\varphi \sum_{i=1}^{n} \xi_i^2 \tag{314}$$

where $= \xi_i$ the distance of the ith pile from the axis of rotation.

The pressure of one pile on the soil is $C\xi^2\varphi$. Substituting we obtain

$$M = K_\varphi \cdot \varphi \tag{315}$$

where $K_\varphi =$ the coefficient of non-uniform resistance within the elastic limit.

D) HORIZONTAL LOADING ON PILE FOUNDATIONS

This analysis should be carried out if pile foundations are intended to reduce natural frequencies or decrease amplitudes. The effect on the coefficient of elastic displacement of driving the piles should be examined. It has been found experimentally that the length of the pile has no influence on the coefficient of elastic displacement, but a minimum depth of driving is required to resist horizontal loads. Relying on practical experience Barkan gives this depth as 1.0 to 1.5 m. The elastic resistance depends to a great extent on the diameter of the pile. Experimental data show, too, that the natural frequency of a foundation cannot be increased to any considerable degree by the use of piles.

Although elasticity analysis problems have been treated in this chapter, in addition to the above sections A–D about the elasticity analysis of pile foundations, further investigations should be mentioned in connection with Chapter XII about the design methods of dynamically loaded foundations. (See Richart [1022]; Yamamoto [1348], [1349]; and Yamamoto et al. [1350], [1351].) Regarding pile foundations, a model for machine–pile and foundation–soil system was published

TABLE 33

Correction factor μ as a function of t/d

t/d	μ
∞	1.0
6	0.63
4.5	0.58
3	0.35

by Madhav and Kamashwara [726]; for details concerning the lateral loading of piles, see also Penzien [941]. Further state-of-the-art summaries were presented in 1972 by Broms [131], and for the design of deep penetration piles for ocean structures by McClelland [815a]. Because of their consideration of the soil as an elastic medium, Tajimi [1227] and Novak [899a] should be mentioned. Soil structure interaction for laterally loaded piles is treated in a progress survey by Richart [1023]. For the vertical vibration of piles, see Mogami and Novak [891a] on the problems of floating piles. A theoretical approach to the torsional vibration of piles is presented by Novak and Howell [901a] depending on soil–pile interaction. With increasing shear wave velocity ratios, pile stiffness and damping increases. For soft soils and a pile slenderness ratio greater than 25, the response is independent of the slenderness ratio and the tip condition. Compared with shallow foundations, pile foundations can have higher resonant frequencies but smaller resonant amplitudes than shallow foundations. (The design of machine foundations on piles is also dealt with by Singh et al. [1147a]. With regard to pile-designing problems, the reader is referred to the relevant sections in Vols. II, III and IV.)

CHAPTER X

THE BEHAVIOUR OF SOILS UNDER DYNAMIC LOADS

Some basic principles will be given here, but it must be emphasized that the vibrations of machine foundations are in general—excepting for instance hammer-like foundations—not excessive and they are consequently not characterized by large amplitude of loadings. Such loadings are likely to occur in the case of intensive vibrations excited, for instance, by nuclear blasts or by compaction devices. As the discussion of similar problems is beyond the scope of this book—we refer here to problems such as stress–strain behaviour, liquefaction of cohesionless soils and failures of soil, samples in triaxial tests, of sands in high amplitude column tests and to the change of volume, further to field compaction problems in the case of cohesionless soils—we refer to the relevant literature and to works of Richart et al. [1024] and d'Appolonia [222]: both of these works are provided with extended bibliographies. About methods for prediction and controlling vibrational settlements mainly in case of machine foundations, Section 11 of this present chapter will contain further data.

1. Soil friction and adhesion under dynamic loading

The increase of settlement can be understood if we remember that vibration and shocks reduce friction and adhesion considerably. Owing to the energy of vibration, the coefficient of internal friction decreases, e.g. for sand by as much as 25 to 30 per cent, but the acceleration of the vibrations also plays a part. Friction decreases as the acceleration of vibration increases and approaches asymptotically a value (Fig. 167) which is characteristic of the soil.

2. Coefficient of viscosity

Vibration and shocks tend to make soil behave like a fluid, by increasing its viscosity. Barkan performed experiments to determine the coefficient of viscosity. The diagrammatic arrangement of the experiment is shown in Fig. 168.

He recorded the penetration of a metal ball (3) loaded by weight (4) into a sand mass (1) vibrated by the vibrator (2). The rate of penetration decreases with increasing depth and after a while it can be assumed to be constant. With constant acceleration of vibrations the velocity of sinking and the load of the ball are shown by the experiment to be in linear relationship. The rate of penetration is plotted on the vertical axis of the diagram in Fig. 169, and the load acting upon the ball is plotted on the horizontal axis. The coefficient of viscosity v, is obtained as the slope (tangent) of this straight line.

The coefficient of viscosity is accordingly a coefficient of proportion between the load acting on the ball and its determined rate of penetration, yet it depends to a great extent on the acceleration of vibration as well. Denoting the ratio of the

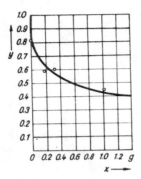

Fig. 167. Internal friction varies inversely with vibrational acceleration and approaches the soil characteristic asymptotically

x—vibrational acceleration, y—coefficient of internal friction

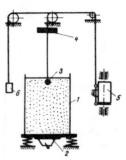

Fig. 168. Device for measuring the penetration of a loaded metal ball into vibrated soil

1—sand vessel, 2—vibrator, 3—metal ball, 4—metal load, 5—recording device, 6—counterweight

acceleration of vibration and of the gravity by η, the product of the coefficient of viscosity and the square of η^k is obtained as an empirical constant a ($k = 1$ if $\eta < 1.40$–1.50, $k = 2$ if $\eta > 1.40$–1.50), that is

$$v\eta^k = a \qquad (316)$$

The coefficient of viscosity is influenced also by the relative moisture content. It reaches a maximum at approximately 13 per cent relative moisture content but at 20 per cent it drops again to the value observed in the dry state (Fig. 170).

Vibration and shocks affect not only the internal friction but also the friction between the vibrating body and the soil. Thus, for example, the force required for drawing a pile is appreciably smaller if it is accompanied by vibration.

3. Void ratio

The density of soil depends on the ratio of the pore volume to the volume of the soil. This is referred to as the void ratio

$$\varepsilon = (1+q)\frac{\gamma_s}{\gamma_0} - 1 \qquad (317)$$

where q is the relative moisture content,
     γ_s the specific weight of the soil material, and
     γ_0 the volume weight of the soil.

The pore volume is minimum when the particles are closest to each other. The void ratio is then denoted by ε_∞; the void ratio of the loosest soil is denoted by ε_0.

For a soil consisting of uniform spheres, these ratios are $\varepsilon_\infty = 0.91$ and $\varepsilon_0 = 0.35$. From experiments carried out by Barkan on soils for different gradation it appears

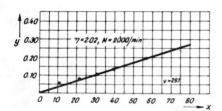

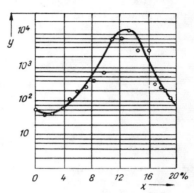

Fig. 169. Relation between load and sinking of the ball is a straight line, the slope of which is the coefficient of viscosity

x—load, y—sinking velocity, in cps

Fig. 170. The coefficient of viscosity as a function of moisture content. Maximum viscosity was observed at 13 per cent moisture content

x—moisture content, y—coefficient of viscosity

that the value of ε_0 depends only to a small degree on the size of the soil particles provided that these are greater than 0.35 mm. Its value is on the average 0.86, and thus it differs by only 5 per cent from the ε_0 value characterizing the system consisting of uniform spheres.

With soils having very fine grains the value of ε_0 is considerably higher, and it can reach 0.91. Sand soils show also higher ε_0 values if clay or silt are present.

The void ratio ε_∞ is more difficult to determine than the value ε_0. The density corresponding to ε_0 can be established neither by static pressure, nor by the simultaneous application of vibration and static pressure. The explanation is perhaps that higher pressures on the soil also increase the friction between the particles; thus the increasing pressure is incapable of changing the pore volume. The solidity of sand increases in the vibrator until it cannot be compacted any longer by vibration. It is then similar to clay which, as is well-known, cannot at all, or but very slightly, be compacted by vibration.

To obtain approximate values for ε_∞, experiments should be carried out with unloaded sand.

With sands loaded only with a dead load vibrated with an acceleration greater than 5 g, a void ratio can be obtained which can be considered to equal ε_∞. Experiments with sand of grain size 1.5 to 0.02 mm give values of 0.49 to 0.54 for ε_∞. With cement of grain size from 0.01 to 0.02 mm, $\varepsilon_\infty = 1.22$. Values relating to finely graded clay should thus also be higher than those obtained for sands.

Experiments with sand showed that the value of ε_∞ was higher than the void ratio calculated for a system of uniform spheres. It is improbable that soil particles could be so densely arranged as spheres. Thus in practice soils approaching this degree of density are seldom encountered. The maximum density of spheres is approached only by the void ratio of sands at the bottom of the sea. The void ratio here is 0.44 to 0.36, that of natural sands 0.60 or even higher.

4. Relative density

Soil aggregation is determined by relative density, derived from the void ratio

$$D = \frac{\delta}{\delta_{max}} = \frac{\varepsilon_0 - \varepsilon}{\varepsilon_0 - \varepsilon_\infty} \tag{318}$$

where D is the factor expressing the relative density of the soil, and its numerical value varies in the range

$$0 < D < 1$$

The counterpart of relative density is the factor of looseness:

$$K = \frac{\varepsilon - \varepsilon_\infty}{\varepsilon_0 - \varepsilon_\infty} \tag{319}$$

where K is the ratio of soil density to maximum density. The two factors are related, since

$$K = 1 - D \tag{320}$$

Sand can be classified according to its relative density into three groups viz.
  (i) dense, where $2/3 < D < 1$
  (ii) medium dense, where $1/3 < D < 2/3$
  (iii) loose, where $c < D < 1/3$.

5. Correlation of density, vibration amplitudes and the direction of vibration

The void ratio depends on the amplitude of vibration, as seen in Fig. 171. But the amplitude of vibration, its frequency and velocity taken separately, cannot characterize the void ratio. According to experiments with vertical vibration, void ratios obtained by vertical and horizontal vibrations of the same frequency are identical.

I would mention here that since 1962 theoretical and practical investigations have been carried out by Schäffner [1085], [1086], [1087] to develop a method using an analytic expression for the settling processes. Based on Fig. 171, Fig. 172 shows a linear relation of ε to frequency f in the case that $(A) = $ const.

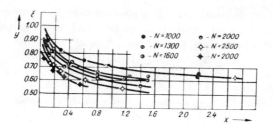

Fig. 171. Void ratio plotted against vibrational amplitude

x—vibrational amplitude, in mm; y—void ratio

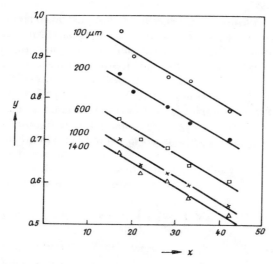

Fig. 172. According to the diagram—based on Fig. 171—for A = const., linear relations of ε to frequency f are given, after [1085]

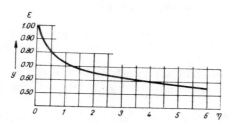

Fig. 173. Void ratio plotted against vibrational acceleration. Compression curve of vibration

η—value proportional to vibrational acceleration, y—void ratio

If there are two vibrations with different amplitudes, A_x and A_y, but with the same phase and the same frequency, the total amplitude determining the void ratio will be:

$$A = \sqrt{A_x^2 + A_y^2} \tag{321}$$

The diagram of Fig. 173 shows the relationship of void ratio and of η, proportional to vibrational acceleration. The diagram was drawn as a result of experiments where vibration was continued for three minutes.

6. Curve of vibrational compression

The above-mentioned curve showing the relationship between the void ratio and the ratio of vibrational acceleration to the gravity constant is called the curve of vibrational compression. If the change in slope of the tangent of the curve is assumed to be approximately linear, its differential equation will be:

$$\frac{d\varepsilon}{d\eta} = -\beta(\varepsilon - \varepsilon_\infty) \tag{322}$$

where β is the proportionality factor. Since for $\eta = 0$; $\varepsilon = \varepsilon^0$,

$$\frac{1}{\beta} = \frac{\varepsilon^0 - \varepsilon_\infty}{\tan \alpha_0} \tag{323}$$

with a_0 denoting the slope of the curve $\varepsilon = \varepsilon(\eta)$ at $\eta = 0$, and the coefficient $1/\beta$ being the vibration acceleration which has the maximum compacting effect on the soil when the void ratio equals ε_∞. The coefficient β may thus be regarded as the coefficient of compacting vibration.

Integrating Eq. (322) we obtain

$$\varepsilon = \varepsilon_\infty + Ce^{-\beta\eta} \tag{324}$$

Here C is the constant to be determined from the assumptions $\eta = 0$ and $\varepsilon = \varepsilon^0$. Hence

$$C = \varepsilon^0 - \varepsilon_\infty \tag{325}$$

and consequently

$$\varepsilon = \varepsilon_\infty + (\varepsilon^0 - \varepsilon_\infty)e^{-\beta\eta} \tag{326}$$

The soil is assumed to have been in a very loose condition up to the starting of compacting by vibration, when $\varepsilon = \varepsilon_0$; the equation of the curve of compacting vibration is then

$$\varepsilon = \varepsilon_\infty + (\varepsilon_0 - \varepsilon_\infty)e^{-\beta\eta} \tag{327}$$

where

$$K = e^{-\beta\eta} \tag{328}$$

If, owing to vibration having an acceleration $\eta=\eta_0$, the void ratio of the soil diminishes to $\varepsilon=\varepsilon^0$, then

$$\varepsilon^0=\varepsilon_\infty+(\varepsilon_0-\varepsilon_\infty)e^{-\beta\eta} \tag{329}$$

Substituting this value of ε^0 into Eq. (327), we arrive at the expression

$$\varepsilon=\varepsilon_\infty+(\varepsilon_0-\varepsilon_\infty)e^{-\beta(\eta+\eta_0)} \tag{330}$$

and

$$K=K_0e^{-\beta\eta} \tag{331}$$

Here η_0 denotes the vibrational acceleration required to transform the soil from the state of lowest compactness characterized by the coefficient ε_0, to the state of natural (initial) compactness, which is expressed by the coefficient ε^0, and where $\varepsilon_0>\varepsilon^0$.

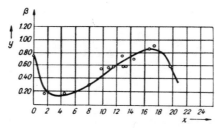

Fig. 174. Changes in the proportionality factor β with moisture content

x—moisture content, in per cent

7. Effect of relative moisture content on compaction by vibration

The equation of the curve of compression depends on the three factors ε_0, ε_∞ and β. The value of β is influenced by the relative moisture content. Variations in β in relation to the relative moisture content are shown in Fig. 174. The optimum value of relative moisture content with sands is 10 to 13 per cent.

8. Effect of duration of vibration on compaction of the soil

According to experience, vibration lasting over three minutes has no considerable effect on dry sand or cement. With wet sand the corresponding time of vibration is longer, 7 to 8 minutes. The void ratio and the time of vibration were found in practice to be related as

$$\varepsilon=\varepsilon_\eta+(\varepsilon_0-\varepsilon_\eta)e^{-\beta_t t} \tag{332}$$

where ε_η is the void ratio corresponding to a given acceleration, and β_t is a factor depending on the physical properties of the soil (for cement $\beta_t=0.048$ sec^{-1}, for one particular sand it was 0.24 sec^{-1}). The declining trend of β_t indicates that the decrease of particle sizes increases the time of compaction, for a given acceleration.

9. Minimum compaction by vibration

Static stresses exceeding the elastic limit cause permanent deformation. Likewise, if acceleration during compaction by vibration exceeds the given limit, the void ratio suffers a permanent change. Further compaction is only possible if the soil is vibrated with higher acceleration. This limit value is called the compaction limit of vibration

If the soil has already been compacted either by a static load or by vibration to a certain ε_k value, further compaction is possible only if the soil is vibrated with a vibrational acceleration η greater than that belonging to ε_k. In this case the value of the compaction limit denoted by η_0 is obtained. The coefficient of looseness was, according to Eq. (328),

$$K_0 = e^{-\beta \eta_0}$$

where

$$\eta_0 = -\frac{1}{\beta} \ln K_0$$

On the other hand,

$$\eta = -\frac{1}{\beta} \ln K$$

The condition of compaction being $\eta > \eta_0$, compactibility is expressed by:

$$K < K_0$$

The amplitudes and the acceleration of vibrations decrease with the distance from the source of vibration. Consequently, the relative density or coefficient of looseness changes too. If

$$\eta = \eta(x,y,z)$$

that is, the value of acceleration is a function of the co-ordinates, the coefficient of looseness becomes

$$K = e^{-\beta \eta(x,y,z)} \tag{333}$$

According to the definition of the limit of compaction by vibration, compaction ensues only if K is smaller than K_0, that is:

$$e^{-\beta \eta(z,y,x)} < K_0 \tag{334}$$

and

$$\eta(x,y,z) = -\frac{1}{\eta} \ln K_0 \tag{335}$$

Acceleration at an amplitude A and frequency ω is $W = A\omega^2$ whence

$$\eta = A(x, y, z)\frac{\omega^2}{g} \tag{336}$$

Substituting this value for η into Eq. (335) we obtain

$$A\,(x,\,y,\,z) = -\frac{g}{\eta\omega^2}\,\ln K_0 \tag{337}$$

It will be perceived that with a permanent source of waves, compaction takes place in an area within amplitudes of equal magnitude. The boundary of compaction by vibration can thus be determined by calculating the range of vibrational acceleration of the soil.

For the determination of the compaction curve of the soil and the compaction limit, vibration odometers are suitable. This device makes it possible to vibrate a soil sample of standard size at any frequency by means of a variable-speed motor. The change of amplitude is effected by pushing a wedge to the required position in a rotating shaft.

10. Settlement due to static pressure and simultaneous vibration

For a soil considered as a viscous medium, the viscosity coefficient of which changes from point to point and depends on vibrational acceleration, the following equation applies:

$$v = f\,[\eta(x,\,y,\,z)] \tag{338}$$

This function describes the settlement due to static pressure and simultaneous vibration. To calculate the velocity of the body and the depth of sinking, we must first consider two fundamental cases.

A) SETTLEMENT OF THE BODY IF THE RESISTANCE TO VIBRATIONAL VISCOSITY OF THE SOIL ACTS ON THE LATERAL SURFACES ONLY

The sort of settlement as indicated in this title is true in the case of piles and sheet walls since the point resistance of the body to be driven is small compared with the resistance acting on the lateral surfaces. It is assumed in the calculations that the coefficient of viscosity at the lateral surfaces is independent of the shape of the body, and the body is incompressible from the aspect of viscous effects. In such an instance, if the body penetrates to depth h, the soil resistance against penetration will be:

$$T = qh\left(2\,\sqrt{\frac{\rho v_0 v}{\pi h}} + \frac{\alpha}{2}\,v_0\right)v \tag{339}$$

where q = perimeter of the driven body
   h = depth of penetration
   ρ = density of soil
   v_0 = coefficient of vibrational viscosity of the soil, corresponding to the vibrational acceleration of the sunken body
   v = velocity of penetration of the body
   a = a factor varying with the type of soil.

Penetration into the vibrated soil is possible only if Q is greater than T. If $Q = T$, the velocity of penetration is:

$$v^3 + kv^2 + lv + m = 0 \qquad (340)$$

where

$$K = -\frac{\pi}{16}\frac{\alpha^2 v_0}{\rho}h$$

$$l = \frac{\pi}{4}\frac{\alpha Q}{q\rho}$$

$$m = -\frac{\pi}{4}\cdot\frac{Q^2}{q^2\rho v_0 h}$$

As is to be seen from the above equation for T the viscous resistance arising in vibrated soils is proportional to the perimeter, the depth and penetration velocity of the body. The resistance of the soil increases with the increase of vibrational viscosity and of density, though the increase is smaller than for variations of perimeter or penetration velocity.

B) SETTLEMENT OF LARGE BODIES DUE TO FRONTAL VIBRATION

Here resistance on the side walls can be neglected. This case corresponds in practice to that of vibrated machine foundations. The resistance acting on the foundation depends on the vibrational viscosity of the soil, the equation of motion being

$$m\frac{dv}{dt} + R = mg \qquad (341)$$

where m = the mass of the foundation
  v = the velocity of penetration (settling) of the foundation
  R = the resistance of vibrational viscosity of soil under the load transmitted by the foundation.

It is assumed that the coefficient of vibrational viscosity of the soil is constant and corresponds to the vibrational acceleration of the vibrating foundation.

For the settling depth and velocity of circular foundations with a base area F Barkan derived the following expressions:

$$h = \frac{g}{b}\left[t - \frac{1}{b}(1 - e^{-bt})\right] \qquad (342)$$

where

$$b = \frac{8}{\sqrt{\pi}}\cdot\frac{v_0\sqrt{F}}{m}$$

and

$$v = \frac{g}{b}(1 - e^{-bt}) \tag{343}$$

After a given time the settlement of foundation becomes uniform:

$$v_\infty = \frac{g}{b} \tag{344}$$

Substituting the corresponding values,

$$v_\infty = \frac{\sqrt{\pi}}{8} \frac{\sigma_{st}\sqrt{F}}{\alpha} \eta \tag{345}$$

From this it can be seen that under the effect of vibration or shocks the settling velocity of the foundation is proportional to the vibrational acceleration, to the static stress σ_{st} acting on the bottom of the foundation, and to the dimensions of the base area. The velocity depends also on the properties of the soil, represented by the factor a in Eq. (316) if $k = 1$.

It should be noted finally that settlement is due not only to the reduction of internal frictional forces, but also to the consolidation of the soil.

When dealing with the limit of compaction by vibration it was established that settlement due to consolidation can arise only if vibrational acceleration is greater than the limit. These settlements are generally related to vibrational viscosity. Settlements due to vibrational compaction decrease with time, or may even cease eventually, and thus Eq. (345) for the determination of v_∞ remains valid.

11. Methods for the prediction and for controlling vibrational settlements

Tschebotarioff and McAlpin stated as early as in 1947 that dynamical settlements will be small provided that the static and dynamic bearing stresses are maintained at less than one-half the permissible bearing stress, where the permissible bearing stress is taken as the static one, which results in the maximum permissible bearing stress. D'Appolonia [220], [221], [222] recommended for machine foundations, a sand densified to greater than about 75 per cent relative density to arrive at small dynamic settlements. As for the relationship between sand density and vibration parameters, if a foundation is subjected to a periodic force P, at an operating frequency of ω, then in designing the foundation the produced accelerations will be less than $1/3$ g. As the soil is undergoing displacements which vary with time, the dynamic stress is due not only to the exciting force P, but also to the inertial force due to the ground acceleration. The maximum displacement during each cycle is related to the inertial stress and at the end of each cycle where the hysteresis loop does not close, a small displacement due to the non-linear behaviour of the soil will arise and will accumulate over many cycles of repeated loading. But there are accelerations in the case of sudden shock loads where the stress changes are small in comparison with the static stress level, while the accelerations are large even causing the collapse of the soil structure. Such effects causing large densifications must also be taken into consideration in the case of machine foundations.

For the evaluation of settlements, laboratory tests are first necessary with soil samples tested to the expected stresses and accelerations. Such tests (published by D'Appolonia and D'Appolonia [223]) show that there is a correlation between terminal density and peak acceleration, in the case of dry fine sand most of the densification occurred until the acceleration reached 1 g and the maximum density was obtained at about 2 g. Another test (Ortigosa and Whitman [916]) showed that a critical acceleration is required to cause densification. Below this critical level, which is the function of the initial density and static confining pressure, no sudden densification occurs. For accelerations less than 1 g sand densification was not observed. It was shown by D'Appolonia and D'Appolonia that for one dimensional loading plotting the vertical strains as a function of the number of loading cycles, low densification is due to repeated stress. Similar results are presented by Luscher et al. [718]. On the basis of the half-space theory, Sparrow and Tory [1170] gave correlations between settlement and density for evaluating the criteria for soil densification; such correlations were found by the stress-path technique of Lambe [661], [662] and were improved by D'Appolonia et al. [224].

In lack of test data for small strains in the case of time-independent linear elasticity, the minimum relative density was suggested by D'Appolonia [222] to be 70; for intermediate strains where the soil has time-dependent and elastic–plastic stress–strain relationships, to be 80; and for large strains, where stress–strain relationships are lacking and the stability bearing capacity is determined from limiting equilibrium, the suggested minimum relative density is 90. In most cases there is a possibility to avoid the application of energy absorbers by increasing the damping characteristics of the soil–foundation system by compaction to a depth of one and one-half times the average width of the foundation and in an annular distance around the foundation at one-half times the average width of the foundation.

The possibility of predicting the settlement of foundations subjected to dynamic loading knowing the limiting amplitude of vibration was investigated by Sridharan and Raman [1178]. It was found by model testing results that although the dynamic modulus of shear is affected by static load, the influence of dynamic load and frequency are less important and the ratio of settlement to amplitude remains at higher dynamic loads essentially uneffected by the frequency and the dynamic loads—which are primarily a function of the type of soil and the static pressure.

As for methods controlling vibrational settlements, it must be mentioned finally that it is generally believed that in existing machine foundations the reduction of settlement due to the combined action of vibration and static loads would require an increase in the dimensions of the foundation. Since this is not possible in most cases, the above-mentioned densification of the soil or stabilization can be used, for example, sand soils with chemicals or compaction with piles could be adopted.

For compaction with piles it must be mentioned here that Barken and his collaborators, Saichev and Smolikov, performed tests with short, wooden piles (3 m long) and found that after using these piles vibrational settlement decreased with loess soils to 1/10 and with dense sand even to 1/30 of the original value.

Piles driven into the ground not only reduce considerably the settlements due to static, but also those caused by vibration.

To summarize, we can state that while methods for the determination of the dynamic motions of machinery based on the elastic half-space theory (see Chapter XII. pp. 270 ff) are progressing and can be applied with some confidence, the generally accepted methods for predicting vibrational settlements are only in the course of development with the result that empirical rules are commonly used for prediction.

CHAPTER XI

DYNAMIC SOIL PROPERTIES
FOR DESIGN PURPOSES

Before treating the dynamic soil properties in detail, more developed knowledge of earth waves is necessary. The theoretical background and practical applications have been given, among others, by Kolsky in 1953 with a general survey, a summary by McNeill in 1969, by Richart et al. in 1970 and by Richart in 1975.

1. Earth waves

Waves most interesting for machine foundation problems are:
(i) Compression waves or B-waves (Fig. 175) depending upon E and ρ travelling with the velocity,

$$v_b = \sqrt{\frac{E}{\rho}} \tag{346}$$

propagated in columns of material with induced particle motions in the travel direction. These are important in laboratory investigations, i.e. in vibrating cylindrical soil specimens in axial compression, where the mass density $\rho = \gamma/g$ ($\gamma =$ unit weight of soil).
(ii) Shear wave or S-wave inducing particle motions transverse to the direction of travel, with the velocity,

$$v_s = \sqrt{\frac{G}{\rho}} \tag{347}$$

travelling inside the earth mass between boundaries of layers including the surface of the ground. This velocity does not depend on Poisson's ratio as shown in Fig. 175 where the relationship between wave velocities is given after Richart [1022] and others.
(iii) Dilatational waves or P-waves (Fig. 175), which induce partial motion in the direction of travel with the velocity,

$$v_P = \sqrt{\frac{E}{\rho} \frac{1-v}{(1-2v)(1+v)}} \tag{348}$$

travelling also inside the soil mass as shear waves, but these are the fastest of all earth waves ($v =$ Poisson's ratio).

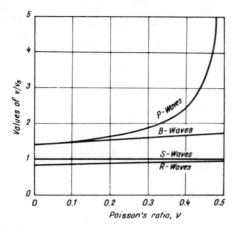

Fig. 175. Relationship between wave velocities after Richart [1022] and others

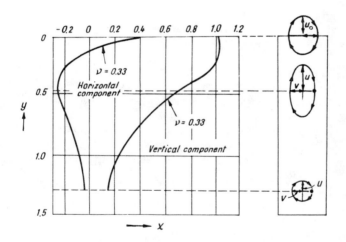

Fig. 176. Character of Raleigh wave after Kolsky [613] and others in case of $v = 0.33$

x—amplitude at depth/amplitude at surface, y—depth/wavelength

(iv) The most important earth wave is the Raleigh wave or R-wave (Fig. 176) which travels with large amplitude near the surface of the ground inducing particle motions in the form of a vertical ellipse, with the velocity,

$$v_r = v_s f(v) \qquad (349)$$

R-waves decrease rapidly with depth and at a depth of one wavelength their motion is considerably less than at the surface. It is assumed in practice that $v_r = v_s$.

Wave propagation below a circular footing is shown in Fig. 177.

Dynamic soil properties are investigated both in laboratory (A) and field (B) tests and soil dynamic investigations are also possible by means of models tests such as, for example, by holography (C).

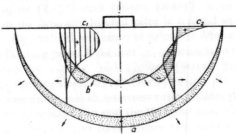

Fig. 177. Wave propagation below a circular footing, after Woods [1343] and Gerb [368].

a—compression wave, b—shear wave, c_1—vertical Raleigh wave, c_2—horizontal Raleigh wave

A) LABORATORY TESTS

Among the laboratory tests the resonant vibration of columns of soil is the most used test. These tests have been described by Shannon et al. (1959), Wilson and Dietrich (1960), Hardin and Richart (1963), Hardin and Black (1966), Drnevich et al. (1967), Humphries and Wahls (1968), Richart et al. (1970), and by Richart (1975).

The wave propagation tests based on laboratory investigation are less popular due to the complexities of the pulse propagation as described by Lawrence in 1961, and 1963; and, using 1.5 m long specimens, by McNeill in 1966. Work on this theme was also done by Afifi in 1970 and by Anderson in 1974.

B) FIELD TESTS

Field tests are based on wave propagation and on models.

Wave propagation field tests use seismic methods for two kind of tests:

(i) Transient tests by measuring the transit time of the induced wave between two points. *P*-waves are, for instance, created by impact or blasting on the surface and the reflections or refractions are sensed by detectors at a given distance from the disturbance. *S*-waves can be investigated, for instance, on the surface using horizontally placed seismographs for the measurement of a hammer effect on a plate in an excavated trench. For the measurement of shear wave velocity at various depths inside the soil, the cross-hole method can be applied. Here in the first hole an impulse rod is used which transmits vertical velocities excited by a transducer while in a second hole a vertical velocity transducer detects the path of the body velocities by means of a second rod. With this arrangement the excited waves are easily shown on an oscilloscope placed above the ground. Resonant column tests were compared with these test results by Richart in 1975 [1023]. Although the cross-hole method refers only to undisturbed soil without any modifications due to the disturbance caused by the built-in construction, the results are in good agreement. Particularly for cohesive soils the v_s values are lower than in the case of laboratory tests and the difference can be minimized if the second effect is included as shown by Anderson in 1974 [29] and Anderson and Woods in 1975 [30]. More details are given on the application of the cross-hole method by Schwarz and Musser in 1971 [1113], by Stokoe and Woods in 1972 [1204], and by Anderson and Woods in 1975 [30].

(ii) Steady-state tests by which vertical oscillators are applied at the ground surface. Miller and Pursey [833] determined the total input energy between different wave forms and found that the most important among the three waves (R-wave, S-wave and bar-wave) is the Raleigh wave with 67 per cent of the total energy, with 26 per cent shear wave and 7 per cent compression or bar-wave. For deep soil investigations heavy vibrating-mass exciters must be used, as in the case of the WES investigations, reported by Fry [340].

Field tests based on models are the small vibrator-plate tests and the cube tests. Plate bearing tests are also applied though these are less useful because they must be cycled about the expected dead load and in the evaluation of the data an assumption must be made as to whether the soil is cohesive or non-cohesive. The most used test form is the small vibrator-plate test using an electrodynamical vibrator on a small plate. Cube tests are useful and can be carried out on the site. The method is to cast a cube of concrete and pluck it in different modes. By observing the decay of the vibrations, stiffness can be calculated. The depths of the model footing are between 1 and 3 m. The vibrational effects are measured by seismographs and as it is possible to back-compute the average properties, this method is also useful in anisotropic soils. Static plate load tests are seldom used nowadays since the application of this test requires the live load to be cycled many times.

Both laboratory and field techniques are used in practice.

As for the analysis of wave propagation in soils, further methods have been developed. In the case of elastic suppositions or for viscoelastic behaviour, exact theories such as the finite element method are suitably applied, but if the problem includes permanent plastic deformations of soils the method of characteristics is the one to be mentioned. This method was proposed as early as in 1933 by Westergard [1314], described by Newmark and Rosenblueth in 1971 [882], applied to one-and two-dimensional problems by Papadakis in 1973 [922], and by Streeter, Wylie and Richart in 1974 [1208]. For the case of the excitation at the base of the soil layer and calculating thereby the soil mass at the surface, the application of the method of characteristics is shown by Richart [1023].

The lattice-work method should also be mentioned for the calculation of two-and three-dimensional transients replacing the use of one-dimensional elements by Streeter and Wylie in 1968 [1207]. Introducing a deformable transfer element, a two-dimensional representation of the continuum was obtained by Papadakis in 1973 [922]. Two-dimensional solutions are progressing further, as reported in 1975 by Richart [1023].

C) TESTS USING HOLOGRAPHY

Holography, lenseless photography, can be used as a means of wavefront reconstruction after Leith and Upatnieks [676]. A coherent light beam is produced by a laser and divided into the object beam and a reference beam as shown by Woods et al. [1344] and Fig. 178a, where an object is shown on a developed photographic plate. If, as according to Fig. 178b, the hologram is illuminated only by the reference beam it is possible to reconstruct the original object beam and by

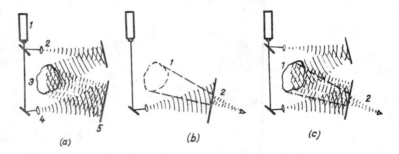

Fig. 178. Process of holography after Woods et al. [1344].

(a) object shown on a developed photographic plate (1—laser, 2—object beam, 3—object, 4—reference beam, 5—hologram), (b) hologram illuminated by the reference beam only (1—virtual image, 2—viewer of camera); (c) hologram illuminated only by the reference beam (1—deformed object, 2—viewer of camera)

looking through the hologram a virtual image of the object can be observed. It is possible in this way to store a wavefront and reconstruct it at any time. It is also possible to interfere with a new wavefront from the investigated object after the deformation as shown in Fig. 178c. First an exposure of the photographic plate is made (but not developed) following the procedure shown in Fig. 178a, and after the deformation of the object the reexposure of the plate is developed.

The undeformed and the deformed wavefront interference patterns are both stored in the hologram and the photograph of this double exposure is an interferogram. Such interferograms of the different wavefronts will result in dark and light fringes on or near the object. Using the double exposure hologram illuminated by the reference beam as shown in Fig. 178b, it will be possible to observe the virtual image of the object with fringes as superimposed equal displacements. The method developed as holographic interferometry can be used to make interferograms in dynamic investigations as shown by Ennos and Archbold [304], by Orr et al. [914] by Sampson [1065] and [1066] and by Brooks et al. [132] as quoted by Woods et al. [1344], shown by Richart [1023] and applied for studying the screening or isolation effectiveness of several types of barriers with results as given in Vol. IV, Chapter I on pp. 62–67.

2. Main soil properties for analytical purposes

There are three main soil properties necessary for analytical purposes. These are the shear modulus (G), the Poisson's ratio (v) and the mass density (ρ) of the soil. Information about the internal damping of the soil can also be of help. The value of Young's modulus (E) being equally of importance can be derived according to

$$E = 2G(1+v) \tag{350}$$

from the values of G and v

A) SHEAR MODULUS

There are different methods for the calculation of the shear modulus G:
  (i) From the velocity of the shear waves the relation:

$$G = \rho \cdot v_v^2 \tag{351}$$

where ρ, the mass density of the soil $= \dfrac{\gamma}{g}$, being the unit weight of the soil and g the acceleration of gravity.

  (ii) From the velocity of the Raleigh wave (v_R) similarly to method (i) because for the range of values of Poisson's ratio for soils $v_s = v_R$. Hence

$$G = \rho \cdot v_R^2 \tag{352}$$

  (iii) From the velocity of pressure waves, (v_p), in the soil by the following relationship:

$$G = \frac{v_p \cdot \rho \cdot (1 - 2\gamma)}{2(1-v)} \tag{353}$$

  (iv) If the dynamic Young's modulus (E) of the soil is given, G may also be calculated according to:

$$G = \frac{E}{2(1-v)} \tag{354}$$

Besides the methods detailed above, there are also empirical relations for G for sandy and clay soil materials depending upon the void ratio and the average confining pressure of the soil (see Hardine and Black in 1966), and for kaolite series (see Humphries and Wahls in 1968).

Measurement methods for density and compressional waves are well known. Procedures for obtaining shear velocity aspecially for seismic waves are given by Mooney [840] together with the relevant literature.

B) POISSON'S RATIO

As for the selection of Poisson's ratio of soils using the main values of the different findings it is enough to take the following values for the various types of soils, taking into account that the results in the analysis because of the effects of an error in v upon the results of analysis, are insignificant:

Cohesionless soils:	0.25–0.35 (0.33)
Cohesive soils:	0.35–0.45 (0.40)

The values in the parentheses may be used as a good approximation in the analysis.

As for the spring constants, and for factors affecting the spring constants, the geometric and internal damping, detailed data are given in Chapter XII

DESIGN METHODS FOR DYNAMICALLY LOADED FOUNDATIONS

1. Tendencies relating to the study of the interaction of soil and foundation

If the methods of design for dynamically loaded foundations are reviewed the related studies may be characterized by the following:

During the period 1928–1936 DEGEBO carried out studies that were first described by Hertwig, Früh and Lorenz in 1933. Later on, between 1950 and 1953, and using the graphical method of Den Hartog (1947) and the apparatus described in Chapter VII—supposing a single-degree-of-freedom system—Lorenz observed a nonlinear response and it was stated that using a mass–spring–dashpot system, the damping constant was completely different in the different tests. It was supposed that a mass of soil moved with the footing but it was found that this mass varied with the dead load, exciting force, base plate area, mode of vibration and with the type of soil upon which the vibrator rested. The supposition of such a quasi co-vibrating soil appeared in the publications of Barkan as a result of some fundamental large-scale experiments in nearly the same period.

The base surfaces of the foundations he used were 2.4 and 8 m^2. According to his results the quasi-participating mass of the soil is by no means negligible and it is from 2/3 to 1/2 that of the foundations. This mass is, however, much smaller than the values suggested by DEGEBO for the quasi-participating soil mass: 4 to 10 times that of the foundation depending upon the mass of the latter. Let us assume that the foundation system is similar to a system supported by a spring. [See Fig. 179a and 179b where m represents the mass and m_0 the mass participating like a spring, but not the effective mass of the spring. The natural frequency of the system supported by a spring of mass m_0 is lower (Fig. 179a) than that of the system which is assumed to be supported by a spring without mass (Fig. 179b).]

The natural frequency will be as follows:

Example *a*
$$n = \frac{1}{2\pi} \sqrt{\frac{c}{m}}$$

Example *b*
$$n = \frac{1}{2\pi} \sqrt{\frac{c}{m+m_0}}$$

Variations in mass m have but little effect on the natural frequency when m_0 is large in relation to m. The magnitude of m_0 varies because the stiffness coefficient c is not constant.

According to experiments by Andrew and Crockett, as well as by Crockett and Hammond [212], and later, by Rao and Balakrishna [991] the natural frequency of the quasi-participating soil mass does not depend on the dimensions of the foundation. This statement would be true if the stiffness of the soil remained the same whatever the size of the foundation; this would also be true if any increase in the size of the foundation were accompanied by a reduction in soil stiffness.

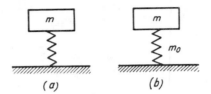

Fig. 179. Masses supported by springs
a—spring without mass, b—spring of mass m_0

With a base plate of small surface the natural frequency of the soil could not remain unchanged unless the participating soil mass were large, i.e. if the foundations were sunk to a depth equal to the several times the width of the foundation. This however, would be impracticable. Crockett and Hammond obtained their results—in all probability—because the relation between the weight and the size chosen was such that it produced nearly equal frequencies under various experimental conditions. It is generally assumed that the size of the participating soil mass is related to the bulb-shaped stress distribution curve mentioned already, which results in elastic ground under the effect of a uniformly distributed load.

Later, in 1965, Awajobi and Grootenhuis [51], and in 1962 Hsieh [485] also supposed the action of an "in phase mass". More details will be given about the results of this supposition later on when treating the theories of the "elastic half space".

A method based entirely on experience is the procedure introduced by Tschebotarioff and Ward in 1948 [1269]. Here a logarithmic relationship was supposed between the base surface area of the foundation and the reduced frequency. It is well known that

$$n = \frac{1}{2\pi} \sqrt{\frac{c}{m}} \tag{355}$$

By substituting for m in the above equation the value

$$\frac{G+G_0}{g}$$

where G is the weight of the foundation,

G_0 the weight of the co-vibrating soil mass,
the natural frequency is obtained as:

$$n = \frac{1}{2\pi} \sqrt{\frac{cg}{G + G_0}} \qquad (356)$$

Denoting the compression modulus of the soil by C_z and the base surface area by F, then $c = C_z F$.

Hence

$$n = \frac{1}{2\pi} \sqrt{\frac{C_z F g}{G + G_0}} \qquad (357)$$

or

$$n = \frac{1}{2\pi} \sqrt{\frac{C_z g}{1 + \frac{G_0}{G}}} \sqrt{\frac{F}{G}} = \frac{1}{\sqrt{o}} n_r \qquad (358)$$

where σ is soil stress,

  n_r the reduced natural frequency.

For the determination of the natural frequency in silty sand soil consisting of very fine particles Kézdi [563] made experiments with a vibrating equipment with interchangeable bottom plates of different surface area with results of measurements at six different points. He arrived at the following conclusions:

(i) The natural frequency of the soil varies between 17 and 20 cps and depends but slightly on the size of the base surface of the plates of the measuring points below ground.

(ii) With increased surface area the natural frequency increases but very slowly.

(iii) Flooding of the soil by water slightly reduces the natural frequency.

Tschebotarioff illustrated his experimental results and those of Barkan, published in 1944, in a graphical form by plotting the reduced natural frequencies per minute against the base surface, as shown in Fig. 180. The series of points thus obtained are scattered about a straight line. The deviation of the points from the straight line can be explained partly by defects of the logarithmic scale and partly by the circumstance that the reduced natural frequency was determined in the same way for very different kinds of foundations. For more details see Tschebotarioff [1263]; also [1264] and [1265a].

On the basis of Tschebotarioff's assumption the Hungarian Institute for Geodetic Survey and Soil Mechanics plotted the linear relation between the reduced natural frequency and the dimensions of the base surface of the foundation (to a logarithmic scale) for both cohesive and granular (sand, gravel) soils as shown in Fig. 181. The results of the Hungarian experiments were good agreement with the above. Further attempts to solve the problem were made by Eastwood, by Slade, by Pauw, all in 1953 and by Polz in 1956. The publications of Goyal and Singh in 1960, and taking into consideration the surface (Raleigh) waves, the work of Jones in 1958 and Foster

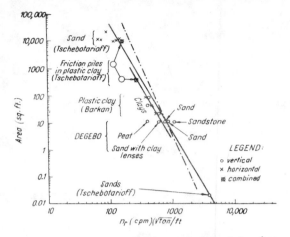

Fig. 180. Reduced natural frequency vs loaded surface

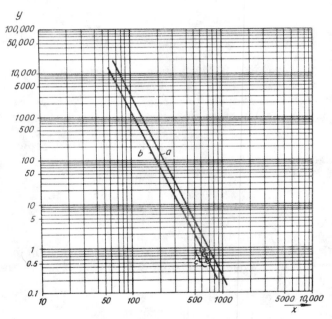

Fig. 181. Reduced natural frequency vs base area in various types of soil

x—reduced natural frequency per minute. y—surface area, in m²; a—granular soil (sand gravel), b—cohesive soil, c—results of Hungarian experiments

in 1960 should also be mentioned. Effects of soil resonance on machine foundations were studied in the light of the above papers by Alpan in 1961 followed by the discussion of F. E. Richart.

Based on the approximative expression of the quasi-participating soil a combined formula was treated by Lorenz in 1960 based on suggestions of Shekhter (1948) and of Novak (1957) for the determination of the dynamic modulus C_z of the soil in the soil in the vertical direction, viz:

$$C_z = \frac{\omega^2 m (1 + \beta \cdot F)^{4/3}}{F} \tag{359}$$

where the constant value $\beta = 0.835$ obtained experimentally was introduced (in dimensions t and m).

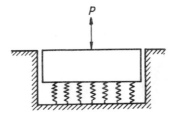

Fig. 182. Spring series replacing soil for dynamic subgrade reaction

Lorenz's approach considered a uniform load distribution only with the assumption that the exciting force of the vibrator is independent of its frequency. The main characteristics of Lorenz's findings were that: the variables of the experiments were Poisson's ratio, the modulus of elasticity in shear and the density as geophysical properties from which the spring constants and further the mass and damping can be determined introducing the constant base area F which is characteristic for the system.

Another method based on the dynamic subgrade reaction discussed by Hayashi in 1921 and by Hetényi in 1946 was introduced by Terzaghi in 1955. As shown in Fig. 182 the soil is simply replaced by a series of springs without considering the damping in the determination of the natural frequencies. Supposing that both model and prototype footings produce equivalent stresses in the investigated soil, the following values are indicated:

For cohesive soils: $$c_z' = c_{z1}' \frac{1}{2d} \tag{360}$$

For cohesionless soils: $$c_z' = c_{z1}' \left(\frac{2d + 1}{4d}\right)^2 \tag{361}$$

where c_z' is the coefficient of the vertical reaction for the dimension of the base of at least of $2d$, width of the beam or base;

c_{z1}' is the coefficient of the vertical reaction for the dimension of the base of the unit.

TABLE 34

Values of the coefficient of uniform compression for various soil types

Soil type	Permissible soil stress σ_{st} kg/cm²		Coefficient of uniform compression C_z metric ton/m³
I	below	1 5	3,000
II		3.5	6,000
III		6.0	10,000⁻
IV	over	6.0	over 10,000

$P_d = \alpha P_{st}$
α = reduction factor
C_z = coefficient of uniform compression for uniformly distributed vertical load
$3.2/\sqrt{F}$ = a magnifying factor of C_z for base areas smaller than 10 m²
F = base area in m²
$C_\varphi = 2C_z$
$C_x = 0.5C_z$

Establishing information for the c'_{z1} values by test data, the two formulae given above, i.e. (360) and (361), can be used for adjusting the subgrade coefficients which correspond to the dimensions of the prototype.

Based also on experience the method introduced by Barkan has been used extensively for the determination of the subgrade coefficients according to the following:

The theoretical determination of the actual coefficient of uniform compression is rather difficult.

In special cases field experiments are warranted for determining the actual value of c_z. Thus the equation for c_z gives only approximate values relying on results of experiments carried out with similar soils. Values of the coefficient of compression are grouped according to four soil types in the USSR specifications CH-18-58 given in Table 34.

Depending upon the permissible stress, soils are classified after the specification TU-127-55 as shown in Table 35. The classification includes also the ε values characteristic of the soil (see Chapter X, Section 3).

Compression moduli to be adopted according to stress are given in Table 34 after the specification TU-60-49. For soils in Class A of Table 35, deep foundations (e.g. piles) should be employed. In extreme cases a value $C_z = 2000$ t/m³ corresponds to Class B of the table. The value 3000 t/m³ given for category I in Table 34 can be used for soils of Class C in Table 35. For Class D in Table 35 a value $C_z = 4500$ t/m³, lying between categories I and II in Table 34 can be assumed.

For cases of $F > 10$ m² the values of Table 34 have been simplified and rectified in the USSR specifications CNiP-II-B.7-70 according to Table 36. Here the value of $C_\varphi = 2c_z$ was found as before. It should be mentioned here that the results obtained by experiments with the vibrator apparatus of the "Centre Experimental de

TABLE 35

Class	Type of soil	Permissible stress kg/cm^2
A	Peat and silt soils; Loose sands (void ratio: $\varepsilon > 0.85$); Fresh fills of clay, if uncompacted	1.0
B	Fine sands and pulverized of medium density, very wet, or saturated; Dense, saturated pulverized pulverized soils; Clayey sands and sandy clays; Loose plastic clays ($\varepsilon > 0.7$); Saturated loess (macroporous) soil; Saturated sand soils; Settled clay fills (at least 5 years old)	1.0 – 1.5
C	Sands of medium grain size and density, regardless of water content; Fine-grained sands of medium density and low water content; Fine sands of great density and high water content or saturated; pulverized soils of medium density and low water content, or dense and of low water content, further of very high water content; Plastic and hard clayey sands, of medium density and dense ($0.7 > \varepsilon > 0.5$); Sandy clays and dense, plastic clays ($0.7 > \varepsilon > 0.5$); Loess (macroporous) soils of low water content ...	1.5 – 2.5
D	Coarse-grained and gravelly sands of medium density, regardless of water content; Medium-grained dense sands, regardless of water and gravel content; Fine-grained, dense sands of low water content; Plastic, and dense, hard clayey sands, sandy clays and clays ($\varepsilon < 0.5$)	> 2.5

TABLE 36

Coefficients $C_z t/m^3$ according to the permissible soil stresses after Savinov [1079]

Permissible soil stress kg/cm^2	1	2	3	4	5
C_z t/m^3	2000	4000	5000	6000	7000

Recherches et d'Études du Bâtiment et des Travaux Publics", elaborated by Davance [233] have verified this supposition for the relations a/b according to the diagram of Fig. 183 for rigid and flexible plates. It was found further that $c_x = 0.7 c_z$ and that $c_\psi = 1.05 c_z$, in the above mentioned Soviet specifications. Values of c_z, c_x, c_ϕ and c_ψ should always be determined, if possible, by one of the familiar experimental methods. The values of the tables should be used only in the absence of experiment and should be treated only as approximate ones since the values are given here according to the permissible soil stresses and not according to the effective stresses of the soil types.

Further results of investigations are given in the following.

If two membranes of infinite strips of the dimensions a and b are supposed, and taking into consideration the crossing of the membranes of the dimensions a and b,

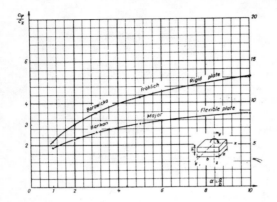

Fig. 183. Relations of C_φ/C_z for rigid and flexible plates

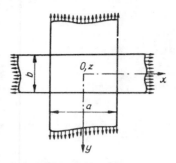

Fig. 184. Supposition of two membranes of infinite strips, after Savinov [1078].

(Fig. 184) the following expressions were published by Savinov [1080]:

$$
\left.
\begin{aligned}
C_z &= C_0\left[1 + \frac{2(a+b)}{\Delta F}\right]\sqrt{\frac{p}{p_0}} \; ; \\[2mm]
C_\varphi &= C_0\left[1 + \frac{2(a+3b)}{\Delta F}\right]\sqrt{\frac{p}{p_0}} \; ; \\[2mm]
C_x &= D_0\left[1 + \frac{2(a+b)}{\Delta F}\right]\sqrt{\frac{p}{p_0}}
\end{aligned}
\right\}
\tag{362}
$$

Here $F = a \cdot b$ is the area of the base slab, $\Delta = 1\ \text{m}^{-1}$;

$$
D_0 = \frac{1-\mu}{1-0.5\mu}\,C_0. \tag{363}
$$

Taking $D_0 = 0.7C_0$ and putting the value E (kg/cm^2) in the formula we obtain

$$
C_0 \approx 2.1E \cdot 10^{-3}\ \text{kg/cm}^2 \tag{364}
$$

The static pressure on the soil $p = G/F$ and p_0 is one reference value of the pressure determined by laboratory experiments on the soil for values of $p_0 = 0.2$ kg/cm^2 (soil pressure coefficients after Table 37 can be taken). The formulae given above are valid only for soils of a static soil stress lower than 2 kg/cm^2.

The modulus of damping is recommended to be taken according to Table 38.

TABLE 37

Coefficients $°C$ for different soils in case of $p_0 = 0.2$ kg/cm² after Savinov [1079]

No.	Type	Soil	C_0 kg/cm³
1	Soft	silt soils, loose sands, fills of clay	0.6–0.7
2	Slightly dense	slightly plastic clay, sandy clay, loose saturated sands	0.8–1.2
3	Medium density	stiff sandy clays, sandy clays, sand of medium density, fine sand	1.3–2.0
4	Hard	hard clayey sands, hard sands, coarse-grained and gravelly sands, rocky soils	2.0–3.0

TABLE 38

Values of coefficients according to Savinov [1079]

Type of soil	
Compact dense sands, plastic clays	0.004–0.006
Sands loose and medium density	0.007–0.008

According to Korenev et al. [630] the values of C_z, C_x and C are found to depend upon the relations $a:b$ using the following formulae:

$$C_z = \kappa_z \frac{E}{1-\mu^2} \cdot \frac{1}{\sqrt{F}}$$

$$C_\varphi = \kappa_\varphi \frac{E}{1-\mu^2} \cdot \frac{1}{\sqrt{F}} \tag{365}$$

$$C_x = \kappa_z \frac{E}{(1-\kappa_z\mu)(1+\mu)} \cdot \frac{1}{\sqrt{F}}$$

The coefficients κ_z, κ_φ and κ_x are shown in Table 39 for values of $a:b = 1$, for $a:b < 1$ and $a:b > 1$.

In the case of different soil layers, a formula is given by Jelen [529] for base areas with the dimensions of a and b and of the height of h_1 supplying a C_{ze} value equivalent for homogeneous soil

$$C_{ze} = \frac{C_{z1}}{n^{2.5}\left[1 - \frac{2}{\pi}\left(1 - \frac{1}{n^{3.5}}\right)\arctan\frac{nh_1}{D}\right]}, \tag{366}$$

where

$$n = \sqrt[2.5]{\frac{C_{z1}}{C_{z0}}} \; ; \quad D = 2\sqrt{\frac{ab}{\pi}}$$

Here C_{z1} corresponds to the first layer of the depth h_1 and C_{z0} is the coefficient for the second layer of unlimited depth.

TABLE 39

Values of κ_z, κ_φ after M. И. Горбумову-Посадову[387] *and κ_x after O. A. Савинову* [1059].

$a:b$	κ_z	κ_φ	κ_x
0.2	1.30	2.31	0.53
0.333	1.21	2.36	0.53
0.5	1.17	2.44	0.54
1	1.14	2.83	0.50
1.5	1.15	3.22	0.45
2	1.17	3.54	0.42
3	1.21	4.15	0.37
5	1.30	5.45	0.29

2. Theory of an elastic half space

The most popular method and the most practical is the model of an elastic isotropic halfspace. Although the soil as a rheological material has many properties, most of the properties are taken into consideration by the theory of this method, using the shear modulus, Poisson's ratio and the density of the soil.

Lamb's was the first paper [660b] about the existence of a homogeneous, isotropic, elastic, semi-infinite body treating the theoretical investigation of ground motions supposing minor tremors on the arrival of P-waves and S-waves, and major tremors on the arrival of the most important R-waves; it was published as early as 1904. Steady state vibrating force or impact loading was supposed at a three-dimensional point along a line, acting for vertical and horizontal loading at the surface, and for vertical and horizontal loading within the body. The vertical vibrating force at the surface has been the so-called "Dynamic Boussinesq Loading". Maxwell's law of dynamic reciprocity has been extended from the static case to the dynamic.

Based on the DEGEBO investigations Reissner [1015] was the first to find the mathematical formulation for the problem of a rigid body of circular area loaded by a system of vertical periodic forces.

The earlier mentioned Hertwig, Früh and Lorenz group [457] experienced many difficulties in their research to determine reasonable values for the damping characteristics from a single response curve. More difficulties arose in the case of several excitations.

Further progress was made in the problem in 1948 by Shekhter [1137]. Having found a sign mistake in the solution of Reiss she supposed the motion of the body to be equal to the average of the dynamic deflection in the middle and at the boundaries of the circular area, loaded uniformly.

The differential equation of vertical forced vibration caused by a force $P \sin \omega t$ is

$$m\ddot{z} + Re^{i\omega t} = Pe^{i(\omega t + \varepsilon)} \tag{367}$$

where R is the amplitude of the soil reaction on the foundation,
$\quad \varepsilon$ the phase shift between the disturbing force and the soil reaction.

When studying the effects of soil characteristics and the nature and displacements of the foundation, both Reissmer and Shekhter assumed that the settlement taken as a basis in the calculation of R, for an elastic circle loaded near the centre, is the mean of the settlements occurring at the centre and at the perimeter.

The values of the amplitude and of the phase shift are, omitting the derivation,

$$a = \frac{P}{Gr_0} \sqrt{\frac{f_1^2 + f_2^2}{\left(1 + \frac{m\omega^2}{Gr_0} f_1\right)^2 + \left(\frac{m\omega^2}{Gr_0} f_2\right)^2}} \tag{368}$$

and

$$\tan \varphi = \frac{f_2}{f_1 + \frac{m\omega^2}{Gr_0}(f_1^2 + f_2^2)} \tag{369}$$

where G is the modulus of sliding of the soil,
$\quad r_0 = $ the radius of the circle for which $r_0 = \sqrt{F/\pi}$ (F being the bearing area of the foundation).

With L_b denoting the wave length of sliding propagated in the soil

$$x = \frac{2\pi r_0}{L_b} \tag{370}$$

and the functions f_1 and f_2 assume the trend according to the curves indicated in Fig. 185. The value of x is plotted on the abscissa and the function values are calculated for the Poisson coefficients

$$v = 0; \quad v = 1/4; \quad v = 1/2.$$

If a coefficient b is introduced, depending on mass, dimensions and density of the soil, as

$$b = \frac{m}{\rho r_0^3} \tag{371}$$

where ρ is the density of the soil, then the expressions for the vibration amplitudes and phase will be altered as follows, substituting into Eqs. (368) and (369) the

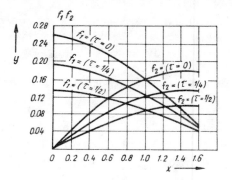

Fig. 185. Curves of functions f_1 and f_2 plotted
against x for $v=0$, $v=1/4$ and $v=1/2$

following values:

$$\frac{m\omega^2}{Gr_0} = x^2 b \tag{372}$$

$$\frac{aGr_0}{P} = \sqrt{\frac{f_1^2 + f_2^2}{(1 + x^2 b f_1)^2 + (x^2 b f_2)^2}} \tag{373}$$

$$\tan \varphi = \frac{f_2}{f_1 + bx^2(f_1^2 + f_2^2)} \tag{374}$$

If the amplitude aGr_0/P is plotted against x given by Eq. (370), as in Fig. 186, the diagrams obtained will be similar to the resonance curves of Fig. 83, plotted graphically for

$$\xi = \sqrt{1 - 2\left(\frac{n}{\lambda_z}\right)^2} \tag{375}$$

It can be seen that, though in the initial Eq. (367) the damping effect of the soil is not taken into consideration, the vibration amplitude is not infinitely large. It follows that even a body assumed as completely elastic has an apparent damping effect on the vibration amplitude of the foundation because the radiating energy of the vibrating foundation will be dispersed in the soil. The curves indicated differ from each other, depending on factor b. Thus they depend on the mass, the density of the soil and the dimensions of the foundation. In Fig. 187, where amplitude Gr_0P is plotted graphically against b, the diagram obtained is almost linear. In the presence of resonance, damping by the soil has but a small effect on the amplitude, the latter is then directly proportional to the static load on the foundation, and inversely proportional to the bearing area of the foundation. Shekhter showed that for equal resonance amplitudes, the apparent damping ratios and the coeficient of the mass increase depending upon the b value.

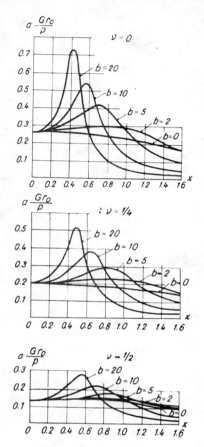

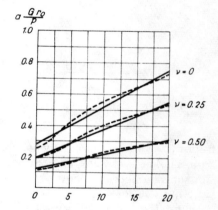

Fig. 186. Value Gr_0/P as a function of the disturbing frequency (x) with different coefficients b

Fig. 187. Value Gr_0/P as a function of coefficient b

Further progress was made in the half-space theory by Quinlan in 1953 [982]. He developed solutions for the rigid base case. For three-pressure distributions for the parabolic, the uniform and the rigid case—which were also mentioned in Quinlan's paper—Sung [1211] established the equations describing the displacement at the centre of the circular base area, thereby giving a qualitative picture about the contact pressure distribution for different Poisson's ratios.

The same problem is discussed for $v = 0$ (Poisson's number, see Fig. 186, top) by Arnold, Bycroft and Warburton in 1955; and further, for forced vibrations of two masses by Warburton, Richardson and Webster is 1955. The reader is also referred to the paper by Zareva in 1956 and the theoretical suggestion by Just and Heidrich in 1959 and 1961 for determining the natural frequency and amplitudes of the soil

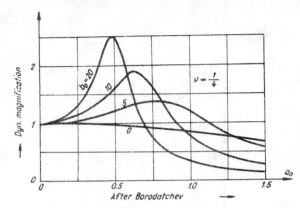

Fig. 188. Response curves of rigid foundations on elastic half space after Borodatchev [122]

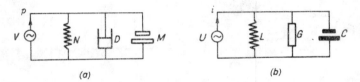

Fig. 189. Electric analogy for mass–spring–dashpot system after Scheiter [1092]

from the results of measurements and soil explorations as revealed by measured data. The method yields an accuracy of ± 20 per cent. In saturated soils having a Poisson's number of about 1/2, the amplitudes are reduced but this is misleading since in these soils a part of the vibrations is propagated to greater distances.

Internal friction in soil was taken into account by Bycroft (1956) showing that this effect can decrease the resonance amplitude in a massless plate. Warburton showed in 1957 [1302] the extent to which the magnification factor was affected by the ratio of the stratum thickness to the base of foundation. Without taking into account the stress distribution below the foundation Borodatchev [122–124] solved the contact problem of a rigid body vibrating on a half-space. The nondimensional response, shown in Fig. 188 somewhat deviates from the curves shown in Fig. 186.

Natural frequencies computed by taking into consideration the damping effect of the soil are about 10 per cent lower than those obtained by neglecting it. Since the error involved in amplitude calculations may be as much as 15 to 20 per cent, the damping effect in the foundation due to soil stiffness can be neglected.

In order to compare the above mentioned results by means of an electrical analogy—replacing the velocity v by the voltage u and the force p by the electric current i—investigations of the Research Institute for Water and Foundation Engineering (GDR) were published by Scheiter [1090]. Here, as shown in Fig. 189, the reciprocal value of springiness (N) was replaced by the inductivity (L), the

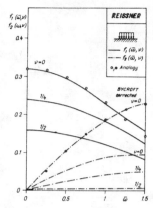

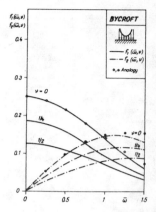

Fig. 190. f_1 and f_2 values depending upon frequency and Poisson's ratio relating to the supposed elastic half space

Fig. 191. For caption, see Fig. 190.

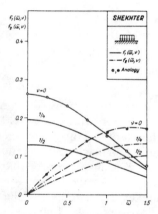

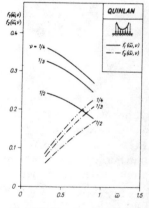

Fig. 192. For caption, see Fig. 190.

Fig. 193. For caption, see Fig. 190.

damping (D) by the conductivity (G) and the mass (M) by the capacity (C) as analogue quantities. Both cases are shown for a mass–spring–dashpot system in the figures. An electrodynamic exciter of Fig. 100 shown in Chapter VII p. 181 was used for model investigations. Rigid circular plates of 5 cm radius were used applying the well known differential equation (367) for the motion. It was possible to investigate by programming with an analogue computer the different results relating to the half-space theory. Using kaolin as a virtually homogeneous material in the first investigations good agreements have been found especially in the case of $v = 0$. In Figs. 190–195 the f_1 and f_2 values depending upon frequency and Poisson's ratio

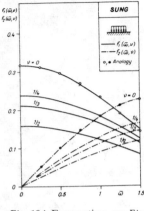

Fig. 194. For caption, see *Fig. 190.*

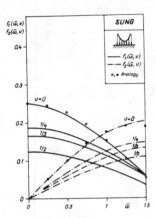

Fig. 195. For caption see, *Fig. 190.*

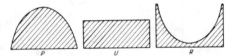

Fig. 196. Different pressure distributions

P—parabolic; U—uniform; R—rigid

are compared for the parabolic distribution of Sung, for the uniform distribution of Reissner, Shekhter and Sung and for the rigid supposition of Bycroft and Sung. The electrical analogue method seems to be a good tool for clarifying further problems relating to the elastic-half-space as model for investigations of machine foundations. Based on experiments on small full scale foundations and using as electrodynamic exciter, an approximative method—useful only in the case of cohesive soils—was suggested by Scheiter in 1971 [1091]. It was also found experimentally by Scheiter [1092] that if the relation of the two dimensions of a rectangular foundation is between 1:1 or 1:2 the same effect was observed as in the case of a circular foundation on equal superficies.

Three base-pressure distributions as shown in Fig. 196, the rigid, uniform and parabolic distributions of Sung, were investigated by Richart and Whitman [1025] according to Fig. 197 in full lines in the case of an exciting force caused by a rotating mass exciter of $Q_0 = m_e e \omega^2$, where m_e is the rotating mass, and e the eccentricity, supposing for $Q = 5$ and $v = 1/4$. It was shown that as the load is progressively concentrated nearer the centre of the loaded area, the peak amplitude increases and a_0 the dimensionless frequency corresponding to this peak is lowered. Supposing weighted average displacements, response curves according to the dashed lines of Fig. 197 were presented by Housner and Castellani in 1969 [480]. This supposition is well suited to the idealized problem and has led to flatter curves; but it can be

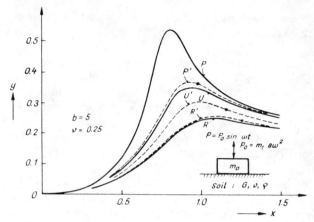

Fig. 197. Response curves for different pressure distributions after Sung [1211], Richart [1024] and Hauser-Castellani [480]

x—amplitudes, y—frequencies

stated that even the full line curves are suitable to present the trend of changes in the response curves showing that the theory of rigid base distribution gives reasonable predictions for the practically acceptable motions of the footings. It can be seen that the response curves for the weighted displacements are even closer to the rigid base case and this fact should indicate the possibility to the designer of influencing the dynamic response of his foundation by controlling the flexibility of the pad. Fistedis reported in 1957 [320] on the usefulness of this fact and on the adjustment of a prestressed concrete foundation by post-tensioning it, changing thereby the soil-contact pressure of the pad. For the effectiveness of such a procedure see further details in Volume III p. 286. It can be stated generally, that in the case of the supposition of an elastic half space the loss of energy due to the radiation of the elastic waves—the so-called geometric damping—does not allow the existence of high amplitudes of motion. In the case of vertical displacements for constant and rotating mass forcing functions the response curves are shown for different damping values in Figs 80–82, Chapter VI.

Expressions for the geometric damping were given in Hsieh's paper in 1962 [485] developed from the elastic theory where the equations were derived for a weightless rigid plate and for a block mass and the damping and spring-reaction term were both functions of the frequency of the vibration.

For the soil participation dimensionless units were derived:

For translation: (vertical or horizontal)

$$b = m_0/\rho r_0^3 \tag{376}$$

For rocking:

$$b = I_{\text{soil}}/\rho r_0^5 \tag{377}$$

For torsion:

$$b = I_{ps}/\rho r_0^5 \tag{378}$$

Here the mass moment of inertia of the soil is I_{soil} and the polar mass moment of inertia about the vertical axis equally of the soil is I_{ps}, and the radius of the foundation is r_0.

Another paper of importance regarding the theory of the vibration of rigid bodies on semi-infinite elastic media is the previously mentioned companion paper of Awajobi and Grootenhuis published in 1965. In order to compare the results of the experiments for vertical vibrations the formulae published were used by Novak in 1970. The vertical vibration on an incompressible nonhomogeneous half space described by Gibson in 1967 [376] in which shear modulus varies linearly in depth starting with zero on the free surface, was further theoretically investigated by Awojobi in 1972.

Further details on: dynamic stress–strain relations for soils; on laboratory methods for evaluating shear modulus and damping; and on the effects of test variables on shear modulus and damping including void ratio, confining pressure, shearing strain amplitude, time of loading, stress history and temperature are given by Richart in 1975 [1023], including approximated analytical expressions by means of a hyperbolic or Ramberg–Osgood [988] type curve representing adequately the test data for shearing stress–shearing strain as adopted by Hardin and Drnevich [427], [428] and shown by Streeter, Wylie and Richart [1208] in 1974; see also Pender [940a].

3. Vibration systems with lumped parameters

More developments in the theory of the elastic half space including its practical application introducing a vibration system with lumped parameters are due to Richart and Whitman together with their co-workers Lysmer, Hall, Hardin, Drnevich and others, who also evaluated the experiments of the large-scale field tests upon machine foundations published by Maxwell, Fry and Ballard in the U.S. Wicksburg WES Station in 1963–1967 and this extended the knowledge in foundation vibrations in the period of 1960–1970.

The WES tests were conducted on model footings in silty clay soil at the WES site, and on nonplastic uniform fine sand at the Egline site in Florida. Both test series used circular footings from about 1.5 m to 5 m. In the sandy soil on Eglin site the average confining stressure distribution from the footing load decreased with the depth according to the Pranges solution of 1965. The average vertical pressure σ_{total} may be taken from the graph of Fig. 198 as

$$\sigma_{total} = \sigma_{soil} + \sigma_{load} \tag{379}$$

where σ_{soil} is due to the unit weight of the soil and

σ_{load} is the stress due to the footing load. In depth d of the footing, the total average pressure is σ_{total}. It was further found that the vibrating body on sand tends to develop a "hard zone" beneath the centre of the footing; see also Converse's supposition of 1953. For vertical vibrations of the model footings the relation of the maximum acceleration to the acceleration of gravity g was

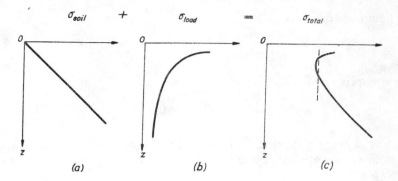

Fig. 198. Values of average confining pressures

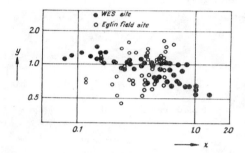

Fig. 199. WES investigation results showing the summary of 94 tests at vertical vibrations of model footing

investigated for 94 computed values with the result that the relationship of the computed values to the measured values was, on both sites, below 2.0 (at the WES site about 1.0) which is in good agreement with dynamic investigations (Fig. 199).

Although connected parameters in the field of vibrations have been used for decades in European practice the approach introduced in the United States defines rightly the behaviour of dynamically loaded foundations using the half-space theory for predicting footing vibrations by means of a "lumped parameter system".

The system was introduced in the paper of Richart and Whitman in 1967. Before this, in 1965, Lysmer had shown that a vibrating system on an elastic half-space could be represented by a mass–spring–dashpot system. The companion paper of Lysmer and Richart in 1966 followed Richart's original suggestion in 1960. A text on the method was published by Richart et al. in 1970 [1024]. This complemented the information published so far in these topics.

This system was introduced for harmonically excited motions in the near resonance state, i.e. frequency range near resonance, a simple damped oscillator defined by the well known differential equation:

$$m\ddot{z} + k\dot{z} + cz = p(t) \tag{380}$$

for the damping constant:

$$\frac{3 \cdot 4}{1 - \gamma} r_0^2 \sqrt{G\rho}$$

(381)

and for the spring constant:

$$c = \frac{4Gr_0}{1 - v}$$

(382)

In the above k is the geometrical damping of the system soil–foundation and the problem is simplified to a simple damped vibrating footing. The theory is a linear

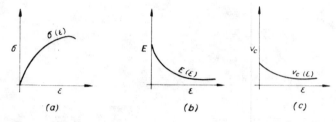

Fig. 200. Dynamic quantities depending upon strain values

(a) Relations of strain (ε) to stress (σ); (b) Relations of strain (ε) to modulus of elasticity $E(\varepsilon)$; (c) Relations of strain (ε) to wave velocity $v_c(\varepsilon)$

one, and acceptable, because the vibrations are small compared with the size of the foundation. It is supposed as well in the practical case, that the footing and soil always remain in contact—free jumping from the ground being excluded. The geometric damping precluding hysteretic damping or internal damping of the soil solely depends upon the three-dimensional geometry of the system.

Before going into the details of spring and damping constants in the lumped parameter system, let us investigate the problems of nonlinearity and the quasi co-vibrating soil mass.

Regarding the nonlinearity in the same period, footing vibrations with nonlinear subgrade support have been investigated by Funston and Hall [344]. Examining in Fig. 200a the strain–stress relation and further the relation of strain (ε) to the modulus of elasticity (E) being $E(\varepsilon) = \dfrac{d\sigma}{d\varepsilon}$ in Fig. 200b and to wave velocity (v_c) being $v_c(\varepsilon) = \dfrac{1}{\rho} \sqrt{\dfrac{d\sigma}{d\varepsilon}}$ in Fig. 200c the related curves are going upward and the variations have their maximum values at seismic strain levels or near zero. Because the wave velocity is proportional to the square root of the modulus it is less dependant on the strain level. Provided that the excursions of stress or strain are small, which is the case in the practice of machine foundations, linear elasticity could be adopted in the analysis. We know as well that the excursions in the resonance curves near the

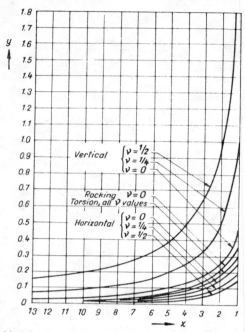

Fig. 201. Soil mass and inertia ratios for different Poisson's values after Irish and Walker [508].

y ratio of: Soil mass/Mass of foundation plus machine or Soil mass/inertia of foundation plus machine, where the ratios are non-dimensional, if the "massess" are inconsistent units. x $b = m/\rho R^3$ or inertia ρR^5, where b is nondimensional, if m, ρ, R, and ff are inconsistent units.

resonance are higher in cases of nonlinearity far from resonance. Therefore, although many efforts have been made in studying nonlinearity, (e.g. by Novak from 1957 until 1971 and by Ehrler in 1968 [290]) in the case of small excursions of stress or strain—as is the case of machine foundations in engineering sense—the linear elasticity can for the time being be used except for large excursions of strain or stress. Experiments on large blocks carried out by Maksimov in 1963 showed considerably lower damping than expected and in consequence the real magnification in the resonance range was much higher than expected. But for real foundations all of this is of little practical importance because the subgrade moduli do not change very much with the size of foundation base as is known from experiments as well as from Novak's work [897].

It should be mentioned that for the simplified estimations for predicting the dynamic response of the prototype footing–soil system—based on the WES tests of Fry [340], on those of Novak [897] and on Lysmer's [719] modified dimensionless mass ratio—a proposition was made by Sridharan and Raman [1178] with suitable tables for the rigid, uniform and parabolic distributions.

As for the quasi co-vibrating soil mass the diagram of Fig. 201 was evaluated after Irish and Walker [508] based on Hsieh [485], and Whitman, Richart [1326] for the

TABLE

Spring and damping constants for

Modes of vibration			Spring constants c	Equivalent radius r_0	
				All shapes of base	Rectangular base
	Vertical	$m_z \ddot{z} + k_z \dot{z} + c_z z = P_z(t)$	$c_z = \dfrac{4Gr_0}{1-v}$	$r_0 = \sqrt{\dfrac{F}{\pi}}$	$r_0 = \sqrt{\dfrac{a_x b_y}{\pi}}$
X–Z plane	Sliding	$m_y \ddot{y} + k_y \dot{y} + c_y y = P_y(t)$	$c_x = \dfrac{32(1-v)Gr_0}{7-8v}$	$r_0 = \sqrt{\dfrac{E}{\pi}}$	$r_0 = \sqrt{\dfrac{a_x b_y}{\pi}}$
X–Z plane	Rocking	$I_x \dot{\theta}_x + k_{\phi x} \theta_x + c_{\phi x} \theta_x = M_x(t)$	$c_{\phi y} = \dfrac{8Gr_0^3}{3(1-v)}$	$r_0 = \sqrt[4]{\dfrac{4I A_y}{\pi}}$	$r_0 = \sqrt[4]{\dfrac{b_y a_x^3}{3\pi}}$
Y–Z plane	Sliding	$m_x \ddot{x} + k_x \dot{x} + c_x x = P_x(t)$	$c_y = \dfrac{32(1-v)Gr_0}{7-8v}$	$r_0 = \sqrt[4]{\dfrac{F}{\pi}}$	$r_0 = \sqrt{\dfrac{a_x b_y}{\pi}}$
Y–Z plane	Rocking	$I_y \ddot{\theta}_y + k_{\phi y} \dot{\theta}_y + c_{\phi y}\theta_y - M_y(t)$	$c_{\phi x} = \dfrac{8Gr_0^3}{3(1-v)}$	$r_0 = \sqrt[4]{\dfrac{4I A_x}{\pi}}$	$r_0 = \sqrt{\dfrac{a_x b_y}{\pi}}$
	Twisting	$I_z \ddot{\theta}_z + k_{\psi} \dot{\theta}_z + c_{\psi}\theta_z = M_z(t)$	$c_\psi = \dfrac{16}{3} Gr_0^3$	$r_0 = \sqrt[4]{\dfrac{2I A_z}{\pi}}$	$r_0 = \sqrt[4]{\dfrac{a^x b^y (a_x^2 + b_y^2)}{6\pi}}$

G = shear modulus; v = Poisson's ratio; $\rho = \dfrac{\gamma}{g}$ mass density of soil

determination of the equivalent mass coefficient depending upon the dimensionless factor $b = M/\rho \cdot r_0^3$. It can be seen from here, that especially in the case of a rigid base pressure distribution in the case of vertical motion the equivalent mass coefficient above $b = 20$ remains very small, below 20 per cent of the foundation-mass inertia and can be neglected in the calculations. The same result was found for rocking and torsional motions in the investigations for values where b is greater than 2. These findings justify, in most practical cases, the recommendation in choosing the inertia of soil and foundation by neglecting the consideration of the "effective soil mass".

40

the six modes of vibration (see Fig. 76)

Mass (or inertia) ratio	Geometrical damping ratio	Damping constant	
		Considering both geometrical and internal damping	Considering geometrical damping only
$B_z = \dfrac{(1-v)}{4} \cdot \dfrac{m}{\rho r_0^3}$	$D_z = \dfrac{0.425}{\sqrt{B_z}}$	$k_z = 2(D_z + D_i)\sqrt{k_z m}$	$k_z = \dfrac{3.4 r^2}{1-v}\sqrt{G\rho}$
$B_x = \dfrac{7-8v}{32(1-v)} \cdot \dfrac{m}{\rho r_0^3}$	$D_x = \dfrac{0.288}{\sqrt{B_x}}$	$k_x = 2(D_x + D_i)\sqrt{k_x m}$	$k_x = \dfrac{18.4(1-v)}{7-8v} r_0^2 \sqrt{G\rho}$
$B_{\phi y} = \dfrac{3(1-v)}{8} \cdot \dfrac{I_{my}+m_s^2}{\rho r_0^2}$	$D_{\phi y} = \dfrac{0.15}{(1+B_{\phi y})\sqrt{B_{\phi y}}}$	$k_{\phi y} = 2(D_{\phi y}+D_i)\sqrt{k_{\phi y}(I_{my}+m_s^2)}$	$k_{\phi y} = \dfrac{0.80 r_0^4 \sqrt{G\rho}}{(1-v)(1+B_{\phi y})}$
$B_y = \dfrac{7-8v}{32(1-v)} \cdot \dfrac{m}{\rho r_0^3}$	$D_y = \dfrac{0.288}{\sqrt{B_y}}$	$k_y = 2(D_y + D_i)\sqrt{k_y m}$	$k_y = \dfrac{18.4(1-v)}{7-8v} r_0^2 \sqrt{G\rho}$
$B_{\phi x} = \dfrac{3(1-v)}{8} \cdot \dfrac{I_{mx}+m_s^2}{\rho r_0^5}$	$D_{\phi x} = \dfrac{0.15}{(1+B_{\phi x})\sqrt{B_{\phi x}}}$	$k_{\phi x} = 2(D_{\phi x}+D_i)\sqrt{k_{\phi x}(I_{mx}+m_s^2)}$	$k_{\phi x} = \dfrac{0.80 r_0^4 \sqrt{G\rho}}{(1-v)(1+B_{\phi x})}$
$B_\psi = \dfrac{I_{mz}}{\rho r_0^5}$	$D_\psi = \dfrac{0.50}{1+2B_\psi}$	$k_\psi = 2(D_\psi + D_i)\sqrt{k_\psi I_{mz}}$	$k_\psi = \dfrac{4.0}{1+2B_\psi}\sqrt{G r_0^3 I_{mz} 3}$

Spring and damping constants have been further developed based on the above mentioned large-scale experiments for horizontal translations, for rocking and twisting. For the six modes of motion of the block-like foundation of Fig. 76 the differential equations are given in Table 40 with the corresponding figures for the modes. It should be mentioned here for orientation, that the rocking and sliding modes of vibrations (including the coupling effect) were investigated by Hall in 1968. As for the spring constants it has been shown that the solutions for a rigid circular base are approximately the same as for the rectangular base of the same area $\left(\text{up to } \dfrac{a}{b}=2\right)$. Since the equations are much simpler for the circular footings, an equivalent circular footing will be used for the calculations of both spring constants and damping ratios. The expressions for the radius of the equivalent circular base and the equations for the spring and damping constants are also given for the six modes of vibration in Table 40. For the determination of the spring and damping constants in the compilation of Richart in 1962 and Whitman and Richart in 1967; for the vertical constants values of Timoshenko and Goodier in 1951 and Barkan in 1948 and 1962; for the horizontal constants values of Barkan and Bycroft in 1956; for the rocking values of Borowicka in 1943 and Gorbunov-Possadov in 1961; and

TABLE 41

Internal damping of soils

Soil type	D_i
Dry sand and gravel	0.03–0.07
Dry sand and saturated sand	0.01–0.03
Silty sand	0.03–0.10
Clay	0.02–0.05

for the torsion from Reissner and Sagoci in 1944 values have been extended for all possibilities.

With regard to the damping constants, there are two types of damping in the actual system that must be considered: one is—as mentioned above—due to the loss of energy through the propagation of elastic waves away from the foundation, the other is due to the internal energy losses within the soil due to hysteretic or viscous effects. The first is the geometrical or radiation damping and the second is called internal damping. Values for internal damping have been developed empirically by Hardin and Music [429] according to the expression

$$D_i = 4.5 \cdot \gamma_{xz}^{0.2} \cdot \sigma^{\frac{1}{2}} \tag{383}$$

where γ is the shearing strain in soil and σ the average effective soil pressure for dry sands.

From other typical values of Weissman and Hart [1309a], Barkan [67], Hall and Richart [410], Whitman and Richart [1326], and Stevens [1200a], Table 41 is given here for the internal damping of soils.

It is additionally mentioned that the torsional vibration of viscoelastic foundations has been investigated further, including the effect of material damping, thereby presenting a simple approximate analysis for a massless disc supported on a perfectly elastic half space; these investigations were by Veletsos et al. [1288] (this publication contains details of the relevant literature).

In the analysis, both the effects of geometrical and internal damping are to be taken into account. In other words:

$$D = D_g + D_i \tag{384}$$

The comparison of the typical damping value of D_i with that of D_g for the various modes indicates that for translatory modes $D_g > D_i$ therefore D_i may even be disregarded, but for rotational modes it may be of the same order of magnitude. This is why resonance should be avoided especially for the rocking mode because even the small damping present for this mode of vibration may result in high amplitudes of motion near the resonant frequency. Therefore for values of $B\psi \geqq 1.0$ and $B\psi \geqq 2.0$ it is advisable to ensure that the resonant frequency for rocking is well above the operating speed of the machine.

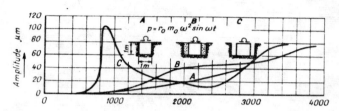

Fig. 202. Effect of embedment for different types of contact between the sides of the foundation after Novak [896]

There are two more factors to be taken into consideration: (i) the embedment of the foundation and (ii) the effect of a hard layer at a shallow depth below the footing.

(i) The effect of embedment was shown by Barkan [66]. Research results published by Pauw [937] followed an analytical approach to determine the spring constants and the apparent mass values assuming rectangular footings acted on by a uniformly distributed load. Both for horizontal and vertical contact surfaces the analysis supposed that the pressure from the footing decreases with the width and depth and is uniformly distributed over rectangular areas bounded by planes from the footing sloping outwards at a constant angle. Details of the investigations are to be found in Leonards [680] after Pauw [937]. According also to Savinov [1078], horizontal vibration amplitudes of a free standing foundation block having a base of 1.0×1.0 m at a height of 3.0 m were three times as large as those of a foundation having the same base area, but being embedded 1.60 m deep in the ground, but the increase of depth of the foundation extended in the direction of the disturbing force had no effect whatever on the horizontal amplitudes. Novak [896] studied the effect of the depth of the foundation under the ground surface examining also the type of contact between the sides of the foundation and the surrounding soil, i.e. whether the foundation was surrounded by undisturbed soil, filler material or air gaps. The differences are shown in Fig. 202. Koloušek et al. [610], supposing H for the depth of the foundation and h the height of the contact between foundation and soil, published the effects for different h/H values of 0, 1/3, 2/3 and 1 (Fig. 203). Whitman [1318] also concerned himself with this effect; the results of Kaldjian should also be referred to, for torsional stiffness [546], while Gereb et al. [371] reported on small and large-scale tests. In these experiments the relations h/H were investigated for values of 0, 1/4, 1/2, 3/4 and 1.

Baranov's theoretical solution [63] was considered as an approach to the dynamic reaction below the base of the foundation resting on a semi-infinite elastic medium while a system of horizontal infinitesimally thin layers was assumed along the sides of the foundation. It was confirmed that the effect of embedment increases the resonant frequencies thereby reducing the maximum amplitudes. This solution was further extended by Beredugo and Novak [90] in 1974, by comparing it with finite element solutions. In the case of hammer foundations a hemispherical footing

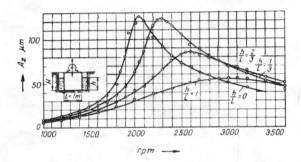

Fig. 203. Embedment effects for different h/H values after Koloušek et al. [610]

was assumed by Toshov [1256]. A more exact treatment of the problem, taking into account a finite element model with appropriate boundary conditions ensuring the complete absorption of the wave energy, was demonstrated by Lysmer and Kuhlemeyer [721] and by Waas and Lysmer [1295]. To explain the frictional effect of the footing with the surrounding soil, a lumped parameter model was supposed by Anandakrishnan and Krishnaswamy [27] in 1973 with the inclusion of a Coulomb friction effect supposing a constant frictional force P. Results of the related steady state tests indicate in general a decrease in the maximum amplitudes and an increase in the resonant frequencies; the field test data have shown a quite satisfactory agreement with the predicted values, and also compared with the results of Novak [897] and of Fry [340]. In his discussion about this latter paper Novak [900] observes that even in the case of embedment, the response curve of an embedded foundation is lying either below the response curve of the surface footing with dry friction or is crossing the corresponding curve of the surface footing thereby showing that the embedment does not act as additional friction only. It is emphasized here that some frictional damping tends to replace the radiation and hysteretic damping lost due to the lack of bond between footing and soil.

As a further means of clarifying the embedment problem, investigations aided by model studies have been reported by Stokoe and Richart [1203] for an air compressor and for two embedded vacuum pump foundations (see also Richart's work of 1975 [1023]). In the first case the actual magnitude of steady state motion was less than 25 per cent below that predicted for a similar circular foundation without taking into account the influence of embedment. In the second case this value was about 20 per cent. Similar to Kaldjian's work [545] and [546] all modes of displacement for circular and strip footings and depth to bedrock were also taken into consideration by Johnson et al. [533] in 1975. It is suggested that under certain conditions the static coefficients may be employed in the dynamic analysis involving soil-structure interaction. (About dynamic stiffness of circular footings see also Kausel and Roësset in 1975 [552] with discussions by Johnson and Epstein in *Proc. ASCE, EM4*, Aug. 1976, pp. 746–748.)

Summarizing with due caution the results so far, the partial embedment of the foundation tests tends to increase the effective damping by only 10 to 25 per cent. Neglecting this effect will result in remaining on the safe side.

We have seen formulae given by Jelen [529] for different soil layers. As to the application of the finite element method, investigations of Valliapan et al. [1279] should be mentioned. The investigations led to the conclusion that for the increased embedment of footings, the reduction in vibration amplitudes is caused by the apparent increase in soil stiffness. Only a slight decrease in the damping characteristic of the soil was found earlier; for a supposed model of Kameswara and Das Gupta the decrease in damping was found more important [547a].

(ii) The effect of a hard stratum or of rock below the footing reflects the elastic wave energy back to the footing thereby causing an increase in the amplitudes. This effect could be taken into account because it tends to increase the values of the spring constants. For more details, see Arnold et al. [44], Warburton [1302], McNeill [818] and Richart et al. [1024]. For both cases—embedment and hard layer—adjusted spring constants according to Table 42 could be used in the analysis. But these are only recommendations since the effect of embedments and those of a hard layer have not yet been fully clarified and more studies are needed in this area.

In the case of strong motions such as earthquakes the dynamic response of overlaying soil deposits on base rock, the pseudo-record of rock motion, the so-called site-consistent rock motion ought to be studied. A simple and direct method was given by Johnston in 1973 [534] with examples showing that the rock motion is amplified by the soil deposit in the transmission process of the motion to the surface of the soil.

We can state that the elastic half space theory remains a good approximation for the evaluation of foundation vibrations. As for small foundations, the soil layer should be considered as a half space. In the case of large foundations the soil behaviour resembles more a limited stratum than an infinite half space. The foundation response can be considerably affected by the depth of the embedment or by a hard layer below the surface of the footing.

To summarize the results, it is clear that the lumped parameter system could be accepted as a suitable tool for approaching the practical behaviour of soil and vibrating foundation by appropriate choice of the spring and damping constants and taking into account separately in each case the effect of embedment or of a hard layer since the soil inertia usually remains small enough to be neglected and the inertial characteristics of the system can easily be determined. However, an

TABLE 42

Factors affecting spring constants

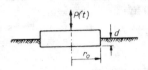

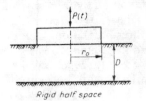

Rigid half space

Effect of depth of embedment

Effect of rigid boundary layer

d/r_0	n_e	
	No skin friction	Skin friction included
0.2	Negligible	1.2
0.5	Negligible	1.3
1.0	1.1	1.4
1.5	1.15	1.5
2.0	1.2	1.6

D/r_0	n_b
0.5	4
1.0	2
2.0	1.5
3.0	1.3
4.0	Negligible or ~ 1.0

$$k'_i = (n_e + n_b) \cdot k_i$$

where k'_1 = adjusted spring constant of mode i
k_i = unadjusted spring constant of mode i
n_e = adjustment factor for the effect of the depth of embedment
n_b = adjustment factor for the effect of rigid boundary layer
d = depth of embedded portion of foundation
D = distance between foundation base plane and rigid boundary

advisable way to obtain the best solutions for the machine–foundation–soil system is to analyse several alternatives using both the subgrade modulus solutions treated before and the lumped parameter system using appropriate electronic computer programs thereby reducing the time required for the analysis and design (see Vol. II, Chap. IV and Vol. III, Chaps. II and III). In this way one can be assured of the most suitable and most economical solution. The application for very large foundations necessitates more theoretical and experimental research. For further experiments see Chapter XIV Sec. 5.

CHAPTER XIII

PERMISSIBLE SOIL STRESSES FOR DYNAMICALLY LOADED MACHINE FOUNDATIONS

The stress in the soil due to a machine foundation depends not only on the maximum displacement characterizing the vibration, i.e. on the amplitude and on the frequency, but also on the static pressure to which the soil is subjected. The settlement caused by vibration increases with this pressure. Therefore the pressure permitted must be smaller than that permitted for static loads. The reduction factor depends on the acceleration of vibration. Thus for instance, for hammer foundations where the acceleration of vibration is very considerable—it may be as much as $1.5\,g$—a reduction factor of 0.3–0.5 must be taken. For machines of high speed (above 3000 rpm), where the amplitude of vibrations is only some microns (μm), a reduction factor of 0.8 is sufficient. Any reduction is unnecessary, i.e. a factor equalling unity can be applied, when the acceleration of vibration is lower than $0.2\,g$. Such vibrations are caused by low-speed machines. By way of summary, the reduction factors for the different types of machines are given in Table 43.

The use of a reduction factor is also indicated when the soil supporting the machine foundation is subjected to vibrations other than those transmitted by the foundation itself. The extent of reduction should be selected according to the distance from the source, i.e. it should be greater in the vicinity thereof.

For vibrations with considerable acceleration (higher than 2 g), *the permissible stress must be diminished in the proportion of* $0.2/\eta$ where η, as mentioned already, is the ratio of the acceleration of the foundation under consideration to the gravitational one. The permissible stress σ_s for the soil is, accordingly,

$$\sigma_s = \frac{0.2}{\eta}\,\sigma_{st} \tag{385}$$

where σ_{st} is the allowable stress for static load. In accordance with the above considerations, the empirical values dealt with in Chapt. XII were specified in the USSR.

Under hammer foundations, according to the specification DIN 4025, para. 3.7, soil pressures due to permanent load and dynamic forces acting in conjunction must not exceed the permissible values mentioned in the Code of Practice DIN 1045 (dealing with permissible loads on the subsoil and pile foundations). On the other hand, soil explorations are required for non-, or slightly cohesive soils (gravel, sand, silt)—which consolidate under vibratory effects—because of the danger of differen-

TABLE 43

Reduction factors according to machine types

Type of machine	Reduction factor (α)
Hammers	0.4
Reciprocating engines with crank drive	1.0
High speed machinery (turbosets)	0.8
Rolling mills	1.0
Crusher	1.0
Mills	1.0
Machine tools	1.0

tial settlement. When indicated, soil compaction or deep foundation methods (piles, or open caissons) may be recommended.

In the case of supports for revolving machinery actual dynamic forces should, as specified in DIN 4024, para. 2.26, be taken into account with half their value. For deep foundations these forces may be reduced still further provided that sufficiently low natural frequencies have been determined for the foundation.

CHAPTER XIV

THE EXPERIMENTAL STUDY OF FOUNDATION
VIBRATIONS

The theoretical results derived in the foregoing chapter were checked and proved by extensive experiments. These included the control of vertical vibrations, determination of the damping coefficient, investigation of vertical vibrations of foundations built on piles, the study of horizontal vibrations and studies relating to the further verification of the half-space theory.

1. Examination of vertical vibration

The first experiments to determine the vertical natural and forced vibrations of foundations were made by Barkan and Mikhaichuk on a 4 to 4.5 m deep layer of sandy clay soil flooded by ground-water. The water cover on the foundation was 20 to 30 cm. The experiments were made with large foundations, with base areas of 2.0, 4.0, and 8.0 m^2. The results of the experiments are compiled in Table 44. Natural vibrations were calculated with the aid of the coefficient c_z obtained by experiments made with static loads.

Figure 204 shows the resonance curves of a foundation having a base area of 8 m^2. The data were taken at various eccentricities of the vibrating machine.

Experiments like the previous ones were carried out by Barkan and Smolikov [69] on a grey, muddy sandy clay soil, saturated with water. The results are summarized in Table 45.

Table 46 indicates the results obtained by experiments on a loess soil. In these experiments the calculated natural vibrations were verified against the actual natural vibrations generated by a single blow and, as a further check, the forced vibrations caused by a vibrating machine were determined.

A comparison of the experimental and theoretical results reveals a fair agreement between the natural and forced vibrations obtained by experiment and calculation. Consequently, the results of calculations offer acceptable values for use in practice. Since the results were obtained in spite of neglecting the damping effect of the soil in the computation, this agreement additionally implies that in the examples studied, the damping effect of the soil was very slight. It should be noted, however, that the experiments were carried out with foundations laid directly on the soil, thus the damping effect of the soil could act only on the base area.

TABLE 44

Comparison of calculated and observed vertical natural frequencies of an experimental foundation

Area of the foundation plane	Weight of foundation	C_z from static results	Frequency of vertical natural vibrations	
m^2	metric tons	kg/cm^3	calculated sec^{-1}	from the forceed vibrations observed sec^{-1}
2	16.30	4.40	72.8	88.0
4	18.80	2.45	71.4	60.0
8	30.00	2.05	73.2	69.0

TABLE 45

Comparison of calculated and observed vertical natural frequencies of small experimental foundations

Area of the foundation plane	Weight of foundation	C_z from static results	Frequency of vertical natural vibrations	
m^2	metric tons	kg/cm^3	calculated sec^{-1}	from the forced vibrations observed sec^{-1}
0.5	3.26	3.5	72.5	72.8
1.0	5.10	2.52	69.5	69.5
1.5	6.70	2.1	67.8	70.2

TABLE 46

Comparison of experimental results obtained by two methods with results of calculation relating to the vertical natural vibration frequencies

Area of the foundation plane	Weight of foundation	C_z from static results	Frequency of vertical natural vibrations sec^{-1}		
m^2	metric tons	kg/cm^3	calculated	natural vibration	from the forced vibrations observed
0.31	4.30	14.2	162	158	159
1.40	10.60	10.8	118	113	107
2.00	10.80	10.3	137	117	117
4.00	17.10	8.2	137	118	121

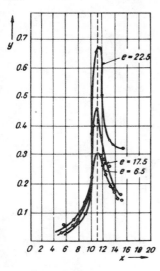

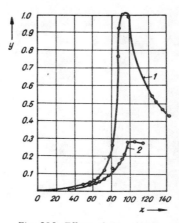

Fig. 204. Resonance curves of an experimental foundation of 8 m² base area with different eccentricities of vibration source. The above resonance curve shows the vibrational amplitudes as a function of frequency

x—frequency in cps, y—vibrational amplitude in mm

Fig. 205. Effect of damping on the resonance curve: curve 1 is the resonance curve of a foundation resting on the soil surface; curve 2 is one of a foundation embedded 2 m in the soil

x—frequency, y—amplitude

2. Experimental studies on the damping coefficient

Table 47 shows the damping coefficients appearing in the range of resonance for various foundations. The value of the damping coefficient depends, to a large extent, upon whether the foundation is completely embedded in the soil or is simply seated on it. Resonance curves obtained by experiments investigating this difference are shown in Fig. 205. Curve 1 is the resonance curve of a foundation laid on the soil; curve 2 corresponds to a foundation embedded to a depth of 2 metres. A comparison of the two curves shows that for embedded foundations, damping by the soil is considerable—about 3.5 times greater than with a foundation simply laid on the soil. For further experiments regarding embedments see Chapter XII.

Damping is also increased if the sides of the foundation are surrounded by ground-water instead of soil. The explanation of this fact is that the surface which transfers energy is increased.

The experimental evidence at our disposal leads us to the conclusion that if the elasticity coefficients of the soil were correctly ascertained on the basis of theoretical assumptions, then the difference between calculated and actual vibrational amplitudes, even in the zone of resonance, would not be greater than 10 to 20 per cent.

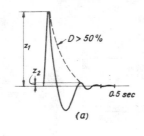

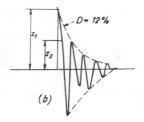

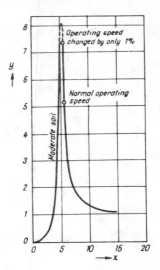

Fig. 206. Test values for (a) vertical and
(b) horizontal rocking modes after McNeill [818]

Fig. 207. Case story of a large
rocking foundation after
McNeill [818]

As for the calculated and measured damping effect we may stress that this effect depends not only on the contact pressure distribution but also on the mode of vibration. The rocking mode assumes a pressure distribution and the actual damping will therefore be less, the actual maximum response will be higher and the actual frequency of maximum response will be lower than the calculated one. As shown in an example by McNeill [818] in the case of the vertical mode (Fig. 206a),

TABLE 47

Results of experiments relating to the damping coefficient

Type of soil	Area of the foundation plane m^2	Weight of foundation metric tons	b	Coefficient I
Sandy clay, saturated with water	2	16.3	16.5	0.145
	4	18.8	6.7	0.133
	8	30.0	4.0	0.131
Silty, water-saturated sand with little clay	0.5	3.25	26.0	0.071
	1.0	5.10	14.5	0.058
	1.5	6.72	9	0.051
Fine-grained, dense, saturated sand	1	6.76	19	0.132
	1	0.82	20	0.190
	1	0.82	20	0.175
	1	16.4	55	0.083

the predicted damping was greater than 70 per cent, the measured one was greater than 50 per cent; the frequency predicted was 4 cps, the measured frequency was 5 cps. In the case of the rocking-horizontal mode (Fig. 206b), the predicted damping value was 9 per cent and the measured 10 per cent; the damping was predicted as 25 per cent against the measured 12 per cent. In the prediction the contact pressure was not taken into account. A further example was shown in Fig. 207 in case of a large rocking foundation also after McNeill [818]. Here the damping was calculated to be 3 per cent. Testing was hereby avoided, because it was to be feared that the foundation might fail running near resonance. Such low damping was disastrous for this rather unfortunate very expensive case.

TABLE 48

Experimental results on vertical natural frequencies of foundations built on piles

Area of the foundation plane, m^2	Weight of foundation metric tons	Data of piles			K_z from static results, kg/cm	Frequency of natural vibrations, sec^{-1}	
		Number of piles	Spacing of piles, m	Length of piles		calculated	observed forced vibr.
10.8	2.94	16	0.81	5.4	$153 \cdot 10^4$	227	201
8.6	2.25	12	0.81	5.6	$104 \cdot 10^4$	215	186
8.3	1.67	12	0.81	5.4	$105 \cdot 10^4$	247	235
6.5	1.96	9	0.81	5.6	$55 \cdot 10^4$	166	138

3. Examination of vibrations of foundations built on piles

Results of investigations of foundations built on piles are compiled in Table 48. The piles were driven into grey, fine-grained, saturated sand. When computing the vertical natural frequencies of foundations the vibrating mass was considered to include only the mass of the foundation. The calculated natural frequencies were found to be somewhat higher than the values obtained from experiments.

4. Experimental study of horizontal vibrations

Forced vibrations caused by a horizontal force were studied on an experimental foundation having a base area of 4 m^2 and built on brown clay. The resonance curve is shown in Fig. 92.

The experiment has proved that at points corresponding to principal frequencies λ_1 and λ_2 the amplitudes suddenly increase and resonance occurs. Static studies, necessary for the determination of c_φ were omitted in this experiment and therefore the extent of agreement between experimentally obtained and calculated λ_1 and λ_2 frequencies could not be established directly.

Similar experiments were made with foundations built on loess soil in which the values of c_φ and c_x were also determined and thus the calculation of the main frequencies λ_1 and λ_2 was made possible. The principal frequencies obtained by calculation and experiment are shown in Table 49. It will be seen that they are in satisfactory agreement.

Experiments in general prove that theoretical concepts agree with the results of calculation for free-standing foundations, according to the possibilites of shaping.

TABLE 49

λ_1 and λ_2 principal frequencies of foundations, obtained by calculation and experiment, for horizontal vibration

Area of the foundation plane	Frequencies calculated from static studies		Values found experimentally	
			From natural vibrations	From forced vibrations
m^2	λ_1 sec^{-1}	λ_2 sec^{-1}	λ_2	
0.81	174.0	58.4	65.3	48.3
1.40	181.0	73.5	73.5	64.0
2.60	140.0	65.2	69.1	50.2
4.00	167.0	89.2	77.8	54.0

5. Experimental studies regarding the further verification of the half-space theory

We have seen some data about experiments regarding the half-space theory (Chapter XII, Sec. 2). Further studies have been published by Novak (1970) [897] who found that prediction, in the case of very large foundations, is difficult as the soil behaves in these cases as a stratum or a layered half-space rather than a homogeneous elastic half-space. But, since practically speaking the effect of soil inertia is small in the case of real foundations, the lumped parameter system based on the half-space theory may be used for the prediction. Extrapolation of small foundation test results for large foundations remains uncertain and further investigations are desirable.

Investigations into calculated and measured vibration amplitudes by Moore were made in 1971 [842] using the small vibrator dealt with in Chapter VII page 180 (Fig. 97) and first found by comparison according to Fig. 208. Considering rigid base distributions, Hsieh's values were always smaller than Sung's values and for the intermediate values for $\nu = 0.25$ for a mass ratio of 4 the deviations were found around 20 per cent as the maximum difference. For many engineering purposes these agreements are acceptable. In was further shown in Fig. 209 that Poisson's ratio has little effect on the acceleration amplitude, deviations are found only in the case of decreasing mass ratios. Another comparison has shown after Fig. 210 that variations for both parabolic and rigid base stress distribution or in Poisson's ratio, have relatively little effect on acceleration amplitudes at frequencies in excess of 800 rpm. Most observed amplitudes generally fall in the vicinity of the theoretical curves. A further result was, after a discussion by Sankaran and Subrahmanyam

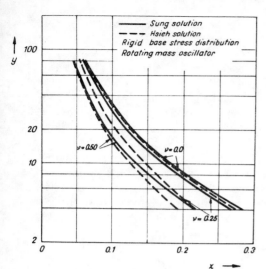

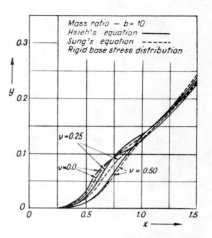

Fig. 208. Solutions for maximum displacement
amplitudes after Moore [842]

x—maximum displacement amplitude, y—Mass ratio b

Fig. 209. Influence of Poisson's ratio after
Moore [842]

x—frequency; y—acceleration amplitude

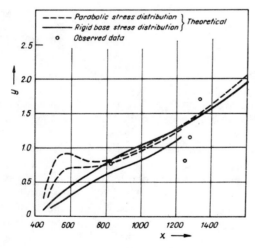

Fig. 210. Comparison of acceleration amplitudes after Moore
[842]

x—frequency, y—acceleration amplitude

[1068], that in the absence of direct measurements it may not be correct to attribute, a particular contact pressure distribution, such as rigid, parabolic, annular ring form, etc. to a given site.

As for the investigations into the inhomogeneous half-space in which shear modulus varies linearly in depth only starting with zero on the free surface, these were described by Gibson [376] and investigated theoretically by Awajobi [48] who concluded that vibration on such a medium will not be transmitted to the free surface except under the buildings from which the vibrations emanate; furthermore, they concluded that a dynamic subgrade reaction of the Winkler model could be used to obtain the amplitude response of the vibration. A finite element program was used by Carrier and Christian [166] to provide a solution for the stresses and settlements of a circular load on a half space defined by $E = E_0/z(D)^n$. Here the diameter of the loaded area is D and Young's modulus E increases monotonically with the depth z according to the power n at a constant Poisson's ration of $1/2$. It was shown that for the case of $n = 0$ and $n = 1$, there is no essential difference between a rough rigid plate and a smooth rigid plate. It was shown by Schiffman [1094] and by Gibson [376] that there are no differences between rough and smooth uniform loads for the same cases and therefore the roughness has no influence for intermediate values of n assuming that $v = 1/2$. Solutions for any value of Poisson's ratio have further been investigated by Brown and Gibson in 1973 [136] with the result that with an increase in inhomogeneity the importance of the Poisson's ratio on the settlement increases as well.

6. Experiments of vibrations by model vibrating tables

Foundations for high-speed machines and especially those for turbines are designed mostly as a slab supported by columns. With this arrangement vibration phenomena, i.e. the mode of vibration, govern the method of measurement to be applied and the selection of measuring points. Hence their determination is of great significance.

Highly instructive experiments with model vibrating tables were carried out by Herrmann [452] at the University for Communication, Dresden. In these experiments vibration phenomena are demonstrated visually. Model dimensions are selected to indicate even forced vibrations of small magnitude. Fibre-board is used for the upper slab, steel wire of 2 mm diameter for the columns, the base slab is of wood. An eccentric mass weighing 10 grams is mounted at a distance of about 20 mm from the axis driven by a small motor, the speed of which can be varied from 500 to 3000 rpm. Vibrations are visualized photographically, partly by time exposures, also by several exposures made on the same film. The photographs were taken by Mr. L. Kaster, Dresden.

In the first of these experiments the columns were fixed in a rigid slab according to Figs. 211 and 212. The aim of this test series was to gain information about the behaviour of columns subjected to violent vibration amplitudes. The lower slab was

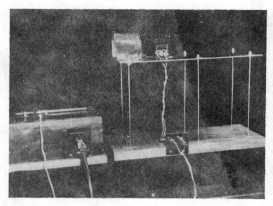

Fig. 211. Model vibrating table made of fibre-board and supported by columns of steel wire fixed in a rigid slab. A transformer and a rheostat for frequency control are to the left. Stationary position

Fig. 212. Movement caused by the operating motor is visualized by a time exposure made during vibration. Amplitudes are largest at the left columns. Simultaneous occurrence of horizontal and torsional vibrations

mounted on a heavy table with the aid of vices. The entire assembly in the stationary position is shown in Fig. 211. A transformer and a rheostat for speed control are to be seen to the left. Movement caused by the operating motor is visualized according to Fig. 212 by a time exposure made during vibration. As revealed by the picture, the largest amplitudes can be observed at the left columns. The protecting hood also shows signs of vibration. As can be seen, horizontal and torsional vibrations appear simultaneously. The upper slab is shown in stationary and in vibrating conditions in Figs. 213 and 214 respectively. Torsional vibrations appear in the latter in pronounced form. Although in the case of properly balanced machines, the

Fig. 213. Upper slab in stationary position
of the arrangement shown in *Fig. 211*

Fig. 214. Vibrations of the upper slab.
Torsional vibrations
occur in a pronounced form

amplitudes due to torsional vibrations are small, their analysis should not, as a rule, be omitted. Torsional vibrations act in phase with the horizontal ones and the vibrating frequency of the column is obtained by the superposition of the two movements.

Columns fixed at both ends are represented in Fig. 215. In order to obtain increased amplitudes, tension has been exerted by means of a thread on the edge of the upper slab. The bent form of the columns can clearly be seen. Three exposures made on the same film are illustrated. The time exposure in Fig. 216 indicates the case where the upper ends of the columns are not fixed but connected to the slab by elastic joints permitting free rotation. An inspection of the deformation line will disclose that rotational movements, although present, remain invisible, contrary to the foregoing photograph where they are clearly discernible. The deformation line is that of a cantilever, as against those of columns fixed at both ends and shown in the preceding pictures.

Summarizing, it can be stated that all kinds of vibrations may well occur in similar experiments so that no kind of vibration that may not have been recorded by oscillographs can be rejected *a priori*. Lines of vibration are closely related configurations to lines of deformation. Herrmann's experiments corroborate the design principle according to which undertuned columns are used in connection with rigid upper slabs and highly tuned columns for less rigid slabs. Hinges at column heads call for rigid upper slabs. Methods of measurement should include all

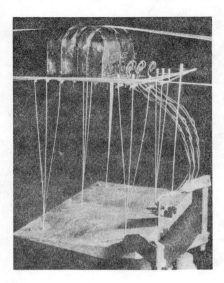

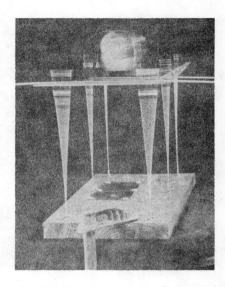

Fig. 215. Tension is exerted by means of a thread on the edge of the slab of the vibrating table. The columns are also fixed at their upper ends. Three exposures were made on the same film. Deformations corresponding to fixed end conditions are visible

Fig. 216. The columns are here fixed at their lower end only. Elastic joints permitting free rotation are used at the head. The edge of the slab is again pulled by a thread. The deformation line of a cantilever is shown by a time exposure, as against the one of columns fixed at both ends according to *Fig. 215.*

vibration phenomena since partial measurements yield no more than certain local information which can only be used with the aid of extensive comparison. The admissible means by which the vibrations were visualized has proved to be very useful for the study of different kinds of vibration.

PART THREE

VIBRATION TOLERANCES

CHAPTER XV

VIBRATION TOLERANCES

Due to the increasing importance of the effects of vibrations attention should be paid to vibration tolerances regarding the terms of limiting values of amplitudes, velocities and accelerations in mechanical and structural vibrations. First of all, the effects of vibrations on the human organism and on buildings, then the determination of these effects and the governing criteria in machine foundation design will be treated.

1. The effect of vibrations on the human organism and on buildings

Some mechanical vibrations are transmitted to the human organism by means of the sense of touch and are felt as vibrations. Slow vibrations from about 1.0 to 2.5 cps affect the sense of balance and the muscles, while faster vibrations (over 10 cps) are registered as pressure and vibration. The resulting psychological problems were discussed in full by Zeller in 1932 and 1933. If the frequency of the vibrations is more than 20 cps: the vibrations are felt by the human organism as sound. Vibrations having a frequency of over 100 cps are mainly noticed as sounds. The vibration of solid bodies is caused by periodic forces produced, for example, by machines, vehicles, by blasting or by natural phenomena such as earthquakes, wind, water, etc.

Vibrations may adversely affect the human organism and may cause harmful loads and stresses in the fabric of buildings. Protection against vibration involves the elimination or at least reduction of these harmful vibrations to a tolerable level at which they do no harm to the human body and will not cause excessive stresses in building materials.

The sensitivity of the human body to vertical and horizontal vibration is illustrated by the diagrams shown in Figs. 217 and 218 after Reiher and Meister [1014]. The diagrams have been found to be very useful in the investigations of various authors, see Steffens [1192], further [145].

It should be mentioned here that the human body can detect amplitudes of 1 μm; amplitudes of 0.05 μm can be detected by fingertips. In the Reiher and Meister investigations, vertical vibrations were detected when people were standing; horizontal vibrations were noticeable when they were laying.

In order to check the results, transient vibration investigations were conducted in 1974 by Wiss and Parmelee [1339] on a vibrating test floor in a test room with 10 persons measuring a total of 202 signals for each subject. It was found that for the

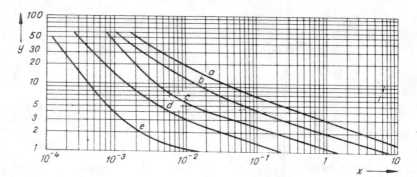

Fig. 217. Sensitivity of the human organism to vertical vibrations

x—amplitude 1 cm; y—frequency, cps, a—harmful vibrations, b—uncomfortable over a long period, c—easily perceptible to uncomfortable vibrations, d—perceptible vibrations, e—just perceptible vibrations

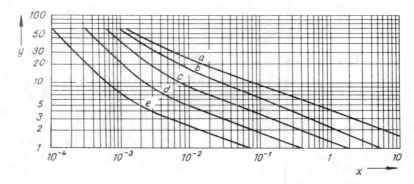

Fig. 218. Sensitivity of the human organism to horizontal vibrations

x—amplitude 1 cm, y—frequency cps; a—harmful vibrations, b—uncomfortable over a long period, c—easily perceptible to uncomfortable, d—perceptible, e—just percebtible vibrations

steady state conditions (zero damping) somewhat less perceptible vibrations were felt than during the Reiher–Meister tests, but it was observed that the transient vibrations of a particular frequency and peak displacement became progressively less perceptible as the critical damping increased from 0.02 to 0.20.

A factor characteristic for the effect of vibrations was given by Zeller in 1931. This factor, related to the mass point m, is given by the following equation:

$$\kappa = \frac{1}{2}(2\pi)\,4a^2 n^3 m \tag{386}$$

For unit mass ($m = 1$ g) this becomes

$$\kappa = \frac{1}{2}(2\pi)^2 a^2 n^3 \qquad (\text{cm}^2\text{sec}^{-3}\text{g}) \tag{387}$$

TABLE 50

Group		κ
I	Imperceptible	1
II	Very weak	2
III	Weak	10
IV	Moderate	50
V	Fairly strong	250
VI	Strong	1,000
VII	Very strong	5,000
VIII	Violent	20,000
IX	Destroying	100,000
X	All-destroying	500,00
XI	Catastrophic	2,500,000
XII	Highly catastrophic	10,000,000

For practical purposes the following formula may be used:

$$\kappa = \frac{b^2}{n} = \frac{[(2\pi n)^2 a]^2}{n} \tag{388}$$

whence, according to Zeller, the following value will be obtained:

$$\kappa = 16\pi^4 a^2 n^3 \qquad (\text{cm}^2\text{sec}^{-3}\text{g}) \tag{389}$$

Vibration frequencies classified by Zeller on the basis of κ can be divided into groups from I to XII (Table 50).

The first damage to buildings can be observed at 25 to 100.

Bendel [85–87] conducted numerous experiments on vibration and compared his results with those of others. On the basis of his research work and making use of the diagrams developed by Reiher and Meister [1014] (see the diagrams in Figs 217 and 218 and that in Fig. 219), he developed several tables containing rates of vibrations both for continuous vibrations and for vibrations due to a single impulse (see Tables 51 and 52).

Standards for comparing mechanical vibrations are given in the Directives of the VDI, and have been incorporated in the DIN Specification 4025, too. For the effect of mechanical vibrations on man the rate of physiological load K is introduced (graduated according to Table 51 from 0.1 to 100). The data contained in Table 52 are average values of informative character and apply to human beings standing upright or sitting, and to essentially continuous vertical, or horizontal vibrations. For intermittent periods of vibration, the next higher class of load in Table 53 can be permitted.

20* Major/I

TABLE 51

Scale of vibrations for continuous vibrations

Group	Acceleration $b = 4\pi^2 a/T^2$ mm/sec^2		Amplitude of the frequency curve[1] $C = an^k$ cm/sec			Factors[2] $x = 16\pi^4 a^4 n^4$		Pal-numbers[2] $P = = 10 \log \kappa/\kappa_0$
	V	L, Q	V	L	Q	L and Q		V, L and Q
1	$0-\quad 0$	6	5	6	6	$2-$		$0-\ 1$
2	$6-\quad 25$	25	14	18	12	$2-$	10	6
3	$25-\quad 50$	$25-100$	40	660	30	$10-$	50	$10-20$
4	$50-\quad 250$	$100-250$	528	4,740	375	$50-$	$1,000$	$25-35$
5	$250-\ 1,000$	$300-500$	3,000	24,400	3,700	$1,000-10,000$		$50-60$
6	$1,000-10,000$					10^5 to 10^7		80

In Table

    V = vertical components at vertical machines

    L = horizontal components at vertical machines

    Q = transverse components at horizontal machines

[1] $C = \dfrac{\text{acceleration}}{4\pi^2 \text{ frequency}}$

    $k = 1$ for $n \geqq 5$

[2] for $\mu > 5$, $A = \dfrac{1}{2}(4\pi^2 a^2 n^2)$ should be considered.

Note: For effect of vibrations on the human organism and buildings the values of Table 52 apply

A vibration evaluation guide is recommended by the ISO Technical Committee 108, [507] for the evaluation of human exposure to whole-body vibration. In this guide, separate limits are specified (Fig. 220) in the anatomically vertical, foot-to-head ($\pm a_z$) direction, and the horizontal ($\pm a_x$) with the x axis corresponding to the back-to-chest position and to the ($\pm a_y$) direction, where y corresponds to the right-to-left side position.

For practical evaluation purposes (a) the preservation of working efficiency, (b) the preservation of health and safety, and (c) the preservation of comfort are the three human criteria distinguished here. As to the working efficiency it should be noted that the most sensitive frequency ranges are 4 Hz to 8 Hz for vertical (a_z) and below 2 Hz for horizontal (a_x, a_y) vibration. For preservation of health the peak value of 1 g or about 10 m/s^2 is permissible; vibrations such as this in the vertical direction can cause the subject to lift off his seat or platform. To maintain comfort, approximately one-third of the health limit levels can be used. Correction factors (e.g. those of Splittberger [1175]) are suggested until more substantial data become available.

Detailed data on the effects of shock and vibration on man are also given by Goldman and Gierke in Vol. 3. of [435], with the relevant literature.

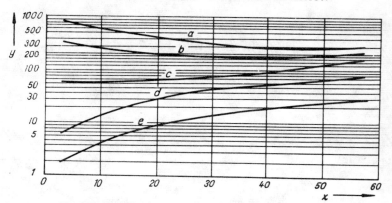

Fig. 219. Classification according to frequency-acceleration values

x—acceleration, y—frequencies in cps; a—certainly harmful, b—possibly harmful (uncomfortable over a long period), c—easily perceptible to uncomfortable, d—perceptible, e—just perceptible

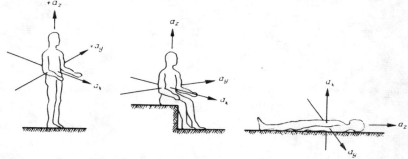

Fig. 220. Sketch for the evaluation of human exposure of the whole body after ISO recommendation [507] with coordinate system for mechanical vibrations

Coordinate system for mechanical vibrations influencing humans: a_x, a_y, a_z—acceleration in the directions of the x, y, z axes, x axis—back-to-chest, y axis—right-to-left-side, z axis—foot-to-head

2. Determination of the effects of vibration

The human organism perceives vibrations in a physiological way. The intensity of the sensation, however, depends not only on the amplitude of the vibration but upon its frequency and direction.

The effect of vibration is usually expressed by means of a dimensionless unit, the "pal-scale" or rather "pal-rate" as follows:

$$10 \log \left(\frac{v}{v_0} \right)^2 \tag{390}$$

where v is the velocity of propagation of the wave, and v_0 the generally acknowledged threshold value of velocity defined as

$$\sqrt{10} \times 10^{-2} = 0.0316 \text{ cm sec}^{-1} \tag{391}$$

TABLE 52

Scale of vibrations for a single impact load

Group	Scales				Effect of vibrations	
	According to the Reiher method	According to Forel – Rossi	Scale of seismic intensity (according to Forel – Mer)		on the human organism	on buildings
			grade	j	value of sensation	
1	0	I	1 – 2	0 – 2.5	imperceptible	–
2	Ia	II	3 – 4	2.5 – 4.5	barely perceptible	not destructive
3	Ib	III	5	4.5 – 5.5	easily perceptible	not destructive
4	Ic	III – V	6 – 7	5.5 – 7.5	easily perceptible and unpleasant	not destructive
5	IIa	V – VIII	8 – 9	7.5 – 9.5	harmful if of long duration	loosening of joints, beyond the tensile strength of the material
6	IIb	IX – XII	10 – 12	9.5 – 12.5	unconditionally harmful, lower limit of pain	destructive

1   the scale of Forel and Mer b denotes acceleration, $\log b = {}^1/_3 (j - 3.5)$, $j =$ intensity (according to Gassmann). For the Reiher method see Figs 217 and 218

TABLE 53

Rate of physiological load K due to vibration on the human organism

K	Description	Work
0.1	Threshold of response, commencement of vibration perception	undisturbed
0.1 – 0.3	Just noticeable, hardly disagreeable, easily tolerable	undisturbed
0.3 – 1.0	Well noticeable, moderately disagreeable if exposed to vibration for hours, tolerable	undisturbed
1.0 – 3.	Strongly noticeable, highly disagreeable, if exposed to vibration for hours, just tolerable	disturbed, yet possible
3 – 10	Disagreeable; intolerable, if exposed to vibration for hours, maximum endurance to be expected: one hour	strongly disturbed, just possible
10 – 30	Very disagreeable, maximum endurance to be expected: ten minutes	hardly possible
30 – 100	Extremely disagreeable, maximum endurance to be expected: ten minutes	impossible
over 100	Unbearable	impossible

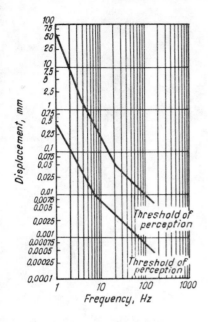

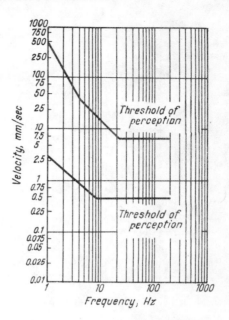

Fig. 221. Threshold of vibration perception and annoyance after Soliman [1161]. Frequency average values plotted against displacement

Fig. 222. Threshold of vibration perception and annoyance after Soliman [1161]. Frequency average values plotted against velocity

In the case of a sinusoidal vibration with an amplitude A and a frequency f' (1/sec) the effective value of the velocity is:

$$v = 2\pi f' \frac{A}{\sqrt{2}} \text{ cm sec}^{-1} \quad (A \text{ cm}) \tag{392}$$

The value corresponding on the pal-scale to the velocity $v = 1$ cm/sec is 30 pals. The individual values of the pal-scale are, according to DIN 4150,

up to 5 pals—barely perceptible
up to 10 pals—easily perceptible
up to 20 pals—very easily perceptible (unpleasant)
up to 40 pals—very unpleasant.

The threshold value of a continuously endurable vibration is about 5 pals, while for intermittent vibrations (e.g. due to traffic) it will be about 20 pals.

According to the Specification DIN 4150 "Protection against Vibrations of Buildings" the permissible amplitude A in cm can be determined either by the equation $An = 0.4$, or by $An^2 = 12.4$, the lower value being significant for the design. Accordingly, the following values are obtained: n, in cps and A in 10^{-1} cm.

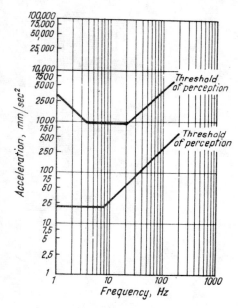

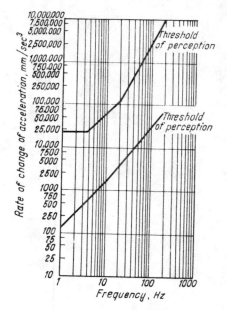

Fig. 223. Threshold of vibration perception and annoyance after Soliman [1161]. Frequency average values plotted against acceleration

Fig. 224. Threshold of vibration perception and annoyance after Soliman [1161]. Frequency average values plotted against rate of change of acceleration

1. Residential areas

(i) special residential areas, i.e. districts to be protected against vibrations, as for example hospitals and schools,

(ii) residential areas of average type.

2. Residential areas mixed with industrial plants.

3. Industrial areas.

In many instances vibrations are caused by rather complicated generating forces. The effect of these forces and the propagation of the waves in newly erected buildings can often be taken into account only on the basis of assumptions. Accordingly, the vibration conditions of completed buildings and structures are usually checked by means of vibration measurements and the results expressed in the pal-scale. If the threshold value of the scale is exceeded, adequate measures for protection must be taken.

At the RILEM Symposium, the First International Conference on Building Vibrations in 1963 Soliman [1161] submitted useful diagrams (Vol. I. pp. 119–122) summarizing the results of 10 investigations regarding lines of the threshold of annoyance and of the perception in the relation of the displacement (Fig. 221), of the velocity (Fig. 222), of the acceleration (Fig. 223) and rate of change of acceleration to the frequency (Fig. 224) being in good agreement with practical findings. Charts for

TABLE 54

Maximum permissible amplitudes of blasting
vibration after Teichmann and Westwater [1237]

Classification	Description of property	Maximum amplitude (thousands of an inch)
1	Structures of great value or frailty ancient monuments, churches, and some badly designed properties	4
2	Closely congregated houses, etc.	8
3	Isolated properties	16
4	Civil engineering structures	30*

* In very exceptional circumstances, e.g. for structures owned by the blasting company, an amplitude of 0.7 in. may be permitted

the pre-assessment of harm due to shock and vibration in building have also been given by Ciesielski [183].

Some empirical formulas have been elaborated further for the limiting displacements:

According to Postlethwaite [965]

$$x_0 = 0.076 \left(1 + \frac{194}{n^2} \right) \text{(mm)} \tag{393}$$

where n is the frequency in Hz.

According to Oehler [907]

$$x_0 = 50.8/n^3 \text{ (mm) for } n = 1 \text{ to } 6 \text{ Hz} \tag{394}$$

$$x_0 = 25.4/3n^2 \text{ (mm) for } n = 6 \text{ to } 20 \text{ Hz.} \tag{395}$$

Dieckman recommends as the limit

$$x_0 = 0.076/1 + \frac{125}{n^2} \text{ (mm)} \tag{396}$$

The results of these formulae deviate slightly from each other.

It should be mentioned here that displacements, velocities and accelerations have been compiled from 15 different sources by Gasch [348] showing considerable deviations from the limits.

Some data are presented regarding the blasting effect after Teichmann and Westwater [1237] in Table 54 where limit values of amplitudes due to explosions are given.

Finally for general orientation Steffens [1192] has given a table containing typical observed data from traffic, blasting and machinery (Table 55).

Summarizing, it can be stated that based on comparative investigations, the effect of the vibration limits on the human organism is of less importance than those with regard to buildings.

TABLE 55

Typical observed data after Steffens [1189]

Vibration from	Authority	Details	Observed		Reiher and Meister classification	Derived	
			Amplitude in	Frequency cps		Max. velocity micro-inches per sec	Acceleration × g
Traffic	Hyde & Lintern (1929)	Single-deck motor bus, 18 m.p.h. 30-ft. away	0.00012	26	just perceptible	19,700	0.0082
Traffic	do.	Light motor-van 13.6 m.p.h. 20-ft. away. Rough road	0.00012	20	just perceptible	15,100	0.0049
Traffic	B.R.S. (1934)	General traffic at Brentford	0.00012	19	just perceptible	14,300	0.0044
Traffic	Tillmann (1933)	Measurements in house 30–50 ft. from traffic	0.00025	24	clearly perceptible	37,700	0.0145
Traffic	B.R.S. (1950)	Vibrations from London traffic as measured inside a building	0.00014	25	just perceptible	22,000	0.009
Traffic	B.R.S. (1950)	Traffic measurements in Queen Street, London	0.00031	14	just perceptible	27,000	0.0062
Traffic	B.R.S. (1950)	Traffic measurements in Farringdon Street, London	0.00036	10	just perceptible	22,600	0.003
Railways	U.S.	Measurements of vibration in Times Building (N.Y.). Underground railway. Floor vibrations	0.00078	15–20	clearly perceptible	85,000	0.024
Railways	Mallock (1902)	Hyde Park area. Building vibrations due to underground railway	0.001	10–15	clearly perceptible	78,000	0.01

Railways	C.C. Williams	Freight train at 65-ft. Passenger train at 25–30-ft.	0.0009 0.0037	to 0.0023 to 0.0060	—	—	—
Pile-driving	B.R.S	Close to occupied building	0.00053	30	clearly perceptible – annoying	100,000	0.049
Blasting	B.R.S. & R.A.E. (1950)	Measurements in bomb damaged tunnel. No damage caused by blasting vibration	0.0015 0.00007	6 80	clearly perceptible clearly perceptible	57,500 36,000	0.006 0.045
Blasting	G. Morris (1950)	Vibrations in villa 1,100 ft. away. Firing 2,000 lb. explosive	0.0017	9.4	clearly perceptible – annoying	100,000	0.015
Machinery	Tillman (1933)	Vibrations from chocolate factory. Measurements in nearby house	0.00056	42	annoying	147,500	0.09
Machinery	Tillman (1933)	Vibration in house (3rd storey) 400 ft. from 120 h.p. diesel	0.0008	3.5	just perceptible	17,500	0.01
Machinery	B.R.S.	Vibrating table. Measurements on table	0.005	25	painful	780,000	0.32
Machinery	Tillman (1933)	Vibration in 70 year old house adjacent to 6 lithographic presses	0.00031	64	annoying	125,000	0.133

Note: From the foregoing results it would appear that the maximum velocities involved at the various stages of perceptibility are (approximately) in micro-inches per second. Just perceptible 10,000 to 30,000; Clearly perceptible 30,000 to 100,000; Annoying over 100,000.

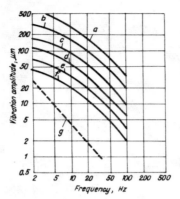

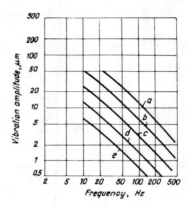

Fig. 225. Charts of vibration tolerances after Rathbone for heavy
machinery

a—very rough, b—rough, c—slighthly rough,
d—fair, e—good, f—very smooth, g—limit of
perceptible vibration

Fig. 226. Charts for electromotors after Schenck and Darmstadt.

a—very rough, b—rough, c—slightly rough, d—
admissible, e—good to very good

3. Criteria for vibration limits in machine foundation design

The governing criteria in machine foundation design are the permissible amounts of vibration that the machine, its surroundings, or the persons in the vicinity of the machine can tolerate.

For steady state vibrations terms of limiting values of amplitudes, or velocity or acceleration under operating conditions are generally given. We have seen in Chapter II that in the case of sinosoidal motion these terms are related to each other.

Beyond the requirement of avoiding damage or harm to buildings the proper and flawless operation of the equipment must be ensured without affecting the machine and foundation thereof.

Different classification charts, formulae and tables are given below for criteria of vibration tolerances.

To obtain the vibration amplitude of a working machine it would be necessary to measure the energy involved. However it is more simple to measure the amplitude itself. Classifications of vibration amplitudes as a function of the frequency were given as early as in 1939 by Rathbone [993a] (Fig. 225), who provided charts for heavy machinery for vibration tolerances. Similar charts are given in Fig. 226 for electromotors after Schenck–Darmstadt, quoted by Buzdugan [152].

The most widely used charts are those of the VDI Recommendations [1286] for assessing vibrations contained in Figs. 227–230.

Concerning the effects of vibration on machines, the adoption of the vibration velocities or amplitudes measured at the bearings should be established as standards of comparison.

TABLE 56

Permissible amplitudes for various machines

Machinery	Harmless		Objectionable	
	Amplitude mm	Frequency per min.	Amplitude mm	Frequency per min.
1. Weaving machines	0.30	140	1.00	—
2. Spinning machines	0.10 – 0.12	200 – 550	—	—
3. Confectionery			—	—
(chocolate press,	0.25	200		
biscuit press)	0.15	350 – 450		
4. Forced draught	0.10	1,000	0.40	1,000
and ventilating				
equipment				
5. Machine-tools				
a) planer	0.35	—	—	—
b) tapping machine	0.03			
milling machine				
slotting machine				
drilling machine				
c) grinding machine				
6. Manufacture of ball				
bearings				
a) grinding machines	0.03	1,000		
b) internal grinding	0.05			
c) presses	0.09			
d) inspection rooms				
with measuring				
instruments	0.005	2,000		

In the directives of the VDI for assessing vibrations, four main groups are described:

Group K: Individual parts of driving gears of prime movers and machine tools, connected finally in operation to the rest of the machine, including mass-produced electromotors meeting no special requirements and being only up to 15 kW (Fig. 227).

Group M: Machines of medium size (electric motors of 15 to 75 kW) without the requirements of special foundations, and rotating machinery up to 300 kW placed on foundations (Fig. 228).

Group G: Major parts of driving gears mounted on rigid or heavy foundations, highly overtuned in the direction of the vibration considered; large prime movers and machine-tools having only revolving masses (Fig. 229).

Group T: Large prime movers and machine-tools with only revolving masses, supported on special foundations, deeply undertuned in the direction of the vibration considered, e.g. turbine sets—especially those with modern, light foundations (Fig. 230).

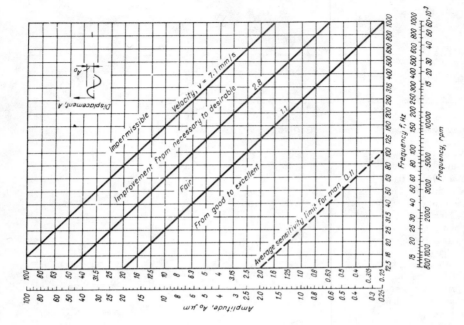

Fig. 228. VDI directives for assessing vibrations: Group M

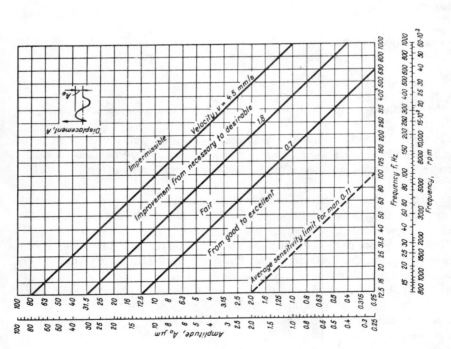

Fig. 227. VDI directives for assessing
vibrations: Group K